Merry Christmas darling.
lots of love
Peter.

AUSTRALIAN PARROTS
IN FIELD AND AVIARY

AUSTRALIAN PARROTS
IN FIELD AND AVIARY

The comprehensive revised edition
of Neville Cayley's standard work

ALAN H. LENDON

Angus & Robertson Publishers

ANGUS & ROBERTSON PUBLISHERS
London ● Sydney ● Melbourne ● Singapore
Manila

First published by Angus & Robertson Publishers, Australia, 1973
Reprinted 1976
This revised edition 1979

© Alan H. Lendon 1973

National Library of Australia
Cataloguing-in-publication data.

Cayley, Neville William, 1887–1950.
Australian parrots in field and aviary.

Rev. ed.
(Australian natural science library)
Index
Bibliography
ISBN 0 207 12424 8

1. Parrots. I. Lendon, Alan Harding,
1903–. II. Title.

598.71'0994

Printed in Hong Kong

CONTENTS

ILLUSTRATIONS

Foreword to First Edition

Forewords to books that speak for themselves are largely superfluous, but as protests upon the point seem to be equally unprofitable, it is best, perhaps, to say at once that I am glad to be associated with Neville Cayley in the rendering of public homage to the parrots and cockatoos of Australia. My feeling in this regard is not only one of admiration for the shapely and beautiful birds; I am moved also by a sense of gratitude for the uplifting experiences they have afforded me, and moreover there is an underlying feeling of contrition for the scurvy manner in which I served full many members of the group in the days of my callow youth.

As is the case, no doubt, with a number of other Australian naturalists, all my years have been bound up with parrots, not in captivity but in their revelling freedom. That is partly because the group is large and one or another species is represented in practically every portion of the continent—they range from the coastal highlands through the open forests of the sub-interior and on through the great inland plains to the "wastes of the Never-Never" in the heart of Australia.

A quaint, lovely, motley throng!

United in general physical characters, and notably that engaging face, they are as varied in disposition as they are in colour; for not only does each species have its own fancy geographically, but some inhabit jungles while others cling to grasses; and others again there be that live variously in swamps, among low vegetation on islands, and among expanses of forbidding scrub that seems unfitted to provide for any self-respecting bird. It follows, therefore, that the wayfarer in Australia, wherever he roam, is never long denied the joyous company of parrots.

In the matter of personal appeal, some of my earliest recollections of any kind attach to these birds. I see the dainty Purple-crowned Lorikeets and kindred honey-parrots feasting and chattering among the blue-gums of winter, the snowy almond-blossoms of early spring, and the ripening pears of summer, while small boys shoot them down with catapults; I see the many-coloured Red Rosellas raiding orchards in the bush; and, among other early impressions, I see the pretty Red-rumped Parrots rise noisily from the paddocks as the wagons rumble by. How beautiful the rosellas in particular appeared as they flashed in flocks among the gum-trees fringing the orchards! Were it not that their innate hardihood has enabled these parrots, in spite of all persecution, not only to persist but to increase their numbers in some parts, they would surely be esteemed as being amongst the most desirable of birds anywhere in the world.

Gazing up the years from boyhood, I see many rich and strange sights provided by parrots and cockatoos in various parts of the continent. I see the multi-coloured crests and underwings of Pink Cockatoos flying among giant gums beside the Murray River; the remarkable change from rose to grey as hundreds of Galahs swoop and turn above plains of the interior; the brilliance of Red-winged Parrots winnowing their way above the free spaces of western Queensland; the beauty of Crimson Parrots flashing among flowering trees on a tropic mountain; and, perhaps most potent of all, the golden glory of Regent Parrots flying through the vivid sunlight of the Victorian Mallee.

All those random memories are of parrots in the mass—in the flock—for most kinds are essentially social. But there abide also memories of individuals, and among them is that of my first and only meeting with a very rare and very beautiful creature, the Paradise Parrot. The story of the search for and discovery of that long-lost bird—the "Ant-hill Parrot" and "Soldier Parrot" of other days—has been told elsewhere; I am now merely toying with a recollection of the varied colours, the shapely form, and the prideful bearing of the exquisite little bird as it appeared on a summer day in a secluded part of Queensland.

How grievous the fact that, on present indications, the Paradise Parrot is on the verge of extinction! Still, one never knows in these matters. The stately Rose-throated (Princess Alexandra) Parrot and the radiant little Scarlet-chested Parrot were supposed a few years ago to have vanished from their haunts in the dry centre of Australia. It was suggested, indeed, that both species were extinct. And yet, only a few days ago, I gazed with rapt admiration at several pairs of both of these beautiful birds from the wastelands sitting side by side in the aviaries of Mr Simon Harvey of Adelaide. Is it too much to hope that the Paradise Parrot will be similarly re-established?

At any rate, although many species of parrots have been seriously decimated since the coming of the white man and his competitive animals—you have only to read pioneering notes to realize how abundant certain species, now rare, were in other days—at any rate, it cannot be said yet that any one kind of parrot has become extinct in the one hundred and fifty years of white settlement in Australia.

It is not for me to discuss here the merits of various cockatoos and parrots as aviary birds. There is, however, a curious point in this respect that demands consideration. Why is it that many species of these birds are admirable "talkers"—that is, faithful mimics of the human voice—when taken young and made captive, and yet do not, apparently, ever attempt mimicry in their natural state? The point becomes emphasized when related to the fact that Australia is singularly well endowed with mocking birds of various kinds. It may be suggested that parrots in their free state are too busy and too joyous to bother about absorbing sounds. But the same circumstance obtains with other birds which are distinguished as "natural" mockers. What puzzles me is why the ability, which apparently is innate with most of the parrot-like birds (including even the honey-parrots of the specialized tongues) does not fade through lack of use. That it does not do so is proved by the fact that there are to-day captive parrots and cockatoos whose ability as "talkers" is almost startling. I heard recently of a cockatoo that, through continually being associated with an auction-room, could repeat phrase after phrase of the auctioneer's patter. In another case a parrot was so assertive that a friend of mine used to go out of his way to avoid the bird—it was, he declared, so human in its chatter that it "gave him the creeps".

There are other points in parrot lore that might be discussed were it not that I have already rambled unduly. Moreover, it seems probable that practically all that we know of the subject will be given somewhere between these covers. All that remains for me to say is that, in my opinion, a book of this kind is a national asset. How can it be otherwise when it deals comprehensively, in story and picture, with one of the beautiful features that distinguish Australia from other lands?

A. H. CHISHOLM,
President, Field Naturalists' Club of Victoria.

Melbourne, 1938.

Foreword to Second Edition

It is a somewhat grim experience, or at least a sobering thought, to reflect that thirty-three years have slipped by since I wrote the preceding Foreword to Neville Cayley's book on Australia's parrots. At that time I was leaving on a journey overseas, and so the manuscript was scribbled on board ship and sent to Neville from Colombo. Now, it would seem, the item figures as something in the nature of a "period piece", and because of that, but mainly because the subject is one that "age cannot wither nor custom stale", it has been allowed to stand in this new edition of a notable book.

There is however one small matter in that earlier Foreword that invites amendment. It was mentioned, as an odd fact, that whereas various kinds of parrots, and especially the amazing little Budgerigar, become proficient talkers when kept as pets, none of them, apparently, practised vocal mimicry in their free state. But to my surprise it has now been revealed that some parrots do at times, when at large, follow the habit of numbers of other Australian birds in "stealing" the voices of their neighbours—this has recently been recorded of the King and Crimson Parrots in New South Wales and of the large Palm Cockatoo in the wilds of Cape York. Do these reports clear the air or do they merely complicate the issue? At any rate, the question remains: why do parrots, as it seems, rarely use their mimetic ability in freedom, whereas with lyrebirds and certain other species vocal mimicry is, so to say, a way of life?

The fact that Cayley's *Parrots* attained popularity is manifest in that within a few years of publication it was listed as rare and appreciated markedly in pecuniary value. Latterly, as the rarity became emphasized, the price of the volume on the secondhand market rose to a point almost prohibitive to most potential buyers, and thus publication of a new edition appeared to be very desirable.

It was known, of course, that in the meantime a number of works either partly or wholly devoted to parrots had been published. But it was also realized that the striking illustrations in the Cayley book still exercised warm appeal, and it was believed that the appeal would be strengthened if the letterpress was revised in the light of modern knowledge possessed by an informed student.

More or less naturally, therefore, Dr Alan Lendon was invited to take the work in hand. An aviculturist of long experience and world status, Dr Lendon has not only specialized during a lengthy period on the study of parrots in captivity—witness his book of 1951 on the subject—

but in recent years has considerably extended his knowledge of various members of the group in the wild. It may be noted, too, that Alan Lendon was one of those who assisted with the original edition. Accordingly, there need be no doubt that if Neville Cayley were still living—he died in 1950, at the age of sixty-three—he would have been glad to hand the torch to the parrot-man of Adelaide.

Men come and go but the birds live on. Inevitably, many species of parrots are much less abundant than they once were. But not one—nor any other kind of bird of the Australian mainland—is known definitely to have vanished since the dawn of settlement. You may read from time to time, even in supposedly authoritative works, assertions that two species in particular, the curious Night Parrot of the arid interior and the beautiful Paradise Parrot of subtropical areas, have become extinct. Such statements, although not baseless, are injudicious, and in fact, at this date, untrue.

What remains true is that neither of the two birds has had a place in any aviary during many years and both are excessively rare in a natural state, so that the menace of extinction, mentioned in the original Foreword as a possibility, continues to be a dark threat. Personally, I have never seen a Night Parrot in life and have not gazed on the proud figure of the Paradise Parrot since 1922—almost fifty years ago. (But here it should be said that I was not responsible for the heading, "The Last of the Paradise Parrots", which appeared upon a contribution of mine to an anthology termed *Discovery: Great Moments in the Lives of Outstanding Naturalists*, published in the United States in 1961; that arresting but somewhat misleading chapter heading, covering an account of the successful search for the bird in 1922, was conceived editorially.)

It may be that the Night Parrot, because of its highly specialized habits—and not, as is sometimes stated, through interference by man—is "on the way out". It is certainly true that the delicate Paradise Parrot, which has been affected by droughts, by competition from stock, and possibly by predators' attacks on its nest-hollows in terrestrial termites' mounds, has vanished from most of its former haunts. Yet, despite the shadowy status of the two birds, "unofficial" reports of sightings of some few examples have come to hand of late; and thus we may say, hopefully, there is still a chance of survival, for some indefinite time, in the case of each of these very distinctive Australians.

Perhaps the only other endemic parrots that have fallen away to an alarming extent—have joined the list of Birds in Danger—are two close relatives of the Paradise Parrot, namely the Golden-shouldered and Hooded species, which also nest in termites' mounds, and a ground-dweller which resembles the Night Parrot but favours marshy areas instead of arid country and therefore is known as the Swamp Parrot. Most of these birds have suffered from the white man's impact, either through the raiding of nests or the indiscriminate clearing of habitats. Their future, at least in a free state, is uncertain.

It is refreshing to remember, however, that some of the most notable members of the band, both cockatoos and parrots, are either abundant or holding on reasonably well. The Galah is, of course, still common. So is the pretty bird that "invented" the Australian-based name Rosella (originally Rosehiller). And, rather curiously, other species that remain fairly familiar include the engaging Red-rumped Parrot, which although belonging to the same genus as the Paradise and Golden-shouldered Parrots appears to have developed, by happy chance, a stronger constitution. Maybe, too, it is more soundly equipped in "temperament" to withstand the pressure of a changing world.

Because the Galah and the Eastern Rosella are familiar there is a tendency to overlook their beauty. Were they less common there would probably be expeditions to seek them. By the same token, there should be full, nation-wide appreciation of all members of this varied assemblage of graceful and picturesque birds which have been, over the centuries, a colourful feature of the Australian landscape.

I hope and expect that the present book will be a strong influence in strengthening such appreciation.

ALEC H. CHISHOLM.

Sydney, 1971.

B

Preface to First Edition

The purpose of *Australian Parrots: Their Habits in the Field and Aviary* is to supply a much-needed and comprehensive manual for the use of lovers of these beautiful birds, and to offer to those who take a more scientific interest in our parrot-like birds information concerning them in their natural habitats, as an inducement for further research in the field. To the aviarist the author expresses the ardent hope that the modern and humane methods advocated in this book will not only help him in his work and increase his pleasure and profit, but will make more contented and happier his lovely captives.

Since the publication of *Australian Finches in Bush and Aviary* in 1932, the author has received numerous requests, both from Australia and overseas, to produce a companion work on Australian parrot-like birds. This book is the response to those requests. Its compilation has been a pleasant task—made possible, very largely, by the kindly assistance of fellow-workers and interested friends.

To them, the author wishes to acknowledge his sincere thanks: especially to Mr R. R. Minchin, Mr K. A. Hindwood, Mr Simon Harvey, Miss Florence M. Irby, Mr A. H. Chisholm, Dr Alan Lendon, Mr C. H. A. Lienau, Mr H. B. Scholz, Dr Garnet Halloran, Dr Frank Marshall, Mr T. Iredale, Mr M. S. R. Sharland, Mr F. E. Parsons, Mr H. J. Cunningham, Mr T. Dunbabin, Mr D. Dickison, Dr E. A. D'Ombrain, and Mr Norman Chaffer. With pleasure he acknowledges the courtesy of the trustees and the staff of the Australian Museum, Sydney, in making available specimens in the collection of that institution.

N.W.C.

Sydney, 1938.

Preface to Second Edition

It must be at least ten years ago that Alec Chisholm suggested to the management of Angus & Robertson Ltd that I should be asked to produce a revised edition of Neville Cayley's *Australian Parrots*. This request I agreed to with the stipulation that I should be allowed to do it in my own time; neither the publishers nor I expected that this would be as long as it has been, but until recently my professional commitments precluded any possibility of really getting down to the task, although over the years I made sporadic attempts to do so. However, this delay has proved to be a not unmixed blessing, since in the intervening years I have been able to extend very greatly my knowledge of parrots in the field, particularly in regard to the number of species (50) with which I am now acquainted, and during the same period a great deal more has been learnt of their habits and behaviour by observation and breeding in captivity. It is therefore, I trust, a mature approach that I have brought to the subject, in contradistinction to many recent publications on Australian ornithology which have been rushed into print in attempts to satisfy an ever-increasing public demand.

In revising this work I have been ruthless in discarding much obsolete historical material which Cayley quoted, largely as padding, in his text; this is all available to the researcher in the appropriate places. I have, however, been meticulous in retaining Cayley's own observations and others of a personal nature which are not recorded elsewhere. As a result the size of the work has been somewhat reduced and it now becomes much more adequate as a field guide to the Australian parrots, a need for which has been apparent for a long time.

A second objective has been to bring the aviary notes up to date. Cayley was limited in this respect because of the lack of avicultural experience of many species at that time and also by the absence of an appropriate medium, apart from the *Avicultural Magazine* published in England, for the recording of what was in fact known. In the last thirty years great strides have been made in the number of species kept, studied scientifically and successfully bred in captivity, both in Australia and in many overseas countries. Where possible I have given an account of my own experiences and, failing this, those of other aviculturists of repute, mainly in Australia and occasionally overseas.

The original colour plates, which were almost uniformly good and particularly adequate from the field-guide viewpoint, have been largely retained, with some rearrangements, minor retouchings and the omission of the colour mutations of the Budgerigar, which were inappropriate for this work. Additional plates have been included, based on Cayley's own paintings in the possession of the publishers, to illustrate the female or immature plumage of species where it differs markedly from the plumage of the depicted male and was not portrayed in the original publication. Black and white reproductions, most of which were of historical interest only, have been omitted, with the exception of the unique photograph of the Paradise Parrot, taken by the late C. H. Jerrard.

All distribution maps have been redrawn and enlarged, based on my paper on this subject published in 1968 in the *South Australian Ornithologist* and on subsequent additional information that has come to hand. In addition, a gazetteer of place-names has been included to facilitate identification of places mentioned in the text.

All species recognized in the 1926 Checklist of the Royal Australasian Ornithologists' Union have been retained, despite the subsequent relegation of several of these to the status of subspecies in amendments thereto, and a sixtieth form, the Fig-parrot discovered on Cape York Peninsula since the original publication, has been added. My policy has been to consider separately those forms which can be readily identified and differentiated in the field, without becoming involved in taxonomic arguments.

Similarly, the vernaculars used in that edition of the Checklist have been retained except where, by virtue of my membership of the Vernacular Names Subcommittee of the R.A.O.U., I am aware of pending recommended alterations.

The text concludes with an Appendix devoted to the housing, feeding and general management of the Australian psittacines in captivity.

I wish to acknowledge the assistance given, particularly in regard to distribution, by A. R. Attiwell, C. N. Austin, Mrs. C. Bevege, G. Chapman, A. H. Chisholm, H. T. Condon, J. Courtney, G. Dibley, Mrs W. Eastman, J. M. Forshaw, Mrs H. B. Gill, Miss A. Griffen, the late Sir Edward Hallstrom, the late K. A. Hindwood, J. N. Hobbs, A. C. Hunt, K. C. Lint, M. McGarvie, A. R. McGill, the late J. N. McGilp, the late G. Mack, J. R. Napier, L. Nielsen, Brigadier H. R. Officer, S. A. Parker, C. E. Rix, L. Robinson, Dr D. L. Serventy and Dr G. M. Storr. Without their help much that has been recorded would have been incomplete.

ALAN LENDON

Adelaide, February 1972

Introduction to First Edition

The birds of Australia include many of the most beautiful members of the large order Psittaciformes or parrot-like birds. They are closely associated with the history of our country, and are greatly appreciated both in Australia and abroad.

For more than one hundred and fifty years Australian parrots have been kept in captivity; yet little has been published regarding their habits. Field observations are by no means complete; in fact, this beautiful group of birds has been neglected by field ornithologists. The records of what has been achieved by Australian aviarists are almost negligible and are scattered in various oversea journals.

This work is the first attempt to combine all that is known about Australian parrot-like birds from the viewpoint of ornithologist and aviarist.

Since soon after the foundation of Australia in 1788, these beautiful birds have been kept in cages. Many species have become quite domesticated; others are still very rare; several are on the verge of extinction.

Owing to the considerable difference of opinion that exists regarding the status of many subspecies, there is much work to accomplish, both in field and aviary. The whole-hearted co-operation of workers in ornithology and aviculture would greatly expedite that work.

Recent successes, both in Australia and abroad, in breeding in captivity several species of the fast disappearing *Neophema* parrakeets, is proof that it is possible, with scientific methods, to breed any of our rarer parrots. One hears the objection that birds bred under such circumstances would perish if liberated. No doubt. But what is the alternative? Is it not far better to see these birds reproducing their kind in captivity than allow them to become extinct? Unless a serious attempt is made to save the few species now on the verge of extinction, only museum specimens will be left to witness to a fate that might have been prevented.

In advocating the breeding of these birds in captivity, especially the rarer species, I do so in the hope that such breeding will be carried out under licence and in a purely scientific manner—not on a commercial basis.

Nomenclature and Classification. The classification and scientific names used in this book are those in the *Systema Avium Australasianarum* (1930) by Gregory M. Mathews.

Vernacular Names. The vernacular names are those used in *What Bird Is That?* with the improvement of parrakeet instead of parrot for the Broadtails and Lesser Broadtails.

Distribution Maps. Considerable research has been necessary in the drafting of these maps. The boundaries, however, are arbitrary, as in many instances the movements of parrots are not fully understood.

The possible, though unrecorded, range of a genus is indicated by broken hatching. Type localities of the species and subspecies of each genus are indicated—the species by binomial names, the subspecies by trinomials. The map showing the distribution of the genus *Geopsittacus* indicates only the most likely area where this "lost" parrakeet may be rediscovered.

The eggs of all parrot-like birds, being white and incubated on rotting wood detritus or soil, always become more or less nest-stained. It, therefore, has not been considered necessary, when dealing with each species, to repeat this obvious and inevitable fact.

A Land of Parrots. Australia is truly a "Land of Parrots". Here are found no fewer than fifty-nine distinct species of parrot-like birds. Although parrots occur in Central and South America, tropical Africa, southern Asia, and throughout the Australian region, nowhere in the world are parrots more numerous, more beautiful or in greater diversity of form than in this island commonwealth of the antipodes.

The earliest Dutch navigators are credited with having named that part of the west coast visited by them in the seventeenth century "The Land of Parrots". Strangely enough, comparatively few species were seen by these early voyagers. Apparently, the White Cockatoo was the first observed. But as this bird would not greatly impress the Dutchmen (who had just come from the Moluccas, the home of the White Cockatoo), we must conclude that it received its name from the extraordinary numbers observed.

A world map of Mercator (issued in 1569) has upon it a place called "Terra Psittacorum, The Land of Parrots". This is marked in 45 degrees south, away to the southward of the Cape of Good Hope. One presumes that Mercator drew his information from either Portuguese or Spanish sources. Probably, the name had something to do with Australia. On the other hand, it may have been derived from the reports of the Portuguese that in a far southern land they had seen "popinjays of marvellous bigness". However, the interesting fact remains that even in those far-off days there was a land renowned for its parrots.

Historical Associations. The earliest known illustration of an Australian parrot was sketched by one of the artists on board the *Endeavour* during the first of the three famous voyages of Captain Cook. After successfully observing the transit of Venus at Tahiti, Cook made for New Zealand waters and later sailed towards Australia. Cruising northwards along the east coast the *Endeavour* put in to Botany Bay for a few days (29th April to 7th May 1770). Many birds were taken as specimens, but only one was sketched at the time, and that by Sydney Parkinson. This historic pencil sketch is an outline of a female Red-tailed Black Cockatoo. Parkinson's drawings passed into the keeping of the British Museum in 1827, together with most of the invaluable manuscripts, specimens, drawings and the library of Sir Joseph Banks, who sailed with Captain Cook on his first voyage.

The second illustration of an Australian parrot was painted during Cook's third and last voyage, the artist, William Ellis, executing a water-colour drawing of the Tasmanian Green Rosella. This painting, dated 1777, is also in the British Museum.

Descriptions, and sometimes illustrations, of the birds brought to England as the result of Cook's voyages appear in several contemporary publications, such as Gmelin's *Systema Naturæ* and Latham's *Synopsis*. The first to appear in print was an illustration of the Rainbow Lorikeet; that appeared in Peter Brown's *New Illustrations of Zoology*, published in 1774.

When the First Fleet arrived in New South Wales and made the first settlement on Port Jackson, the officers and men were greatly interested in the strange wild life they found around them, and many water-colour drawings were made of the flowers and birds. In several collections of paintings dating from about that period there are many figurations of parrots, including the Turquoise Parrakeet and the Ground or Swamp Parrakeet—both now rare and seldom seen near Sydney, where once they were most plentiful.

Publications detailing the life at Sydney Cove (as it was then called) contain coloured plates of parrots. Such books as Phillip's *Voyage*, White's *Journal*, and *The Naturalists' Miscellany* supply ample evidence of the interest shown in these beautifully coloured and attractive birds. And that interest has been maintained and augmented right up to the present time.

One of the earliest, if not the earliest, references to parrots at Sydney— not Botany Bay—is contained in the journal of Arthur Bowes, surgeon of the *Lady Penrhyn*, one of the First Fleet. The passage is quoted in the *Historical Records of New South Wales*, vol. ii, 1893, p. 392.

Most of the First Fleet sailed into Botany Bay on 20th January 1788, but Captain Arthur Phillip, after exploring the surrounding land, and then investigating the possibilities of Port Jackson (the present site of Sydney), ordered the Fleet to the latter place where the colony was established on 26th January 1788. Bowes was much impressed by the scenery and not less so by the bird life as he sailed up Sydney Harbour on that historic day. About the bird life he remarks: "The singing of the various birds amongst the trees, and the flight of numerous parraquets, lorriequets, cockatoos, and maccaws, made all around seem like enchantment."

References to parrots are not confined to those early voyagers who visited our coastal areas. Both Sturt and Mitchell were impressed by their beauty; so much so that they included beautiful coloured plates of several among the illustrations to the accounts of their expeditions into the interior of southern and central Australia.

Feathered Ambassadors. Parrots are the favoured pets of bird-lovers everywhere, particularly in Europe, which cannot claim even one species among its avifauna. Perhaps that is one reason why the lure and cult of these fascinating and gorgeous birds have for centuries possessed European aviculturists. The Romans seem to have been the first to introduce parrots into Europe—some two thousand years ago. From then on, as travelling became less difficult (but no less dangerous) every caravan returning from the east and every ship from the west brought home its pets.

Since Captain Cook visited Australia more than one hundred and sixty years ago, parrots have attracted the attention of scientists, aviarists, artists, bird-lovers and tourists. The first live parrot imported into Europe from Australia seems to have been a Rainbow Lorikeet, which Banks took back with him in 1771. And, following the first settlement, there is ample evidence that each ship returning home from the colony brought its quota of living examples of the native fauna of the new land.

As aviary birds, Australian parrots have become extremely popular throughout the world; apart from their beauty and elegance they are easily kept, and many species breed readily in captivity. They are in every museum and zoological garden worthy of the name; while many thousands of birds, singly or in pairs, are to be found in homes all over the world.

Parrots as Pets. In addition to talking, parrots (and cockatoos) are easily taught to perform simple tricks such as riding bicycles, flying through lighted hoops, dancing, breaking flags and firing off small cannon. Several troupes of Australian talking and performing parrots have delighted audiences in every continent, and have done good work in advertising the country of their origin. Australian parrots have become universal favourites. They may well be called our Feathered Ambassadors.

There is an early record of a talking parrot owned by George Caley (a botanical collector for Sir Joseph Banks), who arrived in Sydney in 1800. So attached did he become to his pet that in his will he bequeathed a sum of money to provide for its upkeep after his death.

There is no authentic data as to the longevity of parrots in the wild, but there are some remarkable records of the age attained by parrots and cockatoos in captivity. One Australian White Cockatoo, at least, passed the century. This bird was the celebrated "Cocky Bennett", of Tom Ugly's Point, George's River, New South Wales, who died a few years ago; his body is preserved and mounted in all its glory—"without a feather to fly with". Cocky Bennett, for half his life, lived naked and unashamed, and many amusing stories are told regarding the bird's comical sayings as to his nudity.

Perhaps the most interesting record of the longevity of parrots is given by Newton in his *Dictionary of Birds*. He quotes Humboldt, who found in South America a venerable bird that spoke in the literally dead language of a tribe of Indians, called Atures, who had become extinct.

Introduction to Second Edition

Much has changed since Neville Cayley wrote the introduction to the original edition of this book. For example, his statement that "this beautiful group of birds has been neglected by field ornithologists" no longer applies, many articles and several books having been written on the group in the last thirty-odd years. His further remark that the records of what has been achieved in Australian aviaries are almost negligible is also no longer applicable, for several periodicals devoted to aviculture are now published in Australia.

At that time it was customary to talk, as Cayley did, of species "fast disappearing", "very rare", and "on the verge of extinction". Very fortunately it has been demonstrated that most species to which these descriptions were applied are not nearly as rare as was considered or else have made a substantial comeback. This should not result in complacency but should highlight the necessity for the preservation of their habitat as being really important and urgent for their ultimate conservation, even though it is possible that some species have adapted to altered habitats or may do so.

Cayley went on to advocate the breeding in captivity of the rarer species, having recently witnessed the initial successes achieved in Adelaide with such species as the Princess, Scarlet-chested, Turquoise and Bourke Parrots, all at that time considered to be extremely rare. He would be gratified to know that hundreds of each of these species continue to be bred annually in captivity, both in Australia and overseas, and this without significant introduction of further wild-caught stock, beneficial though a modicum of such may well be. In more recent years the establishment of aviary-bred stocks of the Golden-shouldered Parrot, largely through the initiative of the late Sir Edward Hallstrom, has to some extent offset the risk to survival of this species in the wild state.

Cayley further made a plea for the whole-hearted co-operation of workers in ornithology and aviculture. There is no doubt that the mutual distrust existing between the two groups has greatly diminished, although it has not entirely disappeared. The professional now realizes that he can learn much about behaviour and plumage changes, to quote two examples, from the amateur, whilst the latter has come to appreciate that, in being permitted to indulge his hobby, he has an obligation to make it as scientific as possible, to record his results and to use accepted methods in the establishment of breeding strains.

Cayley also advocated the carrying out of breeding in captivity of the rarer species under licence and not on a commercial basis. Whilst the various State laws permit aviculture to varying degrees, it is a matter for deep concern that the demand for Australian psittacines overseas is so great that extensive smuggling out of the country is attempted despite the risk of substantial penalties. The losses of valuable birds must inevitably be great and yet the dastardly practice continues. Simultaneously, many species are unprotected and can be shot or poisoned at will, whilst others may be permitted to be destroyed if causing seasonal damage. Surely the rational approach to this matter would be to legalize the export, under rigid supervision, of unprotected and of certified aviary-bred birds. Inevitably there would be some attempts to "ring-in" wild-caught birds, but this would surely be preferable to the losses currently occurring, while fantastic prices continue to be offered overseas even for locally unprotected species.

In this revision of Cayley's book the layout has been modified considerably from that of the original edition. The species included in each genus are now preceded by some introductory remarks concerning the genus as a whole, its relationships, distribution, and behaviour, obviating the needless repetition that would occur were this information to be included under each species.

The fifty-nine species recognized by the second edition of the R.A.O.U. Checklist, published in 1926, are retained not necessarily because they represent one's personal opinion—or, for that matter, current taxonomic opinion—but because they are all well-defined forms which Cayley illustrated in the original edition. To them has been added a sixtieth species, the Cape York Fig-parrot, discovered by the late Professor A. J. Marshall as recently as 1942.

The colour plates, altered in some instances and increased in number and content, have been placed opposite the appropriate generic introduction whenever possible.

The species are numbered consecutively for easy reference and each is described in the following sequence:

VERNACULAR NAME The name used is that recommended by the Vernacular Names Subcommittee of the Royal Australasian Ornithologists' Union; a few names will, in consequence, be relatively unfamiliar.

SCIENTIFIC NAME The currently accepted binomial is given, together with the authority.

ILLUSTRATION The plate and figure numbers are given.

SYNONYMS All widely used alternative names are given under this heading. These include the hitherto commonly used Australian vernacular names, and the names used by aviculturists, particularly overseas.

DISTRIBUTION A distribution map is included for each species; the black area provides a general picture of what is accepted as the usual range of each. Accidental, unusual and doubtful records have been omitted entirely. The map is followed by details, State by State, of the areas of distribution. The place names mentioned can be identified from the gazetteer at the back of the book.

DESCRIPTION This begins with the approximate size, measured from the tip of the bill to the tip of the tail; it must be appreciated that this is variable with the race and also, in the case of measurement from skins, because of the technique of preparation. It should be noted that a slim, long-tailed bird may appear to be larger than a bulky, short-tailed one. The size is followed by a detailed description (usually Cayley's) of the adult male; the adult female is distinguished, either in similar detail when the plumage differs appreciably or more briefly when the differences are slight. There follows a description of the immature plumage,

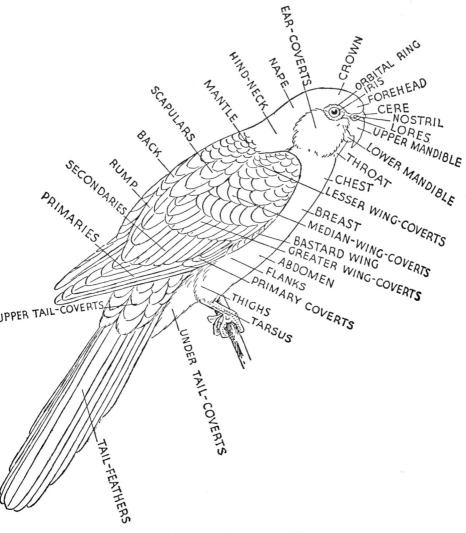

TOPOGRAPHY OF A PARROT

again in detail when necessary. An indication is given, whenever known, of the age of assumption of adult plumage.

GEOGRAPHICAL VARIATIONS This heading is used to describe well-marked subspecies or races, together with their range. If a subspecies is not mentioned it is an indication that it is not considered valid.

FIELD NOTES Under this heading Cayley's own personal observations are repeated, together with any other original notes which he had gathered. These are followed by my personal observations, supplemented on occasions by those of other ornithologists.

AVIARY NOTES Cayley's aviary notes are included when they are considered still to be of value. These are followed by notes of my own experiences in the keeping and breeding of most species, supplemented when necessary by those of other aviculturists, usually in Australia but occasionally overseas.

ALAN LENDON

Introduction to This Edition

When Neville Cayley wrote the first edition of this book in 1938 virtually no accurate popular material had been published on Australian parrots, there had been little scientific study of them and compared to today aviculture in Australia was in its infancy. Cayley therefore was forced to rely on correspondence and old miscellaneous notes to support his magnificent paintings. Some of the material had some historic value but was of doubtful value in other ways. Even so the ornithologists of the day, including ourselves, found the book to be a tremendous stimulus to further work.

Alan Lendon, when he revised the book in 1973 had been one of the country's leading aviculturists for many years. He had abundant personal experience of parrots in captivity and was able to write authoritatively and at first hand. There had been some increase in scientific research and parrots in the wild were becoming better known. The result was that Dr Lendon was able to write a substantial text, increase the illustrations of plumage and produce a well balanced body of information.

Having examined the book, perused the literature and searched our souls we have concluded that the book as it stands needs little alteration. We believe that it should be treated as an important land mark in the study of Australian parrots and as a valuable record of the views of one of the most prominent aviculturists of his day.

Nevertheless there are two areas in which some alteration is desirable. First, Dr Lendon had his own personal views on the taxonomy of parrots and these did not always coincide closely with the weight of opinion of other taxonomists. Second, research on parrots in the wild has accelerated and facts unknown in 1973 are now documented in scientific and popular literature.

With the taxonomic notes and bibliography that follow, this edition should stand as a monument to Neville Cayley and Alan Lendon and as a valuable reference and introduction to Australian parrots for a long time yet.

Taxonomy of parrots

Dr Lendon had a personal and essentially practical view of bird taxonomy. If geographical populations or forms were readily distinguishable in the field or aviary he preferred to regard them as full species. Some of the forms he thus regarded as species, for example, Naretha Blue Bonnet, Cloncurry Parrot, Twenty-eight Parrot, are not recognized as such by most modern authorities. Dr Lendon based his nomenclature on the Second Edition of the R.A.O.U. Checklist published in 1926, the one used by Cayley. A feature of that Checklist followed by Lendon but now largely discarded by ornithologists, is the use of subgenera.

The 1926 Checklist has been replaced by a modern one compiled by H. T. Condon, and published by the R.A.O.U. in 1975. The majority of modern authors follow the Condon Checklist. So that Lendon's book can be used in conjunction with other literature, the following Table has been compiled, in which the common and scientific names used by Lendon are listed together with those used by Condon where the latter differ.

Canberra 1978

H. J. Frith
J. H. Calaby

A Comparison of the Scientific Names for Parrots and Cockatoos used by A. H. Lendon and those used in the Current Checklist of Australian Birds

Lendon (this book)

Condon (Checklist 1975)

1. Rainbow Lorikeet *Trichoglossus moluccanus* (Gmelin)

Trichoglossus haematodus (Linnaeus) The name *moluccanus* is retained for the subspecies of *T. haematodus* found in eastern and south-eastern Australia.

2. Red-collared Lorikeet *Trichoglossus rubritorquis* (Vigors and Horsfield)

3. Scaly-breasted Lorikeet *Trichoglossus* (*Eutelipsitta*) *chlorolepidotus* (Kuhl)

Trichoglossus chlorolepidotus (Kuhl)

4. Red-capped Lorikeet *Psitteuteles versicolor* (Lear)

Varied Lorikeet

5. Musk Lorikeet *Glossopsitta concinna* (Shaw)

6. Purple-crowned Lorikeet *Glossopsitta porphyrocephala* (Dietrichsen)

7. Little Lorikeet *Glossopsitta pusilla* (Shaw)

8. Southern Fig-parrot *Opopsitta coxeni* (Gould)

Fig-parrot Psittaculirostris diophthalma (Hombron and Jacquinot) The three fig-parrots recognized as species by Lendon are considered to belong to a single species, but all three forms are retained as subspecies. The Cape York subspecies is called *P. d. marshalli* (Iredale)

9. Northern Fig-parrot *Opopsitta macleayana* (Ramsay)

10. Cape York Fig-parrot *Opopsitta diophthalma* (Hombron and Jacquinot)

11. Palm Cockatoo *Probosciger aterrimus* (Gmelin)

12. White-tailed Black Cockatoo *Calyptorhynchus* (Zanda) *baudinii* (Lear)

Calyptorhynchus baudinii (Lear)

13. Yellow-tailed Black Cockatoo *Calyptorhynchus* (Zanda) *funereus* (Shaw)

Calyptorhynchus funereus (Shaw)

14. Red-tailed Black Cockatoo *Calyptorhynchus magnificus* (Shaw)

15. Casuarina Black Cockatoo *Calyptorhynchus* (*Harrisornis*) *lathami* (Temminck)

Glossy Black Cockatoo *Calyptorhynchus lathami* (Temminck)

16. Gang-gang Cockatoo *Callocephalon fimbriatum* (Grant)

17. Sulphur-crested Cockatoo
    Cacatua galerita (Latham)

18. Pink Cockatoo *Cacatua*   *Cacatua leadbeateri* (Vigors)
    (*Lophochroa*) *leadbeateri* (Vigors)

19. Little Corella *Cacatua*   *Cacatua sanguinea* (Gould)
    (*Ducorpsius*) *sanguinea* (Gould)

20. Long-billed Corella *Cacatua*   *Cacatua tenuirostris* (Kuhl)
    (*Licmetis*) *tenuirostris* (Kuhl)   There are isolated populations of *C.
                                        tenuirostris* in south-western Australia
                                        that Condon recognizes as a
                                        subspecies *C. t. pastinator* (Gould).
                                        Lendon treats these populations as a
                                        subspecies of *C. sanguinea*.

21. Galah *Cacatua* (*Eolophus*)   *Cacatua roseicapilla* (Vieillot)
    roseicapilla (Vieillot)

22. Cockatiel *Nymphicus hollandicus*
    (Kerr)

23. Superb Parrot *Polytelis swainsonii*
    (Desmarest)

24. Regent Parrot *Polytelis
    anthopeplus* (Lear)

25. Princess Parrot *Polytelis*   *Polytelis alexandrae* (Gould)
    (*Spathopterus*) *alexandrae* (Gould)

26. Red-winged Parrot *Aprosmictus
    erythropterus* (Gmelin)

27. King Parrot *Aprosmictus*   *Alisterus scapularis* (Lichtenstein)
    (*Alisterus*) *scapularis*
    (Lichtenstein)

28. Eclectus Parrot *Eclectus pectoralis*   *Eclectus roratus* (P. L. S. Müller)
    (P. L. S. Müller)

29. Red-cheeked Parrot *Geoffroyus
    geoffroyi* (Bechstein)

30. Red-capped Parrot
    Purpureicephalus spurius (Kuhl)

31. Ringneck Parrot *Barnardius*   Mallee Ringneck
    barnardi (Vigors and Horsfield)

32. Cloncurry Parrot *Barnardius*   Recognized as a subspecies only of
    macgillivrayi (North)   the Mallee Ringneck *B. barnardi*

33. Yellow-banded Parrot *Barnardius*   Port Lincoln Parrot
    zonarius (Shaw)

34. Twenty-eight Parrot *Barnardius*   Recognised as a subspecies only of
    semitorquatus (Quoy and   the Port Lincoln Parrot *B. zonarius*
    Gaimard)

35. Crimson Rosella *Platycercus*   These three forms considered by
    elegans (Gmelin)   Lendon to be separate species are
                                        treated as different subspecies only of
36. Adelaide Rosella *Platycercus*   a single species *P. elegans*. The true
    adelaidae (Gould)   relationships of these three forms are
                                        probably better expressed by the
37. Yellow Rosella *Platycercus*   arrangement adopted by Forshaw
    flaveolus (Gould)   (1973) who considers that *P. elegans*
                                        and *P. flaveolus* are separate species
                                        and the form *adelaidae* a hybrid
                                        linking population

38. Green Rosella *Platycercus caledonicus* (Gmelin)
39. Northern Rosella *Platycercus venustus* (Kuhl)
40. Pale-headed Rosella *Platycercus adscitus* (Latham)
41. Eastern Rosella *Platycercus eximius* (Shaw)
42. Western Rosella *Platycercus icterotis* (Kuhl)
43. Red-rumped Parrot *Psephotus haematonotus* (Gould)
44. Many-coloured Parrot *Psephotus varius* (Clark)
45. Blue Bonnet *Psephotus* (*Northiella*) *haematogaster* (Gould)   *Northiella haematogaster* (Gould)
46. Little Blue Bonnet *Psephotus* (*Northiella*) *narethae* (H. L. White)   Recognized as subspecies only of the Blue Bonnet *N. haematogaster*
47. Paradise Parrot *Psephotus* (*Psephotellus*) *pulcherrimus* (Gould)   *Psephotus pulcherrimus* (Gould)
48. Golden-shouldered Parrot *Psephotus* (*Psephotellus*) *chrysopterygius* (Gould)   *Psephotus chrysopterygius* (Gould)
49. Hooded Parrot *Psephotus* (*Psephotellus*) *dissimilis* (Collett)   *Psephotus dissimilis* (Collett)
50. Bourke Parrot *Neophema* (*Neopsephotus*) *bourkii* (Gould)   Bourke's Parrot *Neophema bourkii* (Gould)
51. Orange-bellied Parrot *Neophema* (*Neonanodes*) *chrysogaster* (Latham)   *Neophema chrysogaster* (Latham)
52. Rock Parrot *Neophema* (*Neonanodes*) *petrophila* (Gould)   *Neophema petrophila* (Gould)
53. Blue-winged Parrot *Neophema* (*Neonanodes*) *chrysostoma* (Kuhl)   *Neophema chrysostoma* (Kuhl)
54. Elegant Parrot *Neophema* (*Neonanodes*) *elegans* (Gould)   *Neophema elegans* (Gould)
55. Turquoise Parrot *Neophema pulchella* (Shaw)
56. Scarlet-chested Parrot *Neophema splendida* (Gould)   Scarlet-breasted Parrot
57. Swift Parrot *Lathamus discolor* (Shaw)   *Lathamus discolor* (White)
58. Budgerigar *Melopsittacus undulatus* (Shaw)   Budgerygah
59. Swamp Parrot *Pezoporus wallicus* (Kerr)
60. Night Parrot *Geopsittacus occidentalis* (Gould)

TRICHOGLOSSUS Stephens
Medium-sized Lorikeets

This genus comprises the best known and most widely distributed of the medium-sized lorikeets, as opposed to the short-tailed lories of the Moluccan, Papuan and Polynesian regions. Most authorities include the very distinct Scaly-breasted Lorikeet, *chlorolepidotus*, in the same genus, as well as the allied species, the Perfect Lorikeet, *euteles*, of Timor and adjacent islands; this inclusion is open to doubt and I have a strong leaning to the retention of *Eutelipsitta*, formerly *Psitteuteles*, for these two smaller, differently patterned species, which are sympatric with one or other subspecies of *Trichoglossus haematodus* throughout their ranges. The widely ranging green-collared forms may be considered to constitute the typical *Trichoglossus*, and the current tendency is to consider them as comprising a single species, *haematodus*, of which the Rainbow Lorikeet, *moluccanus*, becomes a subspecies; this treatment is not followed here.

Recently Peters[1] and Cain[2] have retained the Ornate Lorikeet, *ornatus*, of the Celebes and the Cherry-red Lorikeet, *rubiginosus*, of Ponape in the Caroline Islands as separate species, but have regarded the very distinctly patterned Red-collared Lorikeet, *rubritorquis*, as a subspecies of *haematodus*; in accordance with the intention of following the 1926 R.A.O.U. Checklist in regard to species, this bird with its very different plumage pattern is retained. If *Eutelipsitta* is admitted, either as a genus or subgenus, then it would seem proper to include in it the Yellow-green Lorikeet, *flavoviridis*, of the Sula Islands, Meyer's Lorikeet, *meyeri*, of the Celebes and the little-known Johnstone's Lorikeet, *johnstoniae*, of Mindanao in the Philippines.

The three species of large lorikeets included in this genus do not vary in their behaviour from that of the remainder of the family. Mated pairs sit close together and frequently indulge in mutual preening. The rather comical and elaborate display is the same in each species; Tavistock[3] states that "they perform droll and curious antics, dancing, bowing, bobbing and squirming; they often play together in an amusing and puppy-like fashion, rolling over and over and pretending to bite".

Courtship feeding occurs, and although the male spends much time in the nest during incubation, it has never been satisfactorily proved that he participates in the actual incubation of the eggs, which takes twenty-five days; presumably he feeds the female in the nest during this time and also feeds the young during both the early and later periods of their nest occupancy. All lorikeets spend a longer period in the nest than do young broadtailed parrots, the time between hatching and emergence being about eight weeks.

The colour of the down, although rarely recorded, is reputedly white. In this genus the bill colour is dark, unlike the red or orange of the adult, when the young leave the nest, but changes fairly rapidly. All the lorikeets of the genus have a broad coloured band on the under-surface of the primaries and secondaries; this differs considerably from the spots which make up the wing-stripe of the broadtails and it is constant in immatures and adults of both sexes.

Members of the genus are free bathers, usually in foliage which is wet from rain or dew; in captivity they enjoy a spray but will use drinking receptacles for a bath. They do not use the feet for the purpose of holding articles of food. Head-scratching is performed under the wing.

The flight is direct and fast, with rapid wing-beats. The silhouette is the same as for all lorikeets: noticeably sleek bodies with pointed tails and long, tapering wings.

I Rainbow Lorikeet

Trichoglossus moluccanus (Gmelin)

PLATE I

Synonyms

Blue Mountain Lorikeet, Swainson's Lorikeet, Blue-bellied Lorikeet, Bluey.

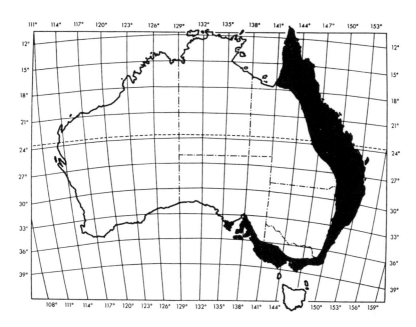

Distribution

In Queensland there are records from some Torres Strait islands and from most of Cape York Peninsula, at the base of which it is believed that there may be some overlap in the range of this and the next species. Proceeding southwards, the species inhabits the whole of eastern Queensland without going much farther west than the limits of the Great Dividing Range.

In New South Wales the recorded distribution is again mainly limited to the Great Dividing Range and to the east thereof, although it extends to the west as far as Moree.

C

In Victoria it is notable that the species is absent from the whole of the north-western corner and indeed from much of the northern half of the State.

In South Australia it appears to be predominantly found in the south-east and the Mount Lofty Ranges with northernmost recordings at Sutherlands and at Melrose in the southern Flinders Range and with further extensions to Yorke Peninsula, Kangaroo Island and southern Eyre Peninsula.

According to Sharland[4] it is a rare visitor to Tasmania, and M. McGarvie has only one record for King Island.

Description

SIZE. About 12 inches (305 mm).

ADULT MALE. General colour above, including back, wings and tail, green, feathers on lower hind-neck and mantle bright scarlet on subapical portion; primary and secondary feathers green on outer webs and dark brown or blackish on inner webs, with a large ovate yellow spot on central portion of feathers forming a band through the wing; outer web of first primary blackish; bases of feathers of scapulars yellow washed with crimson—in some examples this area is entirely yellow, in others crimson; four central tail-feathers bluish-green, outer tail-feathers green on their outer webs, yellow on their inner webs decreasing in extent towards the central feathers; under-surface of tail-feathers yellowish; nuchal collar yellowish-green; head, sides of face and throat dusky-brown with glossy-blue shaft streaks to the feathers; chest and breast crimson, some of the feathers in the centre fringed with deep blue; sides of breast orange-yellow, more or less tipped with crimson; centre of abdomen deep blue, sides crimson mottled with yellow and tipped with green; under tail-coverts yellow, mesially tipped with green and washed with crimson at base; auxiliaries and under wing-coverts bright crimson; bill red; legs and feet ashy-grey; iris orange or reddish yellow.

ADULT FEMALE. Similar to the male, but has a smaller and rounder head.

IMMATURE. Differs from the adult in having a more yellowish breast, a narrower nuchal collar, and a blackish bill.

Geographical Variations

Birds from the northern part of the range have been separated sub-specifically (*septentrionalis*); they are certainly smaller but it has been demonstrated that they are no more brightly coloured than birds from southern Queensland. It seems probable that this is only a clinal variation and unworthy of retention.

Field Notes

Cayley wrote: "These lorikeets are more or less nomadic, their appearance in districts mostly coinciding with the flowering of the eucalypts. In some seasons they are extremely plentiful; their shrill shrieking notes as they fly swiftly overhead or from tree to tree are to be heard in most coastal districts. At one time they were very common in localities in the neighbourhood of Sydney but of late years only scattered flocks are to be observed, and then only in good seasons. Usually they are met with feeding in company with Musk and Little Lorikeets.

"They are amusing birds to watch, either feeding among the blossom-laden gums or sheltering among the leafy branches. They never seem to rest, for when not feeding they are as playful and as full of tricks as monkeys. While feeding they keep up an incessant din, chattering and screeching as they climb, twist and turn in all manner of positions, in and out of the masses of flowers, greedily extracting the nectar with their long brush-like tongues. At times the noise is almost deafening, especially when the flock is accompanied by other honey-loving species. They are exceptionally greedy feeders; gorging until the feathers of their heads, necks, and breasts are a sticky mass, and the nectar pours from their throats. Insects (chiefly beetles), attracted by the honey-laden flowers, are also eaten and form a considerable portion of their diet.

"Like nearly all the species of lorikeets inhabiting Australia, the Rainbow Lorikeet uses as a nesting-place a hole in a tree, sometimes in a dead hollow branch, but often in a living one, the eggs being deposited on the decaying wood usually found in these cavities. The height from the ground of these nesting-sites varies from twenty to sixty feet, and the favourite trees appear to be eucalypts. As a rule the eggs are placed from one to two feet from the entrance, the female doing most of the incubating. When sitting she is fed regularly by the male, only leaving her charges at sundown; after flying round for a while she is joined by her mate when both re-enter the hollow and remain for the night. During the hot summer months the male generally visits and feeds his mate twice during the day, just after daybreak and just before sundown.

"Clutch: Two eggs; white, and rounded-oval to oval in shape, some being slightly pyriform at the smaller end; shell smooth and lustreless. Breeding-season: variable; in northern Queensland young have been observed in May, October, November, December, and January; in New South Wales they have been found breeding as early as June, as late as December, and in each intervening month. Often two or more broods are reared in succession. During the breeding-season they are generally found in pairs, but early in January and February they assemble in flocks."

As far as I can recall, my first sighting of this brilliant bird in the field was at Victor Harbour, South Australia, many years ago; in point of fact, it has usually been plentiful in that district and can often be seen feeding in ornamental eucalypt. planted as street trees. However, I became very much better acquainted with the species in the years following World War II in the course of visits to the south-east of South Australia, where it is often to be found in considerable numbers.

In May 1965, during a tour of north-eastern New South Wales and south-eastern Queensland, enormous numbers were seen everywhere and on one occasion a large number of this species and of the Scaly-breasted Lorikeet were noted feeding on a ripening maize crop; the damage inflicted by them must have been incalculable. In the last few years they have often been seen feeding in large numbers on *Eucalyptus citriodora* and *E. torquata* which have been planted as street and garden trees in the suburbs of Adelaide, and for several months during the winter of 1968 small parties were frequently observed passing over my property in the Mount Lofty Ranges.

In the course of the bird-watchers' tour of eastern Queensland in May and June 1970, large numbers of Rainbow Lorikeets were observed in most areas visited.

Aviary Notes

Cayley wrote: "With its brilliantly-coloured plumage and amusing mannerisms, the Rainbow Lorikeet makes a delightful aviary bird. It is extremely active, twisting, turning and climbing on the perches, or flying swiftly about the enclosure, and is an exceptionally noisy bird at all times.

"The pairs display a marked attachment to each other, often playing together for hours; their courtship is accompanied with much dancing and bowing and droll antics.

"Usually this species lives happily with others of its kind, but generally displays a marked antagonism towards other parrots. Of course there are exceptions; still it is advisable to keep the pairs separately housed. Owing to its activity, and particularly the liquid nature of its droppings, it should only be kept in large aviaries. If suitably housed and fed it will live and breed readily for many years.

"In its wild state it lives almost entirely on honey; but that it soon adapts itself to altered conditions of life, is indicated by its fruit-eating propensities. So, one is not surprised to find it living in captivity on seed. The late Dr W. MacGillivray records a bird that lived in a small aviary for seventeen years, never getting any other food than wheat and canary-seed. A remarkable record. Although other single birds have been kept successfully under similar conditions for several years, one would not advocate such treatment.

"Most aviarists in Australia feed these brush-tongued species on seed and fruit; but as a rule they do not live long on such a diet, usually becoming over-fat and dying of fits. . . .

"A hollow log, with one end blocked and hung horizontally, is all that is required as a nesting-place. When brooding, the male besides feeding the female spends much of his time in the log; he also assists in rearing the young. Male birds often become very spiteful during the breeding-season, especially about the time the youngsters are ready to leave the nest; in an endeavour to make them vacate the log the males savage them unmercifully, badly maiming and sometimes killing them."

This species used to be brought to South Australia from Queensland in large numbers before World War II; since then relatively few have appeared in local bird-shops and it has become much rarer in captivity. The bronze medal of the Avicultural Society of South Australia for the first recorded breeding of this species was awarded in 1929 to Dr W. Hamilton; since that date there have been numerous successes in the Adelaide Zoo.

This species can be kept and even bred on a diet of seed alone, but there seems little doubt that the addition of fruit and sweetened bread and milk provides a more balanced diet.

I possessed a pair of these birds for a short time in 1935, but parted with them as I found them very aggressive towards the other inhabitants of a mixed aviary.

2 Red-collared Lorikeet

Trichoglossus rubritorquis Vigors and Horsfield

PLATE I

Synonyms

Orange-naped Lorikeet, Blue Bonnet (erroneously).

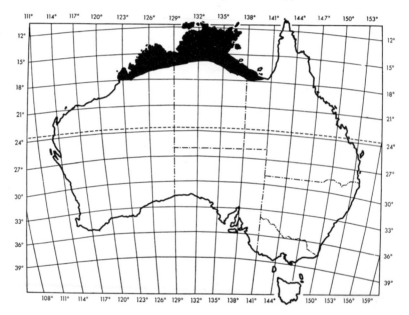

Distribution

This species occurs over most, if not all, of the Kimberley division of Western Australia and the records extend as far west as Broome.

Northern Territory records cover most of the "Top End" north of about the sixteenth parallel of latitude from Victoria River Downs in the west through Daly Waters on the Stuart Highway to Borroloola on the McArthur River in the east and include Melville Island and Groote Eylandt.

The 1926 R.A.O.U. Checklist makes no mention of the Queensland records from the lower Gregory River and Burketown with possible extensions to Normanton and Georgetown at the base of Cape York Peninsula.

Description

SIZE. About 12 inches (305 mm).

ADULT MALE. Head, sides of face and throat dusky-brown with glossy-blue shaft streaks to the feathers; chest, breast and nuchal collar deep orange, more or less streaked with crimson, except at tips of feathers; band on hind-neck deep blue; feathers of interscapular region crimson tipped next to hind-neck with deep blue, and on lower portion with green, bases of feathers yellow; wings green, inner webs of primaries blackish-brown with an oblong spot of yellow in centre forming a band through the wings; two central tail-feathers green washed with blue at tips, the next pair green edged with yellow on inner webs, remainder green on outer webs and yellow on inner ones; under-surface of tail yellowish, deeper in colour on inner webs of lateral feathers; a narrow band on lower throat and centre of abdomen deep blue-black tinged with green; feathers on sides crimson tipped with deep blue or green; flanks and under tail-coverts yellow tipped with green; axillaries and under wing-coverts bright crimson; bill red; legs and feet greyish-brown; eyes reddish-orange.

ADULT FEMALE. Similar to the male, but has a smaller and rounder head.

IMMATURE. Differs from the adult in having a duller coloration generally, a narrower nuchal collar, and a blackish bill.

Geographical Variations

None recognized.

Field Notes

Cayley wrote: "The Red-collared Lorikeet is similar in habits to the Rainbow Lorikeet. From information gathered from bird-trappers, and the few published notes available, this beautiful lorikeet is nomadic, being very numerous during the flowering season of the eucalypts. At other times it is generally met in small flocks or scattered pairs, feeding on the nectar from the flowers of the grevilleas, the cajaput and other flowering trees. It is said to be at all times a restless and noisy bird, constantly on the move from tree to tree, uttering its shrill shrieking note while on the wing. During the breeding-season it is usually found in pairs and nests in the hollow spouts of trees, chiefly eucalypts, bordering watercourses and streams.

"Clutch: two eggs; dull white, similar in size to the Rainbow Lorikeet's. Breeding-season: May to December."

In November 1945 I had a brief glimpse of two pairs of this species during a short time spent in a staging camp on the outskirts of Darwin. In July and August 1964, on a memorable visit to the "Top End" of the Northern Territory, I observed this species in vast numbers, both in pairs and in small and medium-sized flocks, everywhere from Larrimah northwards. At this season of the year they appeared to be feeding exclusively on the lovely orange blossoms of the eucalypt known locally but erroneously as the woollybutt (*Eucalyptus miniata*) which is widespread throughout northern Australia. In 1967, in the course of the R.A.O.U. field outing, the species was still very plentiful in the same areas as three years previously, although *E. miniata* was not flowering profusely, and it was also common in the Nourlangie area on the western fringe of Arnhem Land. In July and August 1969 the birdwatchers' tour of Northern Australia found the species extraordinarily common, although *E. miniata* was again flowering only sparsely; it was seen in all areas noted on previous visits and also westward—that is, at Victoria River Downs, Timber Creek and Kununurra. In the field it gives the impression of being even more brilliant than its close relative, the Rainbow Lorikeet; possibly this may be the effect of the tropical light. The best field guides to its identification, particularly applicable to areas of possible overlap of its range with that of the Rainbow, are the orange-red collar and the black belly as opposed to the light green collar and blue belly of the better known and more widely spread bird.

Aviary Notes

Cayley wrote: "Has the same delightful mannerisms, and does as well in captivity, as its nearest relative the Rainbow Lorikeet with which it will interbreed. The same methods of feeding and housing are recommended.

"Simon Harvey of Adelaide, South Australia, sends me the following notes on his success: 'These birds have been in my aviaries for over twelve years, and have been living on sunflower- and canary-seed, never having honey or bread and milk. Last year the hen laid two eggs and hatched young but did not rear them. I was very surprised to find they had eggs, because whenever I was near the aviary both birds were off the nest. One day I peeped into the nest-box to see if they were breeding, and the eggs were there. This year they commenced nesting early in September; the first egg was laid on 2nd September, and the first young was hatched on 27th September. Their eyes were first noticed to be open on 6th October. Feathers were showing on 12th October, fifteen days from the date of hatching. The head-feathers grew faster than the others; on 19th October the cock had a bright blue head. On 31st October they were well feathered and the red collar was showing distinctly on the cock, the beaks are black. The first young left the log on 28th November, just two months and a day from the date hatched. The colour is almost identical with that of the parents; the body colour is a slightly paler green; the beak changing from black and showing a little red; the eyes are black, whereas the parents have red eyes.' "

Although previously a rare bird in captivity, a number have been brought to South Australia from the Northern Territory since the end of World War II and it is now comparatively common in the State. The bronze medal of the Avicultural Society of South Australia was awarded in 1934 to S. Harvey; it has been bred in the Adelaide Zoo on several occasions since 1938 and also by R. Rowlands with great consistency. The habits of this species in captivity appear to be identical with those of the Rainbow Lorikeet, and to my mind there is little doubt that soft food is desirable, though obviously not essential. I have kept the species myself for only a brief period, in 1956-57 when I housed a pair for a relatively short time; they showed no inclination to breed during the time that they were in my possession.

3 Scaly-breasted Lorikeet

Trichoglossus (Eutelipsitta) chlorolepidotus (Kuhl)

PLATE I

Synonyms

Gold and Green Lorikeet, Greenie.

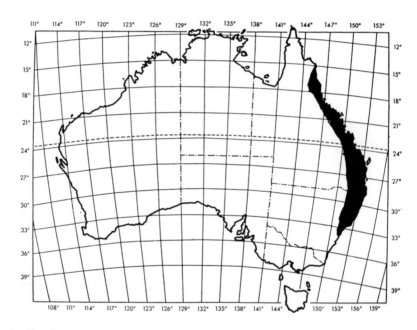

Distribution

The Queensland distribution is best amplified by stating that this species occurs as far north as Cooktown and then follows the coastal belt down to the New South Wales border with westward extensions recorded from Duaringa and Chinchilla.

In northern New South Wales it occurs along the coast and adjacent ranges and extends as far west as Moree; according to the late Keith Hindwood this species is always around Sydney but is comparatively rare and this locality is apparently its southern limit. However, Forshaw[5] states that he is informed that it visits the Illawarra district, south of Sydney, regularly.

Recent sightings in the vicinity of Melbourne are almost certainly the result of liberations.

Description

SIZE. About 9½ inches (241 mm).

ADULT MALE. General colour above and below grass-green: feathers on mantle, hind-neck, sides of neck, breast and sides of body broadly banded with yellow, occasionally washed with crimson on the throat, sides of neck and body; primaries and secondaries blackish-brown, all—except the outermost primary on each side, which is edged with yellow—have the outer webs and tips green, the under-surface of the quills with an oblong spot of pale crimson on the median portion of the inner web, increasing in extent and depth of colour towards the innermost secondaries; this part on the upper-surface of the quills is distinctly spotted with yellow; under-surface of tail yellowish, basal half of lateral feathers slightly washed with crimson on their inner webs; axillaries and under wing-coverts bright crimson; bill red; legs and feet light olive-grey; eyes orange-yellow.

ADULT FEMALE. Plumage as in the male; head more rounded and bill smaller.

IMMATURE. Differs from the adult in having less yellow on the mantle, hind-neck and under-parts, and has a brownish bill.

Geographical Variations

None recognized.

Field Notes

Cayley wrote: "Fairly common throughout the coastal districts of northern New South Wales, where it generally prefers cultivated fields and open forest country. Occasionally small flocks are recorded in the Hawkesbury River and Gosford districts, but it is rare in the neighbourhood of Sydney. More or less nomadic, its appearance in districts mostly coincides with the flowering of the eucalypts. In some seasons they are very plentiful, and cause considerable damage in orchards, especially to the soft summer fruits. It is usually in company with the Musk and Little Lorikeets and resembles them in habits. The nesting-season commences in late May or early June and continues till about the end of February. The nesting-places are generally very high up from the ground, the entrance to the hole often being sixty or seventy feet up in a tall gum-tree. The eggs are placed on the soft decayed wood at the bottom of the hole, sometimes as far as six feet from the entrance. The birds often select a place from which a thin dead branch has fallen, or a small knot-hole, and chip away the decayed wood till they reach the hollow in the centre of the limb.

"H. G. Barnard of Duaringa, Queensland, records that a pair he had under observation close to his home were six weeks eating their way into a limb, until the eggs were laid.

"Clutch: two eggs; white, and rounded-oval in form; shell close-grained, smooth and lustreless.

"Miss Florence M. Irby, Narrango, Casino, New South Wales, writes: 'In the Richmond River district this is by far the most common species of the *Psittaci*; every flowering eucalypt, bean-tree, grevillea or other blossom-bearer attracting its quota of joyously screaming green birds. Although nectar-feeders they come in their hundreds during the autumn months to feast on the sorghum or saccaline heads as they ripen in the fields, often three or four clinging to one head. And they are not easily frightened away; if shot at they will merely fly a little distance and return directly they think the danger past.

" 'In their swiftness and direct manner of flight they remind one of the beautiful Swift Parrakeets. They often fly very high when going to their feeding-trees. I have seen large flocks looking no larger than mosquitoes as they sped across the sky, their gladsome screech making them easily recognizable. Often too they may be heard passing at night. How do they know when the trees are flowering? Waking one morning you find they have arrived in hundreds where there was not even a sign of one the evening before.

" 'In the early spring of 1926 the Scaly-breasted Lorikeets came in thousands to the flowering gums in the Casino district. They were accompanied by many Rainbow Lorikeets. The noise they made as they scrambled among the blossoms was almost deafening; and the ground was carpeted with the flowers they had pulled to pieces.' "

My earliest observation of this species was in August 1939 when I saw a pair flying over the city of Brisbane. In 1942-43, when I was stationed at Redbank, on the outskirts of Brisbane, this was the common lorikeet of the district and could be seen every day in the camp area; it was noted breeding in hollows in the tall eucalypts on several occasions. In May 1961 I again met with the species between Tenterfield and the north coast of New South Wales and also in the Brisbane area where it was plentiful, and in May 1965 it was present in huge numbers in all areas that I visited with my son in the course of a trip from Inverell in northern New South Wales to Gayndah in south-eastern Queensland. As previously mentioned, a large mixed flock of this species and the Rainbow Lorikeet was observed feeding on a ripening maize crop in southern Queensland.

On the bird-watchers' tour of May and June 1970 this species was found to be widely distributed throughout eastern Queensland but did not appear to penetrate as far inland into the drier areas as did the Rainbow Lorikeet.

This medium-sized, predominantly all-green lorikeet is most likely to be confused with the slightly smaller Musk Lorikeet, with which it often associates, particularly in northern New South Wales. The important distinguishing features of the Scaly-breasted are that it is the only lorikeet with an all-green head and in flight it exhibits a broad red band on the under-surface of both primaries and secondaries.

Aviary Notes

Cayley wrote: "Like the other Lorikeets, makes a delightful inmate of an aviary. Generally an easy bird to keep in captivity, being playful and not very noisy. Unfortunately it is as vicious as the other lorikeets in mixed company. Should be fed and housed similarly to the Rainbow Lorikeet.

"W. K. Penney of Plympton, South Australia, successfully bred and reared two young Scaly-breasted Lorikeets in 1935. The parents nested in a horizontal log about 2 feet by 6 inches. They left the log on 31st May, and in June, although not independent of their parents, were feeding from the food dishes while the adults kept all other birds away. This I understand was the first 'record' for South Australia."

Like the Rainbow Lorikeet, this species was imported in numbers from Queensland before World War II, but very few have appeared in the bird-shops in recent years; they used to be fed by the dealers on maize meal with a little sugar added.

My personal experience of this bird is confined to a pair acquired in 1935; they were kept for only a few weeks on account of their aggressive behaviour towards the other occupants of a mixed collection. This species appears to be another of the family that can be kept, in some instances, for long periods on an exclusive seed diet.

In the Adelaide Zoo a single bird was bred in 1946 but this success has not been repeated since. However, the species is relatively hardy in captivity and there have been a few successful breedings recorded in recent years.

PSITTEUTELES Bonaparte
Bare-eyed Lorikeets

This genus, formerly *Ptilosclera*, has as its Australian representative the widely ranging northern species *versicolor*, the Red-capped (formerly Varied) Lorikeet. It seems probable that the Iris Lorikeet, *iris*, of Timor, strangely omitted from Mivart's monograph,[6] fits properly into this genus, as placed by Peters,[1] although it would be interesting to know whether this species exhibits in life the obvious naked periorbital skin so characteristic of *versicolor*. The position of Goldie's Lorikeet, *goldiei*, of New Guinea, also placed in this genus by Peters, is less certain: I have seen the species in life, both at Taronga Park Zoo, Sydney, and at Brookfield Zoo, Chicago, where it was successfully bred, and formed the opinion that it should be retained in *Glossopsitta*, where it was placed by Salvadori[7] and retained by Mivart.[6]

In common with other lorikeets, the Australian representative of this genus indulges freely in mutual preening, and mated pairs frequently sit close together. The display, as I recall it, consists of the pair approaching one another on a perch and then apparently recoiling by leaning away from each other.

Little has been recorded about courtship feeding but it is almost certain that it occurs; both sexes spend a lot of time together in the nest during incubation, which occupies about twenty-five days but, again, actual participation by the male is doubtful. The feeding of the sitting female and of the chicks by the male at all stages is presumed to occur. The young remain for about seven weeks in the nest after hatching.

The bill of the young bird has been recorded as varying from black to a pinkish shade.

There is no semblance of a coloured band on the flight feathers.

Like all lorikeets, birds of this genus bathe freely in the wild state either in wet foliage or in rain, and in captivity under a spray or in a drinking receptacle.

Food is not held in the foot by members of the genus, and head-scratching is under the wing.

The flight is rapid and direct; the short tail is noticeable in the silhouette.

4 Red-capped Lorikeet

Psitteuteles versicolor (Lear)

PLATE I

Synonyms

Varied Lorikeet, Red-crowned Lorikeet, Variegated Lorikeet.

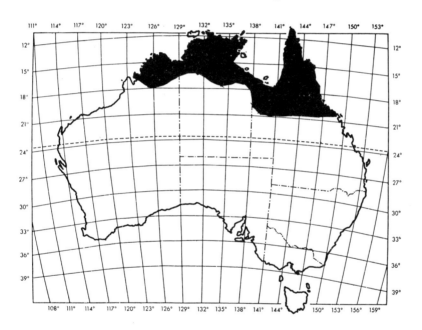

Distribution

In Western Australia the species occurs only in the Kimberley division and it does not appear to have been recorded west of the Fitzroy River.

In the Northern Territory it is found throughout the "Top End" as far south as Victoria River Downs in the west, Elliott on the Stuart Highway and the lower Roper in the east.

In Queensland it has been recorded from most of Cape York Peninsula and farther west from as far south as Camooweal, Mount Isa, Cloncurry and Richmond. There are also isolated records from Mackay and as far south as Gin Gin, and also between Windorah and Boulia.

Description

SIZE. About 8 inches (203 mm).

ADULT MALE. Lores and crown of head cardinal red; cheeks and nape deep blue, the former with bright yellow and the latter with yellowish shaft stripes; interscapular region, back and upper wing-coverts light grass-green, with yellowish shaft stripes; rump and upper tail-coverts light grass-green; tail-feathers light green, yellowish on their inner webs; primaries and secondaries green, margined with blackish-brown on their inner webs; ear-coverts bright yellow; chest dull purplish-red, brighter on sides, each feather with a narrow shaft stripe of yellow; remainder of under-surface and under tail-coverts yellowish-green; bill red; legs and feet leaden-grey; eyes light brown.

ADULT FEMALE. Similar to the male but the red crown is of a lighter shade and the purplish-red colour of the breast is duller.

IMMATURE. Differs considerably from the adult in that all the colouring is duller and the markings less pronounced; also the red cap is replaced by green and there is a small red frontal band.

Geographical Variations

None recognized.

Field Notes

Cayley had no personal notes regarding this species and merely recorded: "Clutch: two eggs; white, shell close-grained, dull and lustreless. Breeding-season: May to January."

My first meeting with this species in the field was in July 1964 when, despite the profuse flowering of *Eucalyptus miniata* in the Northern Territory, it was seen only in several small parties of less than a dozen birds in several different areas. However, large concentrations of the species were met with about twenty miles north of Katherine and also between Warlock Ponds and Larrimah; they were feeding mainly on an unidentified eucalypt with a large white flower. On the R.A.O.U. field outing in 1967 a small party was seen at Nourlangie but they were not observed in any numbers until the return journey when, as before, a moderately large concentration was found between Mataranka and Larrimah. Members of the bird-watchers' tour of July and August 1969 found the species very much more plentiful than on either of the previous visits; it was seen in some numbers at Victoria River Downs, where a pair repeatedly returned to a presumed nesting hollow; also in an area to the east of Kununurra, and once again was quite plentiful between Mataranka and Larrimah.

The call-note of this species is reminiscent of that of the Purple-crowned Lorikeet; the pale bare skin round the eye is very noticeable and has an appearance which is reminiscent of some species of African lovebirds (*Agapornis*).

Aviary Notes

Cayley briefly wrote: "By no means easy to keep in captivity, being very susceptible to cold. Not plentiful in aviaries, and little has been recorded of its habits and behaviour in confinement."

My first meeting with this species in captivity was in the case of a pair kept before World War II by a lady whose husband had procured them from the Northern Territory. This pair of birds lived for several years in perfect condition on a diet of sweetened oatmeal and grapes; unforfortunately, they were never given adequate nesting accommodation or they might well have bred, as I observed them perpetrating their amusing display on several occasions. The breeding record at the Keston Foreign Bird Farm in 1936 reported by Brooksbank[8] appears to be the first instance of the species having bred in captivity.

Thanks to the courtesy of L. C. Webber, of Sydney, I have information regarding an Australian success. The owner of the birds is C. J. Lambert, of the Sydney suburb of Horsley, and they had been in his possession for almost two years before going to nest in a small box, 8 inches by 6 inches, with a short spout. Two white eggs were laid on 16th and 18th September 1949 and were brooded by the hen only. The young hatched after an incubation period of twenty-two days, and the first left the nest on 16th November; both were independent three weeks after leaving the nest. Both parents fed the young, the food provided being Weetbix, milk, sugar, honey, apple and thistle. It was noticed that one young bird had a black beak and the other a pinkish one; these proved to be a cock and hen respectively.

This species has never done very well at the Adelaide Zoo, although eggs were laid in 1948; the species has been exhibited there intermittently since that date, but no further breeding has been attempted.

In 1965 J. L. Mitchell, of the Adelaide suburb of Marion, was awarded the bronze medal of the Avicultural Society of South Australia for the breeding of this bird. His published account of this success reads as follows:[9]

"In my opinion, this brush tongue is the most attractive of the smaller Lorikeet family. Its vivid colouring and amusing antics make it an ideal aviary bird. Approximately three years ago I was fortunate enough to obtain twelve of these birds and it was my intention from the outset to endeavour to breed them in colony. They were housed in an aviary approximately 16 ft x 10 ft x 7 ft with a 6 ft shelter and, even though there were approximately one dozen logs placed inside and out of the shelter, they made no attempt to go to nest in the first two seasons. However, during June, 1965, two pairs commenced nesting operations and a clutch of four eggs was the result in each case—all eggs being fertile. By this time it was well into July and a very bleak winter. Only one egg hatched and the youngster was dead in a matter of hours. All the others were dead in the egg.

D

"Needless to say, this caused me great concern but I managed to convince myself that it was probably due to the extreme cold conditions, coupled with a certain amount of interference and in no way attributable to the type of food supplied. There were numerous instances of interference as perhaps once or twice each day they would all carry on in corroboree style and their screeching would cause the sitting hen to leave the log immediately and join them. I have referred to it as corroboree style because it could not actually be termed a fight although at times it was getting pretty close to it. On one occasion, an inquisitive bird entered the log of one of the breeding pairs and was promptly torn to pieces. The male bird of the other pair seemed to be just as interested in another hen, in fact, more so whilst his mate was sitting, and soon afterwards it was noticed that his other hen friend was trying to get into the same log. He did not try to stop her and she often succeeded in getting inside, whereupon the sitting hen would leave her eggs and push her out immediately. It amazed me that this stray hen did not select another log because she was certainly intent on going to nest. I persevered in the hope that breeding in colony would be successful, but when the second clutch of four eggs went the same way as the first and the second pair went to nest again, I decided to remove all but the one breeding pair. This pair went on with the job and four eggs were laid again—two being noticed on 4th September. Only one young was hatched, this being on 29th September. The young bird left the log on the forty-third day after being hatched (10th November) and was practically independent in three days and, certainly completely independent one week later. The youngster—obviously a male—was practically the same size as his parents when he left the log and at least as bright in colouring as a mature female (if not brighter) with the only real difference being much less red on the head. I am pleased to say that he is as fit as a fiddle.

"The log chosen is one about three feet in length and approximately nine inches in diameter. It was hung at an angle of approximately 45 degrees and about five feet from the ground under the sheltered section. Sawdust and dirt was supplied and the birds added numerous feathers. Needless to say, the eggs followed the parrot fashion and were all white. Before commencing to lay, the hen bird was in the log continually for many weeks, and the male spent most of the time with her. This continued throughout the incubation period: the male only leaving the log to feed and then returning immediately to feed his mate.

"Whilst the young bird was in the log, it was fed by both parents but immediately it left the log, only the male bird seemed interested in feeding it, and then only on one or two occasions to my knowledge. As I mentioned earlier the bird was feeding itself without difficulty three days after leaving the nest. I have stuck rigidly to the same food, this being apples, bread and milk sweetened with sugar and occasionally with honey, pears and flowering gum branches, when available. Pears have never really been appreciated, but apples are relished and I am quite satisfied that they could exist on these alone and probably remain in excellent condition. Whilst feeding the young bird the parent birds consumed more bread and milk than usual, in addition to their supply of fruit which would average one normal size apple per bird each day.

"Instead of the usual type perches I have used two dead trees—one at each end of the flight—and on these, I place the apples which are cut in halves. To see one dozen Lorikeets crawling over the tree feeding and carrying on with their amusing antics as they do I can assure anyone is a sight really worth seeing. The display of the male to his mate is somewhat unusual and slightly resembles the Indian Ringneck. Both birds maintain a constant noise sounding like 'Zrr-zrr', and bob up and down on the perch like a jack-in-the-box, and continually sway away from each other in a circular fashion as if their feet were anchored to the spot.

"Because these birds are from our tropical North and thus come into breeding condition during our winter I am satisfied that it would be wise to remove all nesting facilities until at least August and, if this is done, I think there would be a good chance of spring breeding being successful.

"I am deeply honoured to have been awarded the Society's bronze medal for the first breeding of this species, but full credit must go to my eldest daughter Trina (14 years) who has attended to their requirements regularly over the years when, for business reasons, it has not been possible for me to do so."

GLOSSOPSITTA Bonaparte
Small Lorikeets

This genus of short-tailed, small lorikeets is predominantly an Australian one, with three well-known and widely ranging species; as noted under PSITTEUTELES it seems proper to include *goldiei* of New Guinea as a fourth species in the genus. The members of the genus are all dark-billed forms, as opposed to the birds of the two preceding genera with their red or orange bills. A further interesting point is that the two smallest members of the genus, *porphyrocephala* and *pusilla*, appear to be unique among the lories and lorikeets in producing clutches of more than two eggs, threes and fours being not unusual for these species.

Practically everything that has been said in regard to the genus *Trichoglossus* in respect of preening, courtship behaviour, incubation and feeding of young applies to this genus; however, the display is not as elaborate as it is with the larger birds.

The incubation period is about three and a half weeks and the young remain in the nest between five and six weeks before fledging.

With these dark-billed birds the bill colour of the fledgling is appreciably lighter but it soon acquires the adult colour.

There is nothing resembling a wing-stripe in the members of this genus.

Bathing habits are the same in all members of the genus.

The flight is direct and swift, with rapid wing-beats; the short tail is a prominent feature of the silhouette.

5 Musk Lorikeet

Glossopsitta concinna (Shaw)

PLATE I

Synonyms

Red-eared Lorikeet, Green Keet, Green Leek (erroneous), King Parrot (erroneous).

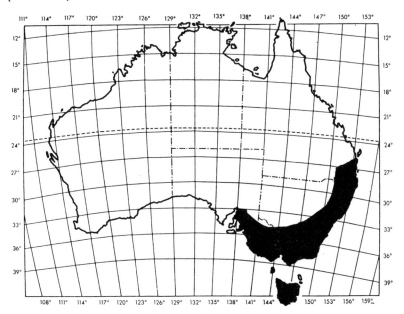

Distribution

In Queensland there are relatively few records of this species, all being from the south-eastern corner of the State with the exception of isolated observations from Duaringa and Maryborough.

In New South Wales most records are from the Great Dividing Range or to the east thereof. A. R. McGill states that he has seen the species as far west as near West Wyalong and J. N. Hobbs states that it reaches south-western New South Wales in the Mathoura-Barham area in small numbers with some regularity; elsewhere only as a bad-season visitor. A. C. Hunt states that in north-eastern New South Wales it is common as far west as Bingara.

In Victoria it appears to occur practically everywhere from east to west, including the north-west corner on occasions.

In South Australia this species occurs throughout the south-east, the Mount Lofty Ranges, as far north as Orroroo and along the Murray eastward from Morgan to the border; Kangaroo Island records need confirmation.

In Tasmania it is plentiful and widely distributed, and small flocks have been recorded on King Island on several occasions.

Description

SIZE. About 9 inches (229 mm).

ADULT MALE. General colour above and below grass-green; forehead and ear-coverts bright red; crown and sides of head washed with blue; centres of feathers of forepart of cheeks rich bluish-green; hind-neck and interscapular region olive-brown; primaries and secondaries blackish-brown, the outer webs and tips green, except on the outermost primary which is narrowly edged with green; an irregularly shaped patch of bright yellow on sides of breast; under-surface of tail washed with yellow, bases of inner webs of the two outer pairs red; bill blackish-brown with an orange-red tip; legs and feet yellowish-grey; eyes orange.

ADULT FEMALE. Similar to the male but has less blue on the head.

IMMATURE. Differs from the adult in being duller in coloration generally, with an incomplete dull red crown and less yellow on the sides of the breast. The bill is uniformly dark coloured without the orange tip.

Geographical Variations

None recognized.

Field Notes

Cayley wrote: "Freely distributed in the coastal districts of New South Wales, being more abundant during the summer and autumn months when they generally congregate in large flocks. Its appearance is greatly governed by the food-supply, and its chief haunts are the forests of flowering eucalypts. Generally it associates with the Little, Purple-crowned, and Rainbow Lorikeets, and like these species is a serious pest to orchardists. During the late spring months they are met with in pairs: it is not uncommon for several pairs to breed in the same tree. The nesting-season depends largely upon the food-supply: usually it breeds in the spring, but often in late summer. A noisy bird on the wing and when feeding among the blossoms, yet its call is not so loud as that of the Swift Parrot, and its flight is much slower. For a breeding-place it usually selects a very small hole or the elbow of a limb of a tree, and mostly in living gum-trees. If one wishes to know, without chopping it out, if a hole in a tree is occupied by this parrot, one has only to place one's nose near the hole; if present the strong musky odour associated with this bird will be evident.

"Clutch: two eggs; white, and nearly globular in form; shell close-grained, smooth and lustreless. Breeding-season: August and the four following months."

I have been familiar with this species for most of my life for it is an extremely common bird in the vicinity of Adelaide at most seasons of the year and is nearly always to be found whenever there are eucalypts in flower in the suburban streets and parklands. At most times of the year, but especially in the summer, odd birds and small parties can be heard and seen coming and going from the large Moreton Bay fig-trees at the northern end of the Adelaide Oval, where they presumably feed on the fruit. The species is also common in the south-east of South Australia and, on one occasion, vast numbers were seen feeding on a crop of ripening wheat near Bordertown; fortunately, this habit does not appear to be widespread. However, this bird has a bad reputation on account of its liking for fruit and there are accounts of numbers becoming intoxicated through feasting on fermenting grapes.

My experience of the species in other States is very limited: I can recall having seen it in southern Queensland only in very limited numbers, and a pair near Launceston in October 1969.

Its relatively large size, distinctive call-notes and absence of red under the wings constitute reliable features in field identifications.

Aviary Notes

Cayley merely stated: "Does not live very long in captivity. An attractive bird with playful habits, but a veritable savage in mixed company."

Although such a common bird in the wild state, it is never very freely kept in captivity and it is undoubtedly one of the lorikeets which will not often survive long on a diet of seed alone.

The bronze medal of the Avicultural Society of South Australia for the first breeding of this species was awarded to Dr W. Hamilton in 1930. In the Adelaide Zoo it was first bred in 1941 and in several subsequent seasons in a hollow in an old, rotted tree stump. These successes were repeated annually at the Zoo between 1963 and 1967.

6 Purple-crowned Lorikeet

Glossopsitta porphyrocephala (Dietrichsen)

PLATE I

Synonyms

Porphyry-crowned Lorikeet, Zit Parrot.

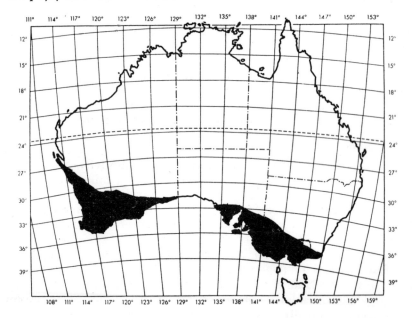

Distribution

In Western Australia, where this species is the only lorikeet other than in the Kimberley division, it is found, according to Serventy and Whittell,[10] in the south and south-west, south of the mulga-eucalypt line and in the Great Victoria Desert and along the coastal mallee fringe to Eucla when the eucalypts are in flower.

The above range probably implies a more or less continuous distribution across into South Australia, where it occurs from southern Eyre Peninsula north to the Gawler Range. East of Spencer Gulf there are records from Yorke Peninsula, Kangaroo Island and from most of the remainder of the south-eastern part of the State, north as far as Wilmington in the lower Flinders Range.

In Victoria the species is widely distributed, especially in the western part of the State, but there is also a suspect record from Mallacoota.

The New South Wales records are few and far between and mainly southern, namely at Euston, Rand, Albury and Bega. However, J. N. Hobbs states that it is a regular winter visitor to far south-western New South Wales and breeds regularly (in October) near Euston; he has recorded it up to fifty miles north of Buronga.

Records from the Tweed River in northern New South Wales and Murphy's Creek in southern Queensland must be regarded as suspect.

Description

SIZE. About 7 inches (178 mm).

ADULT MALE. General colour of upper-surface green; forehead orange tinged with red on lores and in front and above eyes; crown of head purplish-blue; ear-coverts pale orange; occiput, hind-neck and sides of neck yellowish-green; mantle dull yellowish-green; upper wing-coverts and scapulars green; shoulders and lesser wing-coverts bright blue; primaries and secondaries blackish-brown, their outer webs green externally edged with yellow; interscapular region olive-green; rump and upper tail-coverts grass-green; tail green, inner webs and under-surface yellowish washed with crimson at base of lateral feathers; throat, breast and centre of abdomen bluish-grey; flanks and under tail-coverts light green tinged with yellow, the former washed with red; axillaries and under secondary coverts crimson; bill black; legs and feet flesh-grey; eyes hazel.

ADULT FEMALE. Similar to the male, but the ear-coverts are much paler and there is no red wash on flanks and inner webs of lateral tail-feathers; eyes darker.

IMMATURE. Differs in being much duller in coloration generally and completely lacks the purple cap; the red on flanks and tail-feathers of the adult male is absent.

Geographical Variations

The birds occurring in Western Australia, *whitlocki*, are stated to be paler in colour; this is not particularly obvious.

Field Notes

Cayley wrote: "This dainty little lorikeet is commonly called the Purple-crowned Keet and is still fairly plentiful. Usually seen in flocks, frequenting flowering eucalypts and other blossoming or fruit-bearing trees. Those that I have seen were always in flowering eucalypts, and almost invariably in association with the Little and Musk Lorikeets which they closely resemble in habits and economy. Nomadic, its movements being regulated by the various flowering seasons of the different eucalypts. Its flight is swift, the flocks keeping well bunched together as they dart over the tops or between the trees. When on the wing, and constantly while feeding, they utter sharp screeching notes. Nectar, native and cultivated fruits and berries are its food.

"The nesting-site is in a hollow limb or hole in a tree. Clutch: four eggs; white, and round or rounded-oval in form; shell close-grained, smooth and lustreless. Breeding-season: usually September to November."

This is perhaps the commonest and most widely spread lorikeet in South Australia, although not as obtrusive as the two larger local species on account of its small size and rather feeble call-notes. I have been familiar with this species for most of my life, as it is often plentiful in the suburbs of Adelaide and I have also met with it in many parts of the State, as well as in the south-west of Western Australia (where it is the only lorikeet) and in the western half of Victoria.

It is primarily a nectar-feeder, but there are a few records of its having developed a taste for soft fruits.

The small size and the red colouring under the wings constitute the field key for differentiation from the considerably larger Musk and slightly smaller Little Lorikeet.

Aviary Notes

Cayley briefly wrote: "Like the Musk Lorikeet this species does not live very long in captivity. There is no record of it ever having been taken abroad or bred in confinement. One can only suggest that it be housed and fed like other members of the genus."

Although such a common wild bird, this species has seldom been kept successfully in captivity for any length of time, and soft food is undoubtedly essential for its well-being.

It was bred in 1936 by J. Gregg, of Croydon, South Australia. I well remember taking an overseas dealer, L. Behrend, to see these birds, and he subsequently purchased the parents and the two young birds.

Dr W. Hamilton had young of this species in the nest when he left for England in 1930, and he hand-reared them successfully aboard ship. Probably one of the several that he took to England on that occasion was still on exhibition in the Parrot House of the London Zoo when I visited it in 1940.

A pair of these birds laid two clutches of two eggs in 1949, in the collection of R. W. McKechnie, but the eggs were unfortunately clear on each occasion.

It was not until 1963 that the bronze medal of the Avicultural Society of South Australia was claimed for the breeding of this species by J. G. Hamilton of the Adelaide suburb of Walkerville. The published account of his success[11] reads as follows: "This delightful little lorikeet which has been kept by many aviculturists over the years, has somehow missed out on doing the right thing on quite a number of occasions, and accordingly on a number of occasions when they nested for some of the fanciers who were keen to breed them, they just carried on long enough in some instances to hatch the eggs, on other occasions a little longer, but always failed to complete the task. However, this has finally been achieved, and definitely is a very first breeding here in South Australia, and possibly a first all round.

"The successful breeder is Mr J. G. Hamilton of Walkerville, a very keen parrot fancier, housing species of the Neophema group and some of the larger varieties. Considerable success is being achieved with all species, and this fancier really gives them the care and attention they like and respond to, and consequently this in the case of the Purple-crowned brought about the desired result.

"This pair of birds shared the aviary with several other species of Lorikeets, these being four Swifts, one Blue Mountain, one Musk, and an odd Purple-crowned. The aviary they occupied was an open flight type, with a shelter eight feet deep, twelve feet wide and eight feet high, and a flight fifteen feet long. This they had occupied for two years before nesting, and finally they selected a log about two feet six in length and five inches in diameter. This was just inside the shelter, hung horizontal and about seven feet from the ground. The entrance to this was from the front and this was a full opening. The log they selected was one of seven provided for these and all other parrots occupying this aviary. Like most parrots they do not build a nest, and for nesting material sawdust and soil was placed in the log and this they shaped up to their liking. This material is placed in all the logs this fancier provides for his collection of parrots.

"Eventually when the Purple-crowned decided to nest they laid a clutch of two eggs, which were hatched, and for a time the two chicks were being fed, but finally one was lost. Incidentally, it was thought that both birds shared in the incubation of the eggs. No definite period is quoted for incubation as Mr Hamilton did not wish to disturb them whilst they were busily engaged with these duties.

"Following incubation the young bird was fed in the log for over a month, and when it finally decided to emerge from the log it would do so for short periods during the day, and return to the log very quickly when the aviary was approached. Feeding of the young bird was shared by the parent birds, and about a week after leaving the log, the young bird was practically independent. On leaving the nest it was of immature colour and there was no sign of any purple patch on the head.

"The diet supplied consisted of bread soaked with sugar and milk. Equal quantities of sugar, Farex, powdered milk were mixed into a paste, using water to gain the correct consistency of this prepared food. This was fed to the birds freshly mixed every morning and evening. In addition, they were supplied apple. Whilst feeding the young, the parent birds showed preference for the mixture of Farex, etc.

"During the rearing of this bird, no interference was experienced from any of the other species sharing this aviary, and this may be attributable to the fact that all species were released in this aviary at the same time, and space was adequate to permit the selection of an area near the log selected, and logs were well spaced in various positions in the aviary.

"Mr Hamilton has added another breeding of the soft food species to a list that is steadily being compiled by the members of this Society, and this after a few failed to succeed with this species. The breeding of this type of bird involves a great deal of preparation and certainly a lot of patience, and it means that a routine has to be adhered to, and this very rigidly in some instances, and for that reason whenever success is achieved it is a fitting reward for the effort and the venture attempted whether it applies to parrots or any other species of the soft varieties."

7 Little Lorikeet

Glossopsitta pusilla (Shaw)

PLATE I

Synonyms

Red-faced Lorikeet, Tiny Lorikeet, Gizzie, Slit.

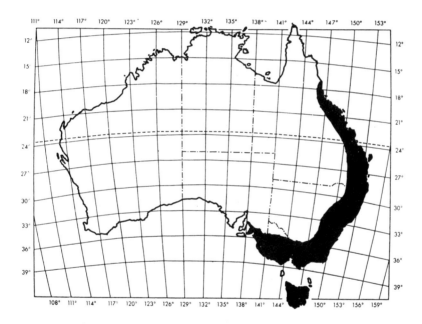

Distribution

Queensland records of this species extend as far north as Cairns and are all from the coastal strip and Dividing Range with frequent observations as far west as Chinchilla.

Those from New South Wales extend from the north to the south of the State but there appear to be few from farther inland than the western slopes of the Great Dividing Range. A. C. Hunt states that the species is numerically stronger west of the watershed of the ranges in northern New South Wales than to the east thereof.

In Victoria the species is widely distributed but there are no certain records from the north-west corner.

In South Australia it is commonest in the south-east, with occasional sightings in the Mount Lofty Ranges and on the Adelaide Plains. The northernmost record is from Sutherlands, and westernmost from Yorke Peninsula.

In Tasmania it appears to be relatively uncommon.

Description

SIZE. About 6½ inches (165 mm).

ADULT MALE. General colour above and below grass-green; forehead, forepart of face and sides of throat red; hind-neck and interscapular region olive-brown; primaries and secondaries blackish-brown, green on their outer webs except the first primary; tail-feathers green, the outer ones red at the base and yellow on the apical portion; wings, under tail-coverts and under wing-coverts yellowish-green; bill black; base of lower mandible dull reddish-brown; legs and feet olive-grey; eyes orange.

ADULT FEMALE. Differs in having a smaller facial mask which is of a duller shade of red.

IMMATURE. Similar to the adult, but with less and paler red on the face, the edge of the wing and the nape yellower, and the breast more yellowish-green; bill olive-brown.

Geographical Variations

None recognized.

Field Notes

Cayley wrote: "The Little Lorikeet (also called Little Keet, Jerryang, and Green Parrakeet) is still fairly abundant, in some seasons, in the neighbourhood of Sydney. Often in association with the Musk and Rainbow Lorikeets, their range being the same. Usually in flocks frequenting chiefly the tall-timbered areas of flowering eucalypts, and is remarkably fearless and noisy, both while feeding and when in flight. From April to the end of June, one often sees large flocks of these birds twisting and turning as they fly swiftly over the tree-tops in search of flowering trees. A voracious feeder, and difficult to disturb when feasting on the nectar— its chief food.

"The nesting-site is in a hollow limb or hole in a tree, usually about twenty feet from the ground.

"Clutch: Usually four eggs, occasionally five; white, some almost globular in form, others rounded-oval; shell close-grained, smooth and lustreless. Breeding-season: August to December."

My first meeting with this species in the field was at Puckapunyal camp in Victoria in September 1942; my attention was drawn to it by the different call from that of the to me familiar Purple-crowned Lorikeet, which was plentiful at Seymour a few miles away. I again saw the species in small numbers in the vicinity of Brisbane the following year but it was not until 1960 when I paid a visit to the home of A. C. Hunt near Inverell, in northern New South Wales, that I became really familiar with the species. It is really a very small bird and its feeble, wheezy calls are often obscured by the noise made by the Rainbow and Scaly-breasted Lorikeets with which it frequently associates. In May 1965 A. C. Hunt and I found the species plentiful everywhere between Toowoomba and Gayndah in southern Queensland. In South Australia it is a comparatively rare species and I have seen it only in the south-eastern portion on a few occasions; I have not met with it in the Mount Lofty Ranges, where it is sometimes recorded.

In May and June 1970 the bird-watchers' tour of eastern Queensland noted this species at Gin Gin and at Cardwell. It was also plentiful at both Scrubby Creek and Kaban on the Atherton Tableland and was observed at the Dawson River crossing near Moura.

The absence of any red under the wings and its small size are the most important field guides when the bird is seen in flight.

Aviary Notes

Cayley's brief notes read: "Another species difficult to keep in captivity, there is no authentic record of it ever having been bred while caged."

This bird is very uncommon in captivity, even in the eastern States, and I know of very few occasions when it has been kept in captivity in South Australia. In R. W. McKechnie's collection, shortly after World War II, a clutch of two eggs was laid, but the sitting hen was unfortunately killed by an unmated bird; a few seasons later a single young bird was hatched in a burrow in the ground in the corner of the aviary but this bird was killed by a rat when half-grown.

N. K. Bush, of the Sydney suburb of Peakhurst, has kindly supplied me with the following information regarding his successful breeding of this species. The birds were housed in a half-covered, planted aviary 15 feet long, 7 feet wide and 6 feet in height. The male bird had been hand-reared, and the female had been caught as a young bird two years previously. They were the only parrots in the aviary, but there were also several pairs of mixed finches housed therein. The nest was under cover, five feet from the ground, in a small box measuring 6 by 6 by 10 inches, with a small hollow log fixed on the front as an entrance. The box was filled to a depth of 2 inches with rotted wood, and the pair spent much time in the box before the hen eventually laid a clutch of four white eggs late in September 1948, the exact date being unknown. Two young birds hatched on 19th October, all the incubation having been performed by the female, who was fed by the male; both birds were very spiteful at this time. Both young birds left the nest about the middle of November, and were independent in two weeks. The food provided was Weetbix, to which was added two teaspoonfuls of Gold Medal condensed milk for each one and a half biscuits; boiled water was then added to form a thin porridge. The hen apparently did all the feeding of the young birds, and it was subsequently noticed that the birds were eating a little canary seed. I understand that Mr Bush was again successful in breeding these birds in 1949.

The Adelaide Zoo has only exhibited the species for a short time on one occasion, during World War II.

OPOPSITTA Sclater
Fig-parrots

The three Australian representatives of this genus are confined to the three major tracts of rain-forest occurring along the east coast of the continent. Keast[12] states: "Those populations inhabiting the two more southern tracts (*coxeni* and *leadbeateri* = *macleayana*) have obviously been isolated for a considerable period of time for they are approaching the degree of differentiation typical of species." Certainly *coxeni* and *macleayana* differ markedly from each other and also from *diophthalma marshalli*, regarding which Keast says: ". . . that inhabiting Cape York, however, is presumably a recent immigrant for it is only doubtfully distinguishable from that inhabiting the Aru Islands."

In New Guinea there are a number of races of *diophthalma* which have a wide range, and also another species, *gulielmiterti*, which has a large number of subspecies and a wide range.

Very little has been recorded in regard to the behaviour of this genus. Tavistock[13] noted that members of the related genus *Psittaculirostris* indulged in mutual preening, and it is presumed that members of this genus behave similarly in this respect.

The late Sir Edward Hallstrom kept numbers of one of the New Guinea races of *diophthalma* and also a few of the allied *Psittaculirostris edwardsi* but did not record anything about either; small, unspectacular birds never appealed very greatly to him. It would appear, therefore, that virtually nothing is known in regard to breeding behaviour.

The wing-stripe is quite extensive and is present in adults of both sexes of the three Australian forms; this may be considered as pointing to a possible platycercine affinity.

J. M. Forshaw has given me the following interesting information regarding a male *macleayana* which has been in his possession for some considerable time. The bird appreciated a spray but was then noted to bathe in the water vessel provided and does this every day; however, Forshaw has seen enough of the genus in the wild, both in Australia and New Guinea, to be almost certain that it is completely arboreal and would therefore bathe during rain or in wet foliage.

The bird under observation scratches over the wing and never holds food in the foot.

The flight pattern of fig-parrots is moderately rapid, and the extremely short, stumpy tail is a characteristic of the silhouette.

E

8 Southern Fig-parrot

Opopsitta coxeni (Gould)

PLATE II

Synonyms

Blue-browed Lorilet, Coxen's Fig-parrot, Red-faced Lorilet.

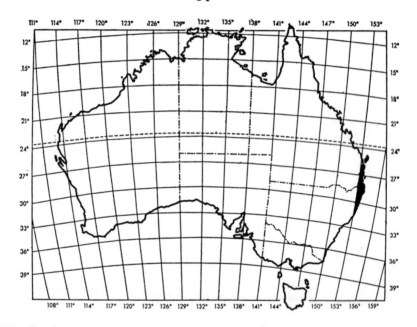

Distribution

Records of this species, which are remarkably few, suggest that it is confined to south-eastern Queensland and north-eastern New South Wales;
the southernmost record is from the Macleay River.

Description

SIZE. About 6 inches (152 mm).

ADULT MALE. General colour above and below green; forepart of face
green flecked with red; ear-coverts, and inner webs of innermost secondaries, red; lower parts of cheeks bright blue, forehead tinged with blue;
outer webs of primaries dark blue, inner webs blackish; tail dark green;

throat and remainder of under-surface yellowish-green, with a yellow patch on sides of body; under wing-coverts bluish-green; bill bluish horn; legs and feet ashy-brown; iris brown.

ADULT FEMALE. Similar to the male but with the red of the ear-coverts extending forward as a band to the base of the lower mandible.

IMMATURE. Undescribed.

Geographical Variations

None recognized.

Field Notes

Cayley recorded the following valuable information: "The species appears to be extremely rare. Why, is difficult to understand, their habitat being the coastal and contiguous scrubs of northern New South Wales and southern Queensland, where large areas are as yet in a virgin state. Perhaps their quiet habits and the difficulty of observing them while feeding in the tall fig-trees are the main reasons why the species has been overlooked.

"When a boy and resident in Casino, Richmond River, New South Wales, I shot one of these birds in mistake. I had fired at a Fruit Pigeon in a tall fig-tree and judge my astonishment when down fell a small parrot along with the pigeon. My father identified it as a Fig Parrot, the only name the species was known by in that district. My shot disturbed several birds, but it was impossible to tell whether they were parrots or pigeons. Visiting the same brush, which was quite close to the town, we were fortunate enough to locate these lorilets on several occasions. They were feeding in the fig-trees, usually in company with pigeons, fig-birds and other fruit-eating species. Difficult to locate, the only indication one had that any birds were feeding in the trees was the quantity of falling fruit dislodged by them. It is a neck-breaking task locating brightly-coloured birds feeding among the tree-tops, and extremely difficult to identify them without the aid of field-glasses. On several visits to the far northern rivers of New South Wales during later years attempts to locate these birds proved fruitless; certainly much of the virgin scrub had disappeared, but there were large areas still untouched by axe or fire. Only the older residents remember the species; they saw small flocks occasionally, especially when felling and clearing the big scrub lands.

"In a letter, dated 12 January 1935, Valdie Christensen of Urangan, via Maryborough, Queensland, wrote me as follows: 'On 2 August 1934, quite near the Urangan Point State School a nest of the Blue-browed Lorilet (*Opopsitta coxeni*) was found by me. The nest was in the hollow of a burnt off log that had been lying on, and half buried in, the ground for years, and contained two pure white eggs, quite fresh.' This letter was read at a meeting of the Ornithological Section of the Royal Zoological Society of New South Wales. It was the considered opinion of the members present, that it was a case of mistaken identity, inasmuch as the bird is strictly arboreal in habits, and the nesting-site, a log on the ground, was the reverse of all known sites. Holes in trees, up to forty feet from the ground, are used by the northern species (*O. leadbeateri*).

"J. R. Kinghorn (*Emu*, vol. xxxvi, pt i, p. 31, July 1936) under the title 'Nests and Eggs of the Blue-browed Lorilet (*Opopsitta coxeni* Gould)' writes: 'The nests and eggs of this little Lorilet were discovered by Mr Valdie Christensen, at Urangan, near Maryborough, Queensland, and are described here for the first time. Mr Christensen informed me that the bird has been a very rare visitor to the Urangan district during a number of years which he has lived there. He first identified the Lorilet as it sat on the limb of a tree near a log which later proved to be the nesting-site. In order that there would be no mistake regarding the identification, I forwarded a packet containing males and females of *Opopsitta coxeni* and allied species, to Mr Christensen who was thereby enabled to confirm his opinion. He informed me that there are many wild fig-trees and berry-bearing trees in the district, mostly growing among the thickets and uncleared land, whilst mistletoe berries are abundant close to the nest, and some large fig-trees are in the hollow near the beach about one-quarter of a mile away. The actual vicinity of the nesting-site is open forest land, near the Urangan Public School.

" 'The nest was in an old, rotted-off, boomerang-shaped stump which was half buried in the ground, thus forming a hollow, and the eggs were laid about twelve inches from the entrance.

" 'The eggs are two in number, pure white, and with a slight lustre on the shell. They are not absolutely oval, one end being slightly more pointed than the other. They measure, in millimetres, 15 by 12. It was observed that they were quite warm when discovered, and examination proved that incubation had commenced. Date of discovery, August 2, 1934.

" 'First clutch in the Valdie Christensen Collection, Urangan, via Maryborough, Queensland.'

"That record is rather an anomaly; a species of arboreal habits resorting to a hollow in a log for a nesting-site, more especially so, when one considers that the other member of the genus nests in holes high up in trees. Certainly other species of parrots resort to logs when nesting-sites are scarce; the Budgerigar for example—through force of circumstances, such as when, during a good season, large numbers of birds congregate where food is plentiful and all the Grass-parrots spend much of their time on the ground feeding on the seeds of grasses and herbaceous plants, whereas the lorilets are fruit-eaters. Again, all the breeding records of *O. leadbeateri* have been obtained from experienced collectors and were accompanied with skins; which, after all, is more satisfactory than records made from memory and by observation only.

"Miss Florence M. Irby, Narrango, Casino, New South Wales, writes: 'I doubt if this little lorilet has ever been otherwise than rare on this extreme north coast of New South Wales. But I do not think they can be any rarer now than they were twenty or thirty years ago when now fast vanishing scrubs covered thousands of acres. The destruction of the rain-forests of the north coast was ruthless and the birds were driven farther and farther back to where isolated patches are still in their virgin glory. Any such areas are naturally far from so-called civilization, and there is little if any observation made on the birds that haunt them.

" 'At rare intervals during the last twenty years I have met with this lorilet in the Tweed River district, where I frequently stayed on my brother's farm. Twenty years ago dense scrubs still covered land that is now devoted to crops or paspalum; every creek had a glorious fringe of almost tropical growth, and there I occasionally saw a pair of these plump little birds feasting with a flock of Crimson Rosellas (*Platycercus elegans*) on the beautiful blue fruit of the Blue Fig (*Placocarpus grandis*). Again I met with them in the same locality in the uppermost boughs of a White Fig—that wonderful parasitical tree that beginning life as a tiny seedling in some small hole or crack in the highest boughs of some forest giant adds its own height to that of its victim which it gradually overgrows and smothers with its octopus-like roots.

" 'The Blue-browed Lorilets have a habit of feeding with other parrots; these being noisier or more arresting in numbers or colouring are apt to draw attention from the plump little green birds pattering about in the same tree.

" 'Again a pair may be found feeding with a flock of Scaly-breasted Lorikeets (*Trichoglossus chlorolepidotus*) among the honey-laden flowers of a Silky Oak (*Grevillea robusta*). Shortage of fruit during the early spring months may account for this, or they may have a natural liking for a change of diet, just as the nectar-loving Scaly-breast will sometimes attack the ripening trees of saccaline or even strip some shrub or tree of its leaves. I incline to the latter theory; for I first saw a pair of Fig Parrots, with Musk Lorikeets (*Glossopsitta concinna*) in a Silky Oak in the Richmond River district many years ago when scrubs with abundance of their natural foods were far more plentiful than now.

" 'The last pair I met with were seen in October 1930; they were in dense scrubs near Mount Warning, on the upper reaches of the Tweed River. With a feeble screech they flew into a tall fig-tree. The birds noted were in pairs except upon a couple of occasions when there were four. As on each occasion it was late in the season it was presumed that two eggs only were laid!' "

Hugh Peddie, of Maryborough, Queensland, has sent me the following valuable information: "*O. coxeni* has been recorded by me at the Kenilworth State Forest (rain-forest) area just some forty miles south of Gympie in September 1960 and again in October and November in 1962 and 1963. On all these occasions there was a party of about a dozen birds quietly feeding on a large and isolated fig-tree species, probably a 'strangler'. My attention was drawn to them while trying to locate cat-birds which were calling and feeding in the same tree. I then noticed these very small lorilets creeping about the foliage near the cat-birds and after observing them for about half an hour through

7x50 binoculars was pretty sure that they were *coxeni*. In November 1966 I also recorded them at the Bunya Mountains National Park. Again my attention was drawn to them only because I was trying to observe a small noisy party of Little Lorikeets which were feeding in the same tree, which appeared to be a forest plum (*Davidsonia pruriens*). As far as I could gather, the Lorikeets were making all the noisy chatter and the Fig-parrots were feeding without calling. When they flew from the tree the flight was swift and direct and again I heard no calls.

"About eighteen years ago, soon after my arrival in Maryborough, I made the acquaintance of Valdie Christensen who at the time was living at the coastal area of Urangan (Hervey Bay) about twenty miles by road from Maryborough. He and his son were (or had been) keen egg-collectors and it was he who had found a *coxeni* breeding in a hollow log on the ground. He was sure the bird was a *coxeni* as he says he had seen them feeding in blossoming melaleucas near Urangan. He left Urangan about 1960 and I have not seen him since. His record of the breeding of *coxeni* in a log on the ground is apparently an isolated instance.

"I have no breeding records at all nor have I been fortunate to sight *coxeni* at Hervey Bay although the Little is there with the Rainbow and Scaly-breasted Lorikeets. Possibly more regular birding at the Bay would produce *coxeni* also."

I have never met with this species in the field. It is noteworthy that none of the Australian museums have skins collected this century, and there is little doubt that it is one of the least-known and possibly also one of the rarest of the Australian parrots.

Aviary Notes

Cayley wrote: "There is no record of the species ever being kept in captivity. But there seems no reason why it could not be kept as well as many other fruit-eating species which thrive well and breed readily under proper management."

I am unable to add anything to the foregoing remarks.

9 Northern Fig-parrot

Opopsitta macleayana (Ramsay)

PLATE II

Synonyms

Red-browed Lorilet, Leadbeater's Fig-parrot, McCoy's Fig-parrot, Macleay's Fig-parrot, Blue-faced Lorilet.

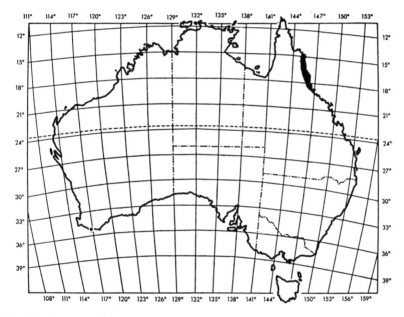

Distribution

Most records suggest that this species is confined to an area bounded by Cairns in the north and Cardwell in the south; however, Forshaw[5] gives Cooktown as its northern limit and suggests that it may possibly reach Townsville to the south; this has now been confirmed.

Description

SIZE. About 5½ inches (140 mm).

ADULT MALE. General colour above and below green, darker on back, wings and tail, brighter on head, hind-neck, sides of neck and breast, paler and more yellowish-green on lower breast, abdomen, thighs, under

tail-coverts and under wing-coverts, the outer margin of the last more
or less blue; bastard wing, primary coverts and outer aspect of primary
and secondary quills dark blue, with inner webs dark brown, a whitish
spot on most of the quills commencing on the third or fourth primary,
some outer webs of secondary quills green; forehead, face and ear-
coverts red, as is also a large patch on the secondaries; lores and a line
below eye turquoise-blue; chin and lower cheeks tinged with purplish-
blue; a large patch of yellow on sides of body; greater series of under
wing-coverts and quill-lining pale brown, margins of former and a band
across latter lemon-yellow; lower aspect of tail (which is obscured by the
under tail-coverts) greyish-brown; bill light blue-grey; legs and feet light
grey; eyes dusky brown.

ADULT FEMALE. Differs from the male in the absence of the red on the
sides of the face, this area being buff brown tinged with bluish-green.

IMMATURE. Resembles the adult female but differs from the adult in
having the under-surface of the plumage a paler green with a decided
yellowish tinge. Bill pale horn colour, darker at the tip.

Geographical Variations

None recognized.

Field Notes

Cayley wrote: "This dainty feathered gem of the parrot tribe has been
sadly overlooked by field workers. All that is known of its habits in the
wild could easily be written in a short paragraph. Like its congenitor
the Blue-browed Lorilet, it usually associates in small flocks and frequents
big scrubs and open forest country alike. It is generally observed in
fruit-bearing trees, chiefly native figs, being at all times remarkably
quiet. Generally, the only indication of its presence is that afforded by
the quantity of fruit it drops while feeding; even then it is difficult to
locate.

"As already mentioned the nest is a hole in a tree, usually about forty
feet from the ground. Clutch: Three or four eggs; pure white; shell
smooth with a slight lustre. Breeding-season: September to November."

In June 1970 I was fortunate enough to see two birds of this species
feeding in a native fig in the main street of Kuranda, North Queensland.
I was looking at some Barred Cuckoo-shrikes in the tree and suddenly
noticed the two small green parrots feeding silently on the figs. They
were either females or immatures, for they did not exhibit any red
colouring on their cheeks. Even when they flew from one part of the tree
to another they did not make any call. After having observed them for
some time, I noticed that the roof of a car parked under the feeding tree
was littered with fragments of chewed-up figs.

An article in the *Emu* by Bourke and Austin[14] contributes a great deal
to the knowledge of this species in the field and draws attention to the
habit these birds have of congregating in roosting trees to which they

return after sunset and which they leave again in the morning when it is barely light. Bourke's and Austin's observations further demonstrate that the species is by no means uncommon, especially in the lowland jungle near Cairns, and they saw it as far north as Mount Molloy, north of Mareeba and also at Lake Eacham. Having seen the bird many times in open forest and partially cleared country along the coast, they reached the conclusion that it was by no means confined to the jungle. They each found a nest in the Cairns area during October 1944; both nests contained two eggs which the authors considered were probably incomplete clutches, in view of Campbell's statement[15] that the clutch is three or four.

It is of great interest to note that Bourke and Austin speculated that "even now it is not too late to discover Fig-parrots on Cape York, far to the north of Cairns". Their paper containing this remark was actually received before Iredale[16] published his account of Marshall's discovery in the region they suggested.

Aviary Notes

Cayley stated: "There is no record of this species ever having been kept in captivity." However, Bourke and Austin[14] state: "It was not until after we had left the area that we heard that a specimen was being kept in captivity in Cairns, and we were unable to follow up the report."

As with *O. coxeni*, I am unable to add anything to the foregoing remarks.

10 Cape York Fig-parrot

Opopsitta diophthalma (Hombron and Jacquinot)

PLATE II

Synonyms

Marshall's Lorilet, Double-eyed Fig-parrot.

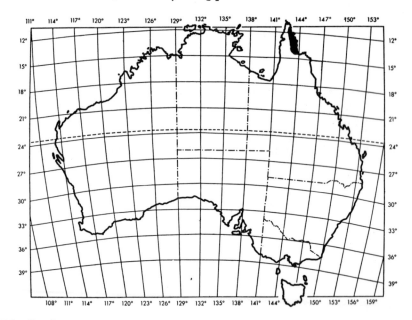

Distribution

The range of this species is probably limited to the eastern side of Cape York Peninsula from the Pascoe River and upper reaches of the Jardine River south to Princess Charlotte Bay. The record of *macleayana* from the Jardine River seem certain to be referable to this species.

Description

SIZE. About 5 inches (127 mm).

ADULT MALE. Forehead, lores, cheeks, ear-coverts and feathers at base of lower mandible scarlet, a line of bright-blue feathers above the eye and another short blue line below the red; all upper-surface bright green, a shade paler on upper tail-coverts, inner web of inner secondaries red, tail dull green; upper wing-coverts and secondaries bright green, primary coverts and primaries brown with outer web dull greenish-blue, the first primary only lacking this edging, as do all the tips; under-surface to under tail-coverts pale green, sides orange-yellow, under tail-coverts yellowish-green, under wing-coverts mottled dull yellow and brown, axillaries green, inner lining of primaries dull yellowish as are the basal parts of the secondaries forming a band; bill dark brown, iris dark, feet and legs pale blue-green.

ADULT FEMALE. Similarly coloured above and below, but complete absence of red on head; forehead bright blue, lores, cheeks and ear-coverts buff brown as are the feathers at base of lower mandible, a blue line of feathers separating this from the green below.

IMMATURE MALE. Similarly coloured above and below, but forehead duller blue than in female, feathers near base of culmen white and red tipped, lores and base feathers of lower mandible pale reddish, line above eye blue, below eye a band of fawnish ending in a blue tip.

Geographical Variations

Several races of *diophthalma* occur in New Guinea; Keast[12] considers the Australian birds, *marshalli*, only doubtfully distinguishable from *aruensis*.

Field Notes

At the time of writing his notes Cayley was unaware of the discovery of this bird, which Iredale[16] reported in *Emu*, stating that Marshall, working on Cape York Peninsula, North Queensland, in September 1942, collected three specimens of a Fig-parrot, which represented a new species, in dense jungle on the Great Dividing Range, behind the Lockhart River.

This species was extensively studied by Forshaw[5] in the course of his visits to Iron Range in 1963 and 1966. He considers the bird to be practically confined to dense forest, it having been observed in open woodland only in the morning and evening in the process of making its way from one patch of forest to another and very occasionally in trees on the margin of rain-forest.

Feeding habits seem to be the same as those of the other species, the food consisting mainly of berries and fruits, particularly native figs. Forshaw, on one occasion, noticed a bird which appeared to be eating either bark or a fungus.

One of the most interesting of Forshaw's observations refers to the use of roosting trees by large parties or flocks of these birds; they occupy these roosts at sunset and leave again at first light and during the following half-hour or so. These observations tally with those recorded by Bourke and Austin[14] in the case of *O. macleayana*.

The eggs have not been described but it is believed that nesting occurs in May, after the end of the wet season, and the hollow is thought to be excavated in the soft fibrous trunk of a particular tree.

Aviary Notes

Although it is highly unlikely that the Australian race of this species has ever been kept in captivity, the late Sir Edward Hallstrom had a number of examples of one of the New Guinea races, presumably derived from the Central Highlands. I am led to believe that this species laid whilst in his possession but did not produce any young; as with so many of Hallstrom's successes, no written record exists. In 1950 he presented me with two birds which both proved to be females—indeed it was subsequently realized that all his stock were females at that time and it transpired that they had all been caught by natives placing their hands over nesting hollows. My birds lived for only about eight months: they could be persuaded to eat only sunflower seed and a little apple and they were always timid and uninteresting. Later, when Sir Edward obtained some male birds, a pair was sent to E. J. Boosey of Keston Foreign Bird Farm in England. Boosey wrote at some length about them, stating, among other things:[17] "Some rare birds prove disappointing, with little save their rarity to recommend them. The little Double-eyed Dwarf Parrot, on the other hand, is as desirable as it is rare, being not only extremely neat and pretty, but also quite one of the most charming and delightful little birds it has ever been my good fortune to keep. The hen of the pair, unfortunately, became ill on the journey and was killed by her mate on being put back in the cage with him after she had recovered from her illness, so it would seem that, despite his small size, a cock Dwarf would need careful watching when a hen was introduced into its aviary."

Since Boosey's article is of unique value, the remainder of it is quoted hereunder:

"Although, owing to its size and general shape, one instinctively compares it with a Lovebird, yet in its quick, rather Lorikeet-like movements, and in its general character and disposition, it is totally different from any member of the *Agapornis* family, and strikes one as having all the intelligence and power of mimicry of the larger parrots.

"The one I have flies very swiftly and has the quick, precise movements of a Lorikeet and also, when excited, their habit of progressing along a perch in a series of hurried jumps, turning in mid-air, so that at one moment he has his back to you and at the next is facing you. If you offer him a titbit he has the curious habit of coming along the perch to take it from your fingers in almost incredibly slow slow-motion, giving exactly the comical effect of a film of a person walking at a normal pace slowed down to a minimum until they move with the most extreme and unnatural deliberation! I don't know the object of this stealthy approach and have never observed it in any other bird.

"It was supposed that, if ever imported, Dwarf Parrots would prove very delicate and sensitive to cold, and would probably need nectar-feeding like the Lory family. My experience of the little Double-eyed Dwarf Parrot, however, shows that they are neither delicate nor difficult to feed. At first I used to take him in for the winter, housing him in a flight cage in a bird room which was heated during very cold spells. When caged, however, he started feather-plucking, so I decided to leave him in his aviary, which faces south, and has a double-wooded shelter into which he is shut each night during the winter, and he never turned a hair even during the coldest spells.

"As to food, he keeps in perfect health on canary, sunflower, monkey nuts and a little hemp, with spinach beet and apple, of both of which he is very fond. He also has, three times a week, a small piece of bread that has been soaked in diluted sweetened milk, which would prove an excellent rearing food if one were ever lucky enough to breed them.

"I think I am right in saying that the Double-eyed Dwarf Parrot I have is the first member of the family ever to be imported into this country and judging by this my first experience of keeping one, I should say that once acclimatized they are quite as hardy and little more difficult to cater for than any of the better-known Australian Parrakeets, so it is doubly to be regretted that there seems little chance of any more being imported, as they are most attractive.

"They are full of character, and my bird is an excellent mimic. He does not actually talk but he imitates very cleverly in his small voice the evening cries of Ringnecks and the alarm note of a pair of Brown's Parrakeets whose aviary is just behind his.

"He has a quick and fiery temper, and if you dare to pass his aviary without taking any notice of him he gives vent to angry screeches of protest of extraordinary volume and carrying-power for a bird of his size. Nor are you at once forgiven if you offer him sunflower or a piece of monkey nut, for he will ignore such peace-offerings, and bang angrily on the wire netting with his beak! However, he soon gets over his temper, and within an hour or so will once more be his delightfully tame and charming self again.

"Incidentally, he is every aviculturist's dream of perfection when the time comes to shut him into the aviary shelter for the night. Some birds just *won't* go in unless driven; others will go in quite readily, but have the infuriating habit of dashing out again as though they had seen a ghost just as you are about to close the shutter.

"My Dwarf Parrot does neither of these things. He is never inside already, as some of the other birds are, but is always sitting in the flight waiting for me, and the moment I say: 'Now then . . . in you go!' he most obligingly does so at once; uttering the quick 'Chee . . . cheet, chee . . . cheet' he always does when on the wing."

PROBOSCIGER Kuhl
Palm Cockatoo

This monotypic genus is confined to New Guinea (including some of the adjacent islands), the Aru Islands and Cape York Peninsula, Queensland. Several subspecies have been described, mainly on the basis of size, with one, *stenolophus*, having more slender crest feathers. There is little doubt that the genus has no very close relations and it may deserve an entirely separate subfamily. Although superficially it may be regarded as a black cockatoo, it bears very little relationship to the genus *Calyptorhynchus* either in appearance or in behaviour.

Palm Cockatoos do not preen their mates, although the pair bond is a close one. The display is most elaborate and spectacular. Forshaw[18] observed it many times at the congregating tree. It was always accompanied by the disyllabic, whistle-like contact call. As the first note of the call was given, the bird adopted an upright stance, with the crest half raised. With the emission of the shrill, drawn-out second note the cockatoo lunged forward, extended the wings and raised the crest and tail. This display was frequently performed two or three times in succession by different birds in the tree. At first it was thought to be a mating display but was subsequently seen being performed by individual birds, including an immature male and an adult female, at their roosting trees. This seemed to indicate that all birds, irrespective of sex, may display in this manner. In captivity this display has been observed being given only by the male and it is often accompanied by stamping of the foot.

Courtship feeding has not been recorded, but it is known that both sexes share the duties of incubation, which, according to R. T. Lynn, of the Sydney suburb of Condell Park, takes thirty-four days. Both birds feed the young both in the nest and for a considerable time after fledging. The down colour is not recorded; the bill of the young bird is a light colour when it first emerges.

Palm Cockatoos bathe freely in a shower of rain.

The foot is used for holding articles of food, such as nuts and large seeds.

Head-scratching is under the wing.

According to Forshaw the flight is heavy and laboured, with slow, full wing-beats and the bill held down against the breast.

11 Palm Cockatoo

Probosciger aterrimus (Gmelin)

PLATE III

Synonyms

Goliath Aratoo, Great Palm Cockatoo, Cape York Cockatoo, Black Macaw (local and erroneous).

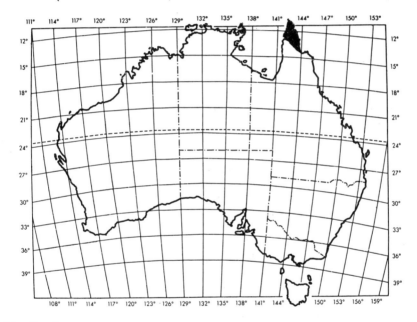

Distribution

The extra-limital distribution comprises New Guinea and the Aru Islands. The Australian distribution is from the extreme tip of Cape York Peninsula extending, according to Thomson,[19] as far south as Massey Creek at the northern end of Princess Charlotte Bay on the east coast and to the Pennefather River on the west coast. Forshaw[5] stated that J. H. Calaby extended the west coast distribution farther south to the Mission River.

Description

SIZE. About 23-27 inches (584-686 mm) according to race.

ADULT MALE. General colour above and below black, with a steel-grey tinge that is more pronounced on the crest feathers, which are much elongated, narrow, and lanceolate in form, and on the upper wing-coverts, scapulars and outer secondaries; hinder portion of ear-coverts black; base of forehead and lores deep velvety-black, the feathers being short and close-set; bare facial patch red; bill black, lower mandible slaty-black; legs and feet blackish; iris brown.

ADULT FEMALE. Similar to the male but, not invariably, smaller. The bare facial patch is usually smaller and the bill is considerably smaller.

IMMATURE. Differs from the adult in its more dusky-black coloration and has the feathers on the under-surface and under-wings barred towards the tips with yellow. Terminal part of bill yellowish-white.

Geographical Variations

Birds from Cape York, *macgillivrayi*, are indistinguishable from some of the New Guinea races and do not warrant recognition.

Field Notes

Cayley had not seen this bird in the field and merely reproduced the interesting notes of Barnard[20] and Macgillivray.[21]

The most recent accounts are those of Forshaw,[18] who described his observations of the species on Cape York in November 1963 in *Emu* and further elaborated on that visit and a subsequent one in January 1966 in his *Australian Parrots*.[5] He found the bird to be numerous in the Iron Range district and drew attention to its habit of roosting singly in the top branches of tall trees on the edge of the rain-forest. In the morning these birds were noted to be late movers, and not until about an hour after sunrise did they commence calling; this resulted in the joining-up of a party of about half a dozen birds in a tall tree in open woodland. After a period spent in this tree, which was accompanied by much displaying and calling, one bird would leave for the feeding areas and the rest would follow almost immediately.

The feeding trees were invariably pandanus, the bird's bill being an obvious adaptation for the purpose of cracking the extremely hard nuts. These trees were occupied until about mid-morning; thereafter the birds sought the shelter of the rain-forest for the remainder of the day, not leaving it till near nightfall, when they returned to the roosting trees.

Aviary Notes

Cayley quoted at length from Dr E. A. d'Ombrain's account in the *Emu* of his pet Palm Cockatoo.[22]

Most of my early knowledge of this species was derived from a study of the specimens in the Adelaide Zoo where, in 1950, three out of a consignment of six obtained twenty years earlier were still surviving. A pair of these birds nested there on several occasions, laying a single egg each time, and twice a young bird was hatched, but in neither case did it survive for more than a few days. As is apparently the case in the wild state, the birds make a rough nest of pieces of bark and sticks, on which the egg is laid.

This cockatoo is quite unlike its relatives in its behaviour and habits generally. Its main call-note is a shrill, quite indescribable whistle, it has a peculiar habit of stamping one foot when excited or alarmed, and the colour of the bare facial patch becomes brighter with the same emotions.

In 1968 the late Sir Edward Hallstrom was kind enough to give my elder son a pair of these birds, for which we constructed a special aviary. The hen laid an egg on the ground within a couple of weeks of arrival and we hoped for further breeding attempts but, strangely, none eventuated and after about a year we were forced with great reluctance to part with the birds because of their incredibly shrill calls, particularly in the early morning and late afternoon.

R. T. Lynn, of the Sydney suburb of Condell Park, has bred two of these birds in the last few years, the first of which I saw when I visited his magnificent collection of cockatoos in October 1969; unfortunately he does not appear to have published any account of this outstanding success, which is certainly a "first" as far as Australia is concerned.

F

CALYPTORHYNCHUS Desmarest
Black Cockatoos

Mathews[23] divided this genus into three subgenera, but Peters[1] accepted only two. The subgenus *Zanda*, comprising the closely related Yellow-tailed and White-tailed Black Cockatoos, does not exhibit marked sexual dimorphism, whereas in the two red-tailed species, the Red-tailed and Casuarina Black Cockatoos, the difference between the sexes is very striking, especially in the former. I have so little personal experience of the Casuarina that I feel unable to express a firm opinion on the desirability of its separation as the subgenus *Harrisornis*, but it is doubtful, to say the least, if *Zanda* warrants retention.

Mutual preening does not take place in the members of this genus, and in captivity, at any rate, pairs do not often appear very attached to each other; males, particularly when tame, are often more interested in humans.

The display of all four species is practically identical; it consists of elevation of the crest and spreading of the tail-feathers in order to display the coloured band, accompanied by a purring or growling note as the male struts along a perch and bows to the female.

This genus is unique amongst the cockatoos in that the males do not participate in the incubation of the eggs; Vane[24] was in error in stating that all the Cacatuinae share the duties of incubation. Courtship feeding has rarely been observed, but the male feeds the female when she leaves the nest during the period of incubation, which is twenty-nine days. It is not established whether he feeds the young bird whilst it remains in the nest for the long period of twelve or thirteen weeks, but he does so after fledging. It is an interesting feature of the breeding behaviour that if two eggs are laid there is an interval of several days between laying and hatching and there appears to be no record of a second chick ever being reared.

The down of the young bird was believed to be cream coloured in all species but Taylor[25] has recently stated it to be white in the White-tailed species. The bill is pale coloured when fledged and very slowly turns black in the males and horn colour in the females.

Black cockatoos enjoy bathing in rain or, in captivity, in a spray.

Food is held in the foot and the head is scratched under the wing.

The slow, flapping flight is buoyant in character and appears lazy. The long tail is a prominent feature of the silhouette.

12 White-tailed Black Cockatoo

Calyptorhynchus (Zanda) baudinii **Lear**

PLATE III

Synonym

Baudin's Black Cockatoo.

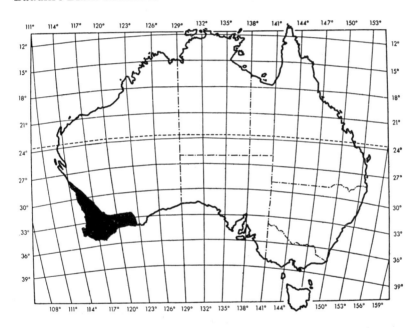

Distribution

Writing of this Western Australian species in 1967 Serventy and Whittell[10] stated that it was confined to the south-west corner, from the lower Murchison River to the eastward of Esperance (recorded to Mississippi Bay) and extended inland as far as Wongan Hills, Kellerberrin and Norseman. No extensions of this range have been found.

Description

SIZE. About 24-26 inches (610-660 mm).

ADULT MALE. General colour above and below greyish-brown with pale edges to the feathers, those on the under-surface being broader; lores, feathers below eye, cheeks, and forehead black with a greenish tinge; ear-coverts dull creamy-white; tail-feathers blackish-brown, all but the central pair crossed in the middle with a broad band of white except on outer edges; bill black; legs and feet dull greyish-yellow; iris hazel, the periorbital skin bright pink.

ADULT FEMALE. Differs in that the ear-coverts are a clearer white, the pale edges to the feathers on the under-surface are broader, the bill is whitish-horn and the periorbital skin is black.

IMMATURE. Resembles the adult of each sex but duller; bill coloration not as well marked and periorbital skin not pink in young males.

Geographical Variations

Serventy and Whittell[10] made the following statement in 1967: "Two well-marked sub-species occur. In the forested south-west corner is a form with a narrow bill (tenuirostris) and inland and to the east of Albany, in the sandplain and mallee areas, is found a heavier-billed race with the mandible shortened (latirostris I. C. Carnaby[26])." More recent observations suggest that this difference may not be constant.

Field Notes

Cayley wrote: "The nesting-site is a hole in a tree, as already described.
    "Clutch: two eggs, white, and oval in form; shell lustreless, fairly smooth, with the exception of a few limy excrescences, but having numerous minute pittings. Breeding-season: August to October."

My earliest meeting with this species was in August 1948 when I observed a pair flying around in the vicinity of the Museum, in the heart of the city of Perth, much to the discomfiture of the local feral pigeons who mistook them for hawks! In the course of the same visit to Western Australia I saw the birds in several areas in the south-west of the State and also found a very large flock, of over a hundred birds, at the Canning Dam: it was noticed that these birds kept very largely in groups of three, which consisted of a pair of adults and, by its behaviour, a young bird of the previous nesting season which continually called to its parents for food.

    In July 1954 a similar threesome of a pair of adults and a young bird was observed between Bindoon and New Norcia, about sixty-five miles north of Perth, and in June 1961 a party of six birds flew low and silently over the Zoo at South Perth; possibly they had been attracted thereto by captive specimens, although they are not uncommonly seen in King's Park and in the suburbs of Perth.

    D. H. Perry[27] has published an interesting article on black cockatoos and pine plantations, from which it is apparent that the seeds of Pinus pinaster form a very large part of the food of this species for a consider- able portion of the year; in addition, the cones dropped by the birds have appreciably reduced the labour required to collect the seeds!

Although Gould[28] recorded that this species occasionally fed on the ground, this habit does not appear to have been often noted; however, on one occasion I disturbed a small party of these birds in the Darling Range near Perth that were feeding on the fallen seed capsules of the marri (*Eucalyptus calophylla*).

Aviary Notes

Cayley wrote: "There is no published record of this cockatoo ever having bred in captivity. The only examples I have seen in the life are a pair in the Adelaide Zoological Gardens which I was told had been only recently received. They were being kept under similar conditions to other black cockatoos that have been in the Gardens for some time."

The first time that I ever saw this bird alive was when an overseas dealer passed through Adelaide, not long before World War II, with a lovely specimen in his possession. Subsequently the two young birds referred to by Cayley were obtained by the Adelaide Zoo but, although they survived for several months, they never appeared to be in very good condition. E. J. L. (later Sir Edward) Hallstrom had quite a number in his collection when I visited him in Sydney in June 1949, and he informed me that they had laid eggs on occasions. This species appears to be very like the Yellow-tailed Black Cockatoo in its habits, as indeed would be expected, for it is obviously a very close relative.

In life the plumage gives the impression of being a rather greyish shade as opposed to the more brownish tinge of the Yellow-tailed.

This bird has become better known in captivity during the past twenty years or so but I have still never heard of a successful breeding; even R. T. Lynn, of the Sydney suburb of Condell Park, does not appear to have succeeded yet, although he had two fine pairs when I saw his collection in October 1969. The C.S.I.R.O. Division of Wildlife Research has carried out investigations into the ecology of the species in its laboratories in Western Australia and has kept examples in captivity, but I have not heard of any successful breedings on their part either.

G. F. Taylor,[25] of the Sydney suburb of Terrey Hills, recorded that in November 1970 a pair of these birds in his possession laid and incubated an egg which hatched and the chick survived for about six weeks.

13 Yellow-tailed Black Cockatoo

Calyptorhynchus (Zanda) funereus (Shaw)

PLATE III

Synonyms

Funereal Cockatoo, Yellow-eared Black Cockatoo, Wyla.

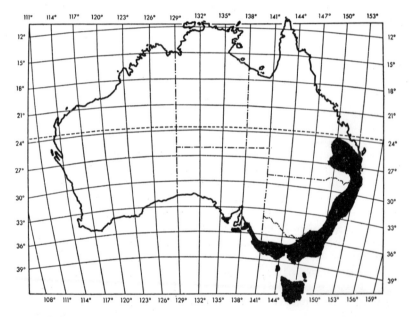

Distribution

In Queensland, apart from an old record from Duaringa and a pair seen in June 1970 in the Dawes Range, between Biloela and Monto, the northern limits of this species appear to be in the vicinity of Gin Gin and Gympie, and the western limit in the region of Chinchilla. From these points there is a relatively unbroken distribution southward along the Great Dividing Range throughout New South Wales into eastern Victoria, where it extends throughout most of that State, with the exception of the north-western and mid-northern portions.

In South Australia the species is widely spread through the south-east and the Coorong into the Mount Lofty Ranges. It is plentiful on

Kangaroo Island and is also, rather surprisingly, found on southern Eyre Peninsula.

In Tasmania it is widely spread and also occurs on King, Flinders and Cape Barren islands.

Description

SIZE. About 24-26 inches (610-660 mm).

ADULT MALE. General colour above brownish-black, including the head, sides of face, back, wings and tail, with paler margins to most of the feathers on hind-neck, sides of neck, back and upper wing-coverts; primary coverts and primary quills have whitish margins at tips; central pair of tail-feathers brownish-black, the remainder brownish-brack crossed (except a narrow margin on the outer webs) with a broad yellow band which is freckled and spotted with brownish-black; ear-coverts light yellow; under-surface dark brown with pale yellowish margins to the feathers; bill greyish-black; legs and feet dull mealy-brown; iris dark brown; periorbital skin bright pink.

ADULT FEMALE. Similar to the male, but usually the yellow band on the tail-feathers is thickly covered with zigzag lines of blackish-brown; ear-coverts brighter yellow; margins of feathers of under-parts broader and a brighter yellow; bill horn-coloured, periorbital skin black.

IMMATURE. Duller in coloration than the adults of each sex; bill coloration not as definite and periorbital skin in young male is not pink.

Geographical Variations

None are accepted; the Tasmanian birds, formerly given specific rank (*xanthonotus*), do not appear to differ in any important feature from the mainland birds. Hallstrom maintained that birds derived from the Blue Mountains had appreciably longer tails.

Field Notes

Cayley wrote: "This species is perhaps the best-known of the black cockatoos, owing to its wide distribution, and frequenting, as it does, the more inhabited portions of the eastern States. This slow-flying bird is the largest of the group, and is still not uncommon in the neighbour-hood of Sydney. Its favourite haunts are the coastal districts, the contiguous mountain ranges and open forest lands. Generally flocks of from six to a dozen birds are met with. They usually make their presence known by their harsh and discordant cries, which when once heard are not easily mistaken for any other species. As a rule the flocks are shy and wary. Its food consists chiefly of the seeds of banksias, casuarinas and hakeas, and the larvae of harmful timber-boring insects. In habits and economy it resembles the Red-tailed species. From my own observations I would class it as even far more useful in helping to keep in check injurious insects, the larvae of which infest valuable timber-trees.

"The nesting-site is a hole in a tree, usually in the main trunk of a dead tree in a clearing, and placed very high up from the ground.

"Clutch: two eggs: white, and varying in form from a very rounded-oval to a thick oval, tapering somewhat sharply towards the smaller end; shell very finely granulate, and covered with minute shallow pittings; some specimens are almost lustreless, others are slightly glossy. Breeding-season: variable, but chiefly during May and June. Eggs have also been taken in each month from October to March."

I have known this species in the Mount Lofty Ranges since boyhood and it was always present in the Victor Harbour district in the summer, feeding on the numerous stands of pines in that area. There is little doubt that, as in Western Australia, pine plantations have contributed enormously to its food supply and it is very plentiful in the south-east of South Australia and in many parts of the hills near Adelaide.

Since I have resided in the Mount Lofty area, I have often seen and heard parties of up to ten or a dozen birds moving through and feeding on pines in the district, but they are practically never seen other than in the summer months.

On the occasion of a conference of fauna authorities held on Kangaroo Island in April 1965, delegates were interested to see a flock of over a hundred of this species feeding on the ground near the western boundary of Flinders Chase. On a visit to Tasmania in October 1969 I was surprised to find a party of a dozen birds feeding on low shrubs near the summit of Mount Barrow, some twenty odd miles east of Launceston.

G. B. Ragless, of Unley Park, South Australia, has supplied me with the following valuable and extremely interesting notes on his experiences with this species:

"In this State the birds frequent suitable areas in the south-east, Kangaroo Island and the Mount Lofty Ranges. There is very little published information about their breeding habits and in South Australia almost none. Eggs were taken at Kangaroo Island, Forest Range and more recently in the south-east but details have not been given. Having seen the birds frequently in the South Coast area, I became interested in where and when breeding took place. Information was hard to secure until I obtained news late in 1955 that, while bull-dozing timber during land-clearing operations in the Hindmarsh Tiers, many eggs were being destroyed. This is where I have done all my work, although I have since learned that during recent years nesting has taken place at Basket Range, Prospect Hill, Mount Jagged and at Delamere. The latter place and the Hindmarsh Tiers would appear to be where the species congregates in the greatest number.

"My inquiries among timber workers and people who take young from the hollows indicated that the birds usually lay two eggs, but only one bird is reared.

"My first visits were unsuccessful except to find a young bird and realize that my equipment for climbing was inadequate. On 24th November 1956 the first clutch of eggs was secured and in blowing them it was found that one egg was much further incubated than the other. The eggs were given to the South Australian Museum, being the first from this State to be in the McGilp Collection. Since the above date further trips have been made and the following briefly represents the information gained.

"When two eggs, which comprise the majority of clutches (others are a single egg), are laid there is an interval of four to seven days between the laying. The larger egg is the first laid and consequently this egg hatches some days ahead of the second one. I have never handled an infertile egg and I have only once seen an egg (still incubating) with a freshly born young. For some time it was a matter of conjecture as to what happened to the second egg or young bird. I have now established that when the second young hatches (some days after the first) it is neglected by its parents and dies of starvation during the first day or so.

"The country used as a nesting area is at an elevation of from 1,100 to 1,300 feet above sea-level. The only kind of tree used is the stringy-bark with hollows varying between thirty and seventy feet above the ground. The favourite position is in the main trunk with an entrance available where the tree has broken off or where a limb has fallen out. Usually this part of the tree is dead or has been burnt in bushfires, but the lower part is alive with green boughs growing. Derelict dead trees are also used occasionally. The hollows are often almost vertical, but a few of a sloping type have the entrance on the underside. On the outside of the entrance the birds tear away the wood, letting the splinters and chips drop inside the hollow to form a heap on which the eggs are placed. Some chips are torn away from the inside for the same purpose. The 'wood heap' varies from two to six feet from the entrance, but on one occasion the eggs were situated eighteen feet from the entrance. This is the greatest distance I have ever known any species of bird deposit eggs down a hollow. In this instance the main trunk of the tree was used, the bird taking quite a time to climb up the inside wall to reach and leave the exit. Where the timber cutters have operated and thinned out the trees, particularly upon the ridges, appears to be the most sought-after nesting location. The closest I have seen nests to one another would be about forty yards.

"In view of the fact that taken young require up to six months of hand feeding prior to being able to look after themselves, I at first thought that the birds only bred every second year, but I have now abandoned that theory. I now know that some pairs raise young each year. I have evidence which indicates that the young bird of the previous year remains with its parents while they nest the following season. I have not previously seen this recorded. Of course, this would only be evident where the family party has suffered no loss from season to season.

"Most birds flush from a hollow easily. One bird with eggs was observed to leave readily, but later when with young simply came to the edge of the hollow, peered down to the ground then backed in and refused to leave despite a determined effort on my part. Frequently both birds leave the nesting area, go out to feed and return towards evening. I have been unable to reach any conclusion as to why some pairs do this and others do not. Possibly temperature of the day and degree of incubation have a bearing upon this behaviour.

"The main period of laying is during November and December. The size and shape of eggs vary a lot, also the texture of the shell. When a tree has been in a fire the eggs become very dark, due to the fine dust lodging upon them when it is disturbed by the birds moving in the hollow. Eggs are evenly covered, which indicates that they receive regular turning. Quite a number of eggs are damaged by the bird, thus causing a cessation of incubation. On one occasion a bird was found still brooding a single egg which had been fractured some time after incubation had commenced. The bird was apparently unaware that the egg was damaged and that its efforts at attempting to hatch it were a waste of time. Quite 25 per cent of the hollows known to me are unclimbable as the situation is unsafe due to the high position in weak trees. Many of the others require the use of a rope ladder to make their inspection possible.

"A lot of clearing has taken place mainly for pasture purposes, but the birds have adapted themselves to the changed conditions. Nests have been found in trees in semi-cleared land and adjacent to tracks. Two nests were close to a gate on a track used frequently by heavy trucks moving logs, but apparently the birds did not mind the noise created when starting etc.

"Pine plantations close to the nesting area are often visited by the birds for the purpose of procuring seed from the cones for food. Pines used as windbreaks etc. on farms in the district are also visited, and it would appear that the cones are available when most needed, i.e., the breeding period. The birds are only present in the area from about October to April or May. They appear to arrive in pairs or small groups and depart in large flocks. Where they are the remainder of the year is uncertain, but I think it is the Coorong or on Kangaroo Island. I know of about 40 nesting hollows, but there is a lot of country available that I do not visit.

"From what I can gather from people who have known the area for some time the birds are as numerous now as twenty to thirty years ago, despite the clearing that has occurred. This would be offset to a great extent by the pine planting providing food. Much of the country is very rocky and will never be cleared to pasture. The whole area is very rough and in many places the undergrowth is very thick, making walking most difficult.

"The veteran ornithologist Mr Frank Parsons informed me that some years ago many of the birds were shot and it was suggested that they should be removed from the protected list. Their habit of perching close to the top of the main stem of the pine trees and severing it, thus causing double shoots, was the reason for their destruction."

Aviary Notes

Cayley wrote: "There are no published records of this cockatoo ever having been bred in captivity, although there are instances of young birds taken from the nest and hand-reared to maturity."

This species used to be rare in captivity, for it was believed that wild-caught adults would not survive and the hand-rearing of young birds taken from the nest was a most tedious and lengthy performance. However, some fifteen or so years ago, large numbers of wild-caught adults appeared on the local market and many were exported, no trouble being experienced in inducing them to feed. In consequence, in the last couple of decades this species has become far commoner in captivity than the red-tailed species, both in Australia and overseas.

A number of these birds have been kept in the Adelaide Zoo over the past two or three decades, and it is from a study of these that most of my observations have been derived. These birds have laid eggs on several occasions, but seldom in a nesting log and even then incubation did not follow. Pairs of this species seldom appear to be as well disposed towards each other as do pairs of the Red-tailed Black Cockatoo. The display, consisting of erection of the crest and fanning of the tail, is much the same as in that species; on such occasions the relative shortness of the crest feathers is easily observable.

The only recorded breeding success is the unique one of R. T. Lynn, of the Sydney suburb of Condell Park. The story of his success, recorded in the magazine of the Avicultural Society of New South Wales and in the journal of the Parrot Society,[29] is as follows: "I acquired a pair of Yellow-tails in 1961 and turned them into a breeding aviary which I felt would possibly be suitable to their requirements. As I had no prior knowledge of their aviary breeding requirements, I was however prepared for some experimentation if any success was to be achieved.

"The aviary chosen for them was forty feet long, ten feet wide and nine feet in height. The front section, facing north, was covered in with horticultural glass and about one-third of the roof was similarly covered. The shelter portion was at the southern end of the aviary and measured about ten feet in length. The aviary was constructed of strong chain wire on a waterpipe frame—any construction of less rigid strength would have been completely unsatisfactory.

"The floor was earth except for a small section round the base of the nesting log which was cemented for support. Native grasses grew abundantly in the aviary, of which the birds are still sole occupants apart from a pair of Cockatiels.

"A natural log was found in a creek bed not far from my home and I hoped that this would eventually be the nesting box for the birds. It stood about four feet high and had two small U bends at the top which made an ideal entrance to the nesting chamber.

"The seed mixture fed to the birds at first consisted of eight parts of sunflower, two parts of corn, one part of wheat, two parts of oats, one of safflower and some raw peanuts.

"Any chance of success in the first year was thwarted by the hen laying clear eggs, and the cock was replaced for the 1962 breeding season. At this time both birds were about four years old and it has been my experience that this species will not breed until they attain at least this age. Some specimens may not breed until they are six years old. The second year—with the new cock bird installed—saw two eggs laid,˙but these were again clear.

"At about this time I began feeding the birds a spoonful of raw mincemeat about twice a week, a fact to which I gave a lot of credit for my eventual success, as on this addition the birds came into fine feather and looked a picture of vitality. Previously I had given chop bones freely, but although the birds show a liking for them now, they were not readily accepted then.

"In the third year (1963) the hen showed her usual interest in the nesting box in late January. At breeding time the birds show great interest in their log and chew continuously at its exterior. Small chewed wood chips find their way into the actual nesting chamber. The birds do not continue chewing at the log after rearing the chick, or at any time of the year other than when breeding begins.

"It is also interesting to note that each year the eggs are laid, incubation begins and the chick hatches on almost exactly the same days.

"At this time the birds particularly appreciate banksia nuts, although these are fed all the year round. The branches of small trees are also chewed vigorously: an activity which is most time-consuming and keeps the birds occupied and contented in confinement. It should be permitted all the year round, not only in the breeding season.

"In this season two eggs were laid, the first of which duly hatched thirty days later. During the incubation and feeding period, the parents were fed sweet corn, mealworms, canary seed and cultivated pine cones in addition to the diet previously mentioned. The cock bird showed a particular liking for canary seed.

"The young bird took ninety days to leave the nest but he was delicate from the very beginning and I partly hand-reared him. At about one year old he died, never having gained the strength and vitality of the parent birds.

"During the fourth breeding year (1964) the birds went to nest at about the same time and one chick was hatched. This bird was strong and vigorous from the outset and at ninety days old it flew from the nesting log into the aviary for its first solo flight. During the feeding period both parents fed the youngster and this continued for three months after it left the nest. After this period the cock bird continued the feeding alone and the chick remained reliant on its father till the next breeding season.

"My experience has been that about this age the young birds tend to be frail and can easily succumb in this period. Great care is required to get the chick over this weaning stage.

"The parents were seven years old at the time of this successful breeding. This year—their eighth—two eggs were laid but one was clear and the other youngster died in the shell. Any further success will be at least twelve months away."

14 Red-tailed Black Cockatoo

Calyptorhynchus magnificus (Shaw)

PLATE IV

Synonyms

Banksian Cockatoo, Great-billed Cockatoo.

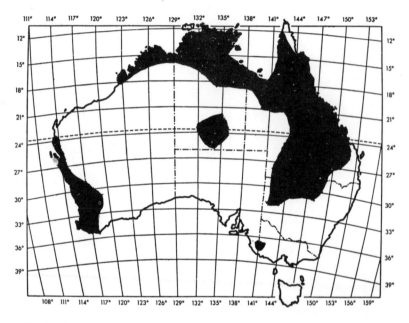

Distribution

A species with a very wide range, particularly in the northern parts of the continent.

For Western Australia, Serventy and Whittell[10] wrote in 1967 that the species was distributed throughout the State but was rare in the south-west. Published records, however, show that the small, short-crested race, *naso*, of the south-west does not occur farther north than the Murchison or possibly the Minilya River; the eastern limits of this population do not appear to be known.

The race *macrorhynchus*, characterized by its large crest and bill and by the almost complete absence of red in the tails of the females, is encountered in the Kimberley division of Western Australia, extending from Broome eastward into the Northern Territory, where it ranges as far south as Victoria River Downs in the west, Elliott on the Stuart Highway and the Nicholson River in the east.

In Central Australia there occurs the doubtfully distinct race *samueli*, which is found throughout the Macdonnell Ranges and probably extending into northern South Australia. Easterly extensions of this population are uncertain.

In Queensland the species extends widely from Cape York Peninsula over most of the State but is absent, according to the late G. Mack, from the south-eastern corner, although it reaches Gayndah on the Burnett River. It seems probable that the Queensland population merges with those of northern and Central Australia.

In New South Wales the species is well distributed throughout the north-western part of the State, extending down the Darling as far as Menindee. Coastal and near-coastal records are few and far between— Macleay and Williams rivers, Illawarra and Australian Capital Territory —and none of them are recent. A. R. McGill states that "the species is somewhat of a mystery in New South Wales. I know of no recent records anywhere near the coast. I saw fair numbers near Tottenham and photographed them, in belah trees, in 1966." Forshaw[5] records the species from Griffith, but this seems likely to be a mistaken identification of *lathami*, which occurs nearby in the ranges at Leeton.

In Victoria there is a small distinct but unnamed population occurring in the western part of the western district and transgressing into the adjacent south-east of South Australia. The record from Mallacoota in eastern Victoria has been shown to be erroneous, the skins collected at the R.A.O.U. camp there having been examined and found to be examples of *lathami*.

The record from King Island, referred to in the 1926 R.A.O.U. Checklist, has not been traced but there seems little doubt that the species no longer exists there, if in fact it ever did. M. McGarvie states, "An old resident says red-tailed black cockatoos were on King Island fifty or more years ago; these were likely to be the Glossy, the habitat being more suitable in those days."

Description

SIZE. About 23-27 inches (584-686 mm) according to race.

ADULT MALE. General colour above and below black with a greenish gloss, which is more distinct on the upper parts, many of the feathers also having a waved appearance; all but the central pair of tail-feathers and the outer webs of the outermost feathers on either side crossed with a red band; bill slate-grey; legs and feet mealy-black; iris blackish-brown, the orbits black.

ADULT FEMALE. General colour above and below black tinged with brown; the feathers on the upper parts also have a greenish gloss and many are edged with brown; back, scapulars, primary and secondary quills and central tail-feathers black; second, third, fourth and fifth primaries incised on the outer webs and the first to the fourth on the inner webs; upper wing-coverts and bastard wing black fringed with pale brown and with whitish markings to the feathers; outer tail-feathers barred and mottled with yellow and red on middle portion of feathers, bars becoming narrower towards tips, under-surface of tail much duller in coloration than on upper parts; crown of head, occipital crest, and sides of face black with pale yellow subapical markings to the feathers; breast and abdomen brownish-black, feathers on former barred with dull yellow and those on latter with a mixture of yellow and red; under tail-coverts black broadly margined at tips with yellow; bill whitish-grey with greyish-brown tip; legs and feet mealy black; iris brown, the orbits black.

IMMATURE. Resembles the adult female but in most instances young males are not as extensively spotted and speckled, and the bill tends to be darker. Young males assume adult plumage gradually by a series of incomplete moults in which they become progressively less speckled generally and the tail-feathers gradually get less barred; in most instances full plumage is not attained till the fourth year.

Geographical Variations

As noted under DISTRIBUTION, the race *naso* which appears to be isolated in the south-west of Western Australia is smaller and with a relatively short crest. *C. macrorhynchus* of the Kimberleys and the Northern Territory is principally distinguished by the almost complete absence of red in the tails of the females. As far as the birds inhabiting eastern and Central Australia are concerned, it is extremely doubtful whether they differ from the nominate form, although the unnamed population based on western Victoria appears to exhibit more yellow barring on the breasts of the females.

Field Notes

Cayley wrote: "This cockatoo was at one time fairly plentiful in close proximity to Sydney, and is still met with in the Illawarra district, the north coast, and on the Blue Mountains. Unfortunately, its numbers are dwindling, and one has to travel to the more unsettled parts of the country to observe it. Usually it is found during the breeding-season in twos and threes (in small flocks of about half a dozen at other times) and is generally exceptionally shy and wary, flying shrieking away at the slightest approach of an intruder. The food of these birds consists chiefly of the seeds of the different banksias, acacias, casuarinas, and eucalypts; they are also partial to the larvae of wood-boring insects, doing excellent service in helping to keep in check these pests so harmful to the timber industry.

"The quantity of litter the birds make when feeding is remarkable. The ground beneath a tree is literally covered with the refuse of cracked seed cones, green leaves, twigs, blossoms, and small branches, or pieces of bark and wood. This tells at once what they are feeding on. The species is more or less nomadic, moving about the countryside following the seeding period of their favourite food-trees. It is extremely fond of the seeds of She-oak (*Casuarina*). The ease with which they extract the seeds from these hard cones—which one has great difficulty to dislodge even with the aid of a heavy hammer—is really remarkable.

"The nest is a hole in a tree, generally in the main trunk and at a great height from the ground. Usually a dead tree situated in a clearing is selected, the nesting-hollow being practically inaccessible to all but the most expert climber.

"From my own observations the female appears to do most of the incubating, the male generally visiting the nesting-hollow only in the early morning and at sun-down, evidently to feed his sitting mate as she rarely leaves her charges. At all times the male approaches the nesting-hollow most cautiously. The first indication one has that he intends visiting the nesting-hollow is his distant call repeated while on the wing, but ceasing as he nears the nesting-site. Usually he perches on a selected elevated position in a tall tree at the edge of the clearing from which he carefully surveys the surroundings before flying to the nesting-tree. He is very alert and will take flight instantly at the slightest suspicion of danger.

"Clutch: one or two eggs; white, and varying from elongate-oval to slightly swollen-oval; shell rather coarse grained, minutely pitted and lustreless. Breeding-season: May to July."

My first meeting with this species in the field was in Western Australia in July 1954 when in company with Dr D. L. Serventy and G. M. Storr: a flock of about fifty birds was located feeding on the ground in a roadside paddock near Carnamah, about 190 miles north of Perth. These birds were remarkably tame and allowed easy observation; we considered that they were feeding on the seeds of double-gees, sometimes known as prickly jacks.

My next encounter was with representatives of the small isolated population in western Victoria. In April 1960 a nesting site had been located a few miles east of Penola just across the Victorian border; it was in an old dead stump about twenty feet from the ground and the single young bird was well feathered and was banded by J. B. Hood. After a long wait, the parent birds were seen to return to the nest almost at dusk, and as far as could be ascertained in the gloom the female entered the nest and presumably fed the young bird.

On a visit to the Northern Territory with three friends in July and August 1964 I saw small flocks passing over the town of Alice Springs, and a party of fifteen birds came in to water at a dam which we had visited at dawn in the hope of seeing Bourke Parrots. At the "Top End" the species was very common, in small parties and in flocks of up to fifty birds; they were feeding on eucalypt seeds, both on the ground

G

and in the trees. It was noted that in this area the females exhibited little or no red coloration in the tail-feathers, which accounts for the oft-repeated erroneous statement that Yellow-tailed Black Cockatoos occur in the Northern Territory.

At Gayndah, in southern Queensland, in May 1965 a flock of eleven birds was seen feeding on the berries of the white cedar. In May 1966 a pair were seen in the course of a brief excursion I made into the Darling Ranges near Perth; it was of great interest to me to confirm the continued existence of the species in this area.

During July and August 1967, on the R.A.O.U. field outing to the Northern Territory, this species was seen in large numbers in most areas visited to the north of Mataranka, including the Nourlangie area. A very large flock, estimated at four hundred birds, was also seen on the Santa Teresa road, several miles south of Alice Springs.

In August 1968, when I made a brief visit to the Alice Springs area, a very large flock, presumably the same birds, was again located on the Santa Teresa road, and in July and August 1969, in the course of a bird-watchers' tour, the species was found to be extremely common in the Northern Territory in all areas north of Elliott, but was not seen in the Kimberleys.

During the bird-watchers' tour to eastern Queensland in May and June 1970 a trio of black cockatoos seen in the distance at Calliope River, central Queensland, were thought to be this species, and another trio was identified with certainty at Big Mitchell Creek, north of Mareeba. Their unmistakable call was heard on another occasion in the same area without the birds actually being seen.

Aviary Notes

Cayley wrote: "In Taronga Zoological Park is a fine old male; he and Jessie the Elephant are the only survivors of the inhabitants transferred from the old Moore Park Zoo. His age is estimated at well over fifty years, and he is still in excellent feather and condition. For several years past he has had a mate; the pair keep constantly together and are among the friendliest of the bird inmates. At present they are housed in a large aviary with a mixed collection of cockatoos, but I understand that in the near future an attempt will be made to breed them in specially-built breeding aviaries now under construction. A female in the Marquess of Tavistock's collection has been at least twenty years in captivity, and another female at the Regent's Park Zoological Gardens has also achieved a very respectable record in close confinement. Many years ago I saw a fine male Banksian in a troupe of performing parrots and cockatoos that appeared on the Australian vaudeville circuit. This bird performed several simple tricks and was devoted to its trainer and owner."

This species is by far the best known in captivity of the black cockatoos, the young birds being usually taken from the nest and hand-reared, an extremely tedious and laborious procedure. When so treated, most males become very tame and well-disposed towards humans, and will often display to them; in such cases, they will seldom become friendly with birds of the opposite sex. Hand-reared females, on the other hand, usually lose their friendliness as they become independent of human feeding.

This species was apparently first hatched in captivity in 1939, in the collection of the then Marquess of Tavistock, and the young bird was ultimately hand-reared by one of his aviary attendants. According to a brief account in the May 1940 issue of the *Avicultural Magazine*,[30] incubation would appear to have lasted approximately two months; however, the late Sir Edward Hallstrom, of Sydney, who bred a number of young birds of this species in his collection, informed me that the incubation period was twenty-nine days, and it would therefore appear probable that one of the months referred to in that account is incorrect.

In 1945 two pairs of this species nested at the Adelaide Zoo, and each successfully reared one young bird. The first pair consisted of a male of one of the large races, which was in adult plumage when acquired in July 1913, mated to a female obtained from the south-east of South Australia in 1936 or 1937. Two eggs were laid, the date not being recorded, and one of them proved to be infertile. Incubation was carried out by the hen only, and a young bird was first seen in the nest on 3rd February. It flourished, and was observed looking out of the nesting log on 12th April, but it did not leave the nest until 10th May; a total period of ninety-six days since hatching. It was first noticed feeding itself on 8th September, four months after leaving the nest! This bird was from the first regarded as a male, and it attained full adult plumage late in 1949 by a series of gradual incomplete moults.

The second pair were relatively young birds obtained from Western Australia a few years previously, and belonging to the subspecies *naso*. Their first egg was laid on the floor of their aviary, and was broken. About a month later another egg was laid in a hollow scooped out in the ground in a corner of their enclosure. This egg was incubated, and hatched on 5th April; the young bird was easily observed and appeared to grow very quickly, and after a time it began to roam about the floor; consequently, bricks were placed around its corner to prevent this. This bird eventually flew to a perch on 18th June, when seventy-five days old, and it was first noticed feeding itself on 13th October, again approximately four months after leaving the nest. From the first, this bird was correctly considered to be a hen, being much more heavily spotted and barred than the other young bird; time proved this to be correct, its plumage having altered very little over the years. The parents of these birds were fed on a mixture of sunflower seed, hulled oats and boiled maize; in addition, lettuce was supplied and a few pine nuts were relished whenever available.

The display of this cockatoo consists of the crest being erected, the feathers of the cheeks puffed out so as to hide the beak, and the tail being fanned to show the red bar; a soft, almost purring, note is uttered at the same time.

Since that time this species has been bred frequently at the Adelaide Zoo from several pairs; seldom has a season passed without one young bird being reared there. The late Sir Edward Hallstrom also bred a goodly number in Sydney at the height of his avicultural career.

15 Casuarina Black Cockatoo

Calyptorhynchus (Harrisornis) lathami (Temminck)

PLATE IV

Synonyms

Leach's Black Cockatoo, Glossy Black Cockatoo.

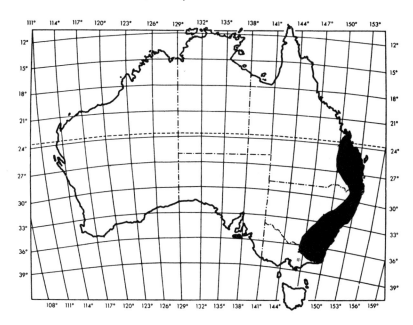

Distribution

There are surprisingly few records of the occurrence of this species; in its identification there is always the possibility of confusion with the Red-tailed Black Cockatoo.

In Queensland the northernmost records are from Yeppoon and Duaringa. Reliable recent records are from Gympie, the Condamine River and Toowoomba and Warwick districts.

New South Wales records of the species are from Tenterfield, the Bellinger and Macleay rivers, Cobbora, Dubbo, Barrington and Leeton. A. R. McGill comments that Leeton, Dubbo and Cobbora records seem too far west but the species is not uncommon in the eastern range country. The late Keith Hindwood stated that the species had been observed on a number of occasions in Nadgee Faunal Reserve in the south-east of New South Wales, and J. N. Hobbs states that it is common in Chichester State Forest which extends up to Barrington Tops, and that he had also seen it at Bateman's Bay and Katoomba. G. Dibley refers to several recent records in the Dharug National Park, on the northern side of the Hawkesbury River between Wiseman's Ferry and Spencer.

In Victoria this species certainly occurs at Mallacoota and has been recorded from Strathbogie and Wangaratta.

In South Australia there is a small isolated population on Kangaroo Island, and towards the end of the last century specimens were seen (and reputedly taken) in the southern Mount Lofty Ranges.

Description

SIZE. About 20 inches (508 mm).

ADULT MALE. General colour above, including back, wings, and central tail-feathers black, glossed with green; all but the central pair of tail-feathers crossed in the middle with a vermilion band, except on margin of outer webs; entire head, including the short crest, sides of face and throat smoky-brown, middle of feathers somewhat darker; under-surface, including under wing-coverts and under tail-coverts, black with a smoky shade; bill greyish-black; legs and feet mealy-grey; iris dark brown.

ADULT FEMALE. Differs from the adult male in having the red of the tail-feathers crossed with black bands and margined with yellow along edge of their inner webs; under-surface of tail-feathers shows more yellow than on upper-surface, and in most specimens scattered, asymmetrical yellow feathers are present on throat, sides of neck and head.

IMMATURE. Resembles the female but has some yellow spots on the under-parts. Young males assume adult plumage gradually, with the tail-feathers becoming less barred with each moult; it seems probable that the process is completed in the third year.

Geographical Variations

None recognized.

Field Notes

Cayley wrote: "The Glossy or 'Leach's' Black Cockatoo is the smallest of the 'blacks' and is remarkable for individual variation in plumage of the females. It is usually met with in pairs or small flocks and frequents heavily timbered mountain ranges and open forest lands, and like the Yellow-tailed and Red-tailed, is becoming very rare.

"I have frequently observed it in the heavily timbered ranges of the Illawarra district, on the Blue Mountains, and in the open forest lands farther inland; also in many parts of the near North Coast, and as close to Sydney as National Park and Kurnell, where they were at one time fairly plentiful. In habits it resembles the Red-tailed and Yellow-tailed species, but is much easier to approach.

"While residing at Cronulla, a seaside resort between Botany Bay and Port Hacking, I had many opportunities of observing this species as well as the Red-tailed and Yellow-tailed Black Cockatoos. All three species were in the habit of visiting the same banksias and casuarinas, but each species kept quite to themselves. I never saw the Glossy feeding upon anything but the seeds of the casuarinas, of which there were several species. It is astonishing how speedily it cracks open the seed-cone and extracts the kernel, soon stripping a tree of its seed and littering the ground underneath with cracked seed-cones, leaves, and twigs.

"One favourite feeding-ground, where large tracts of casuarinas flourish, lies between Cronulla and Kurnell. When the seed was ripe, the flocks that used to visit it passed regularly over my residence to and from their roosting places, the tall timbered ridges some fifteen or twenty miles inland from the feeding-grounds. Just after daybreak one could hear their wailing cries long before the birds were visible. It became quite a habit of mine to wait for their arrival, identify the species, count their numbers and watch them out of sight. As the district became more settled, their numbers dwindled, and it is doubtful if any are to be found in that locality today.

"Like the other species of black cockatoos, it resorts to a hollow limb, trunk, or stump of a tree, when nesting. A favourite site is in the hollow of a tree-trunk where a large branch has been broken off, the egg being laid on the decayed wood at the bottom of the hollow, sometimes as far as four feet from the entrance. The nesting-places I have seen were all in the main trunks of dead eucalypts, and were fully forty feet from the ground. Only two were accessible; one contained an egg, the other pieces of broken shell. In nearly every instance the nests were in trees in clearings of ring-barked timber adjoining heavily timbered ridges.

"Clutch: one egg; white, and oval to swollen ellipse in form; shell fairly smooth and lustreless with minute pittings. Breeding-season: in eastern Australia from March to the beginning of August."

My first meeting with this species in the field was in April 1954 when, in company with Dr and Mrs J. A. R. Miles and my two sons, I visited Kangaroo Island over the Easter weekend. We were discussing this bird with Mrs Sheridan of Western River station on the north coast of the island and she had just remarked that she had not seen them for some time and suddenly she exclaimed, "That is their call." We hurried out of the house and had a most satisfying view of a pair, which drank, first one and then the other, at a nearby dam. They then flew a few hundred yards up the river and indulged in some preening for a time. They then moved on farther and the female was seen to enter a burnt-out hollow stump on the hillside, where they had been known to breed in previous years. When disturbed, the pair flew farther upstream and were lost to sight. As we drove away from the property, a single bird was seen in flight.

During several subsequent visits to Kangaroo Island, I saw the species on only one occasion. This was in November 1965 when, in the course of a day visit I made to Flinders Chase, the ranger, George Lonzar, heard their unmistakable but difficult to describe call and pulled up the car. I alighted and had a good view of three birds feeding, as is almost invariably the case, in she-oak (*casuarina*) trees in the vicinity of Sandy Creek.

At Mallacoota in December 1968 my elder son and I were unable to locate these birds although they are frequently seen in the district.

Aviary Notes

Cayley had no aviary notes on this bird, which is not surprising, for the species had rarely been kept in captivity until Sir Edward Hallstrom became interested in it and its problems and peculiarities.

His initial success with the species has been recorded in the *Avicultural Magazine*[31] and is of such outstanding interest that it is reproduced in full here: "The Glossy Black Cockatoo is the only Black Cockatoo that has proved really too difficult for the ordinary aviculturist or the amateur to raise from the baby stage after being taken from the nest. The feeding is so highly specialized that they gradually lose weight when given ordinary food. I had some failures until I commenced experimenting with matured birds to see if I could produce substitute food. It was no use putting food before them, they would starve themselves to death unless, of course, they were given food they were used to—the seed of the Casuarina tree. This is not easy, as for many years, particularly around Sydney, the wood of this particular tree (which burns with a great heat) has been used for bakers' ovens. Its use is now being replaced with newer methods of baking bread, but the inroads on the trees were so considerable that it was hard to locate the seed anywhere near to Sydney.

"The seed is contained in a hard cone, and it is very difficult to extract it from the cone. Even when the seed has been extracted the birds will politely refuse to eat it—they must tear the cone to pieces themselves. This is tremendously important, as their mandibles have been especially designed by nature for dealing with the cones. If the birds do take to softer foods, such as sunflower seed, maize, etc., their top bill begins to extend, the bottom grows out in two long horns, and it is very soon of no use to the bird whatever. It will be understood, therefore, that this was a real problem. As previously stated, in my experimental work I used matured birds, giving them just sufficient of the cones to keep their bills in trim, and fed them on a mixture of canary seed flour, plus peanut butter and peanut oil. This was administered directly into the crop by means of a syringe and a rubber tube that was pushed down the throat. This could be accomplished with the greatest of ease provided, of course, one knew how to handle the bird.

"My aim was to induce the creature to eat sunflower seed, or canary seed. Canary seed was useless, as it did not have sufficient oil, but the oily content of the sunflower seed made it more suitable. I calculated that if sunflower seed, plus some Casuarina nuts daily to keep their mandibles in trim, were used, it might be possible to keep these birds in captivity. The experiments were carried out over six years. Eventually a satisfactory method was found, and the birds now do well on the before-mentioned diet. Unfortunately, they cannot be tempted to eat any other type of food.

"In my aviaries there are nine of these birds, and to feed them it is necessary for a man to drive, every day, into the country to gather fresh nuts. Two separate aviaries were set up with a nice pair in each and suitable hollow logs were provided. One pair were noticed mating, but the other pair, although friendly, did not appear interested. Suddenly the latter pair produced one egg. Several days later another. The female sat closely, and in twenty-nine days hatched one chick. It was then noticed that the male was losing condition, and I am convinced that he had been starving himself in the feeding of the female who rarely emerged from the log. This really was a desperate position. After very careful observations, I decided to remove the male, and found he had really lost a lot of condition. It was necessary to recommence feeding him by inject-ing canary seed flour plus peanut oil directly into the crop. In a few days he was showing good progress, and was returned intermittently to the mother and youngster. It again appeared as though the double feed-ing was too much for him and although, at this stage, he had an ample supply of Casuarina cones, I found it necessary to remove him again.

"At the moment of writing (1st June 1954), the baby is over two weeks old and is being well cared for by the mother. The father, who is still separated from the female and the youngster, is now doing well again. A peep into the nest hollow this morning revealed a fluffy cream-coloured youngster about the size of one's closed fist. I am sure that this is the first time ever that one has been hatched in captivity. They are really a lovely bird, and I think it will be remembered in my talk in Sweden I described them as a Cockatoo which does not have a gizzard, similar to the other Black Cockatoos.

"As feeding is so highly specialized and consists of a great amount of oil, it makes it most difficult to solve the problem of keeping them in captivity, let alone the successful nesting and producing of a youngster. From all appearances, the youngster is doing so well I am sure it will be successfully reared.

"Additional note, 25th June.—The young Glossy Black Cockatoo is doing exceptionally well. It is in faultless condition (the mother having done all the feeding) and is now almost fully feathered and shows itself at the entrance to the nest. I did not return the male to his mate for fear of disturbing the progress the mother had made with the rearing of this singularly glorious youngster.

"Further additional note, 20th August.—The Glossy Black Cockatoo has now left the nest, and is accompanying its mother to the food con-tainers, and I should say has been successfully reared by the mother alone. The youngster has a considerable amount of down protruding through the now matured feathers on the head. The down is quite long and gives the bird an attractive appearance."

See also "Some Breeding Results in the Hallstrom Collection",[31] also published in the *Avicultural Magazine,* part of which is reproduced below.

"Further additional note, 1958.—These were again successfully bred. Two of the earlier youngsters have now reached maturity and are now interested in one another and the nest, and I am hoping that they will go to nest very soon. My keeper had a peep into the original nest of the parent birds and for the first time we saw two eggs which is exceptional as we have never before seen more than one. Their food is so highly specialized and the work of the parents in feeding the youngsters is so constant that I very much doubt their ability to rear two young. I have no intention of interfering, and will on my part give them an abundance of food and all the encouragement I can, should the two eggs hatch."

At the time of Sir Edward Hallstrom's death there were thirteen adults of this species in his collection, and Gus Beilharz, the attendant, told me that several had been successfully bred over the years. However, all had been bred from the same pair of birds, which had a half-grown youngster in the nest about the time the collection was to be dispersed. Several other pairs had laid eggs but they had always been infertile. I believe that R. T. Lynn, of the Sydney suburb of Condell Park, who has been remarkably successful with most of the black cockatoos, has bred this species on at least one occasion. When I was in Sydney in May 1970 a pair of Sir Edward's birds were on exhibition at Taronga Park Zoo and the hen appeared to be incubating—with a successful result, I have since heard.

CALLOCEPHALON Lesson
Gang-gang Cockatoo

This monotypic genus may well form a link between the "black" and the "white" cockatoos; indeed it may be closer in its relationship to the latter than to the former. Forshaw[5] has for some time considered that it is most nearly related to the Galah, mainly on the evidence of flight behaviour, supported by the slender evidence of an instance of hybridization between the two species.

Pairs of Gang-gangs are very closely attached to each other and indulge in much mutual preening. The display does not appear to have been adequately described; an unmated male in my possession at one stage used to advance purposefully along the perch and then take a hop with the crest erected. Courtship feeding has not been recorded; incubation duties are shared by the sexes, the male brooding for most of the day and the female at night. The incubation period is approximately four weeks and the chicks remain in the nest for about eight weeks after hatching; they are fed by both parents, both before and after fledging.

The colour of the down does not appear to be recorded; the bill of the immature bird is darker than that of the adult.

Bathing takes place in rain and possibly in wet foliage; a spray is enjoyed in captivity.

Food is held in the foot, and head-scratching is under the wing.

The flight is heavy, with slow, sweeping wing-beats; it is remarkably silent and owl-like.

16 Gang-gang Cockatoo

Callocephalon fimbriatum (Grant)

PLATE V

Synonyms

Red-crowned Cockatoo, Red-headed Cockatoo, Helmeted Cockatoo, Galah (erroneously).

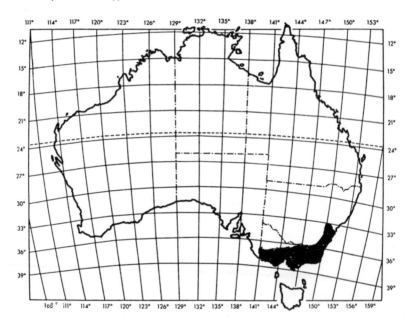

Distribution

In coastal New South Wales this species was thought not to occur farther north than the Hawkesbury River, but A. R. McGill informs me that it extends to the Hunter River near the coast. The late K. A. Hindwood stated that he saw it at Breakfast Creek, seventy-five miles due north of Lithgow, and both he and A. R. McGill recorded it north-east and east of Mudgee. More recently, G. Chapman has seen a pair near Dorrigo, considerably farther north. It is widely spread throughout the mountainous parts of the south-east of the State.

In Victoria this species occurs throughout the State with the exception of the north-western and mid-northern portions, but it is much more plentiful in the eastern than in the western part; it occasionally transgresses the border into the south-east of South Australia.

M. McGarvie states that it was present in some numbers till the 1940s in the Pegorah area on King Island; the records from the north-west coast of Tasmania are almost certainly accidental.

Description

SIZE. About 14 inches (356 mm).

ADULT MALE. General colour above and below dark slate-grey, with pale margins to the feathers, more pronounced on hind-neck, sides of neck, back, and upper tail-coverts; upper wing-coverts like the back; primaries, greater wing-coverts and outer webs of secondaries slate-grey faintly washed with pale sulphur-yellow; tail-feathers dark slate-grey; forehead, crown of head, crest and sides of head scarlet; feathers on lower breast, abdomen, flanks and under tail-coverts have dull red margins with a greenish tinge; bill horn-grey, greyish-white at base of upper mandible; legs and feet mealy-grey; iris dark brown.

ADULT FEMALE. Resembles the male, but head and crest grey, feathers on upper parts mottled with bands of the same colour and narrowly barred with white; feathers on under-surface crossed with yellowish-white bands and broadly margined around the tips with dull scarlet, the subapical band being of a clearer yellow on the lower breast; under tail-coverts grey crossed with pale yellow bands freckled with grey.

IMMATURE. The young male resembles the adult female except on the feathers of the back, which are without pale cross-bars; the yellow and dull-scarlet margins to the feathers on the under-parts are brighter; some of the feathers on the forehead are tipped with dull scarlet, and the crest feathers are dull scarlet with grey bases. The young male is thought to take at least two years to acquire full adult plumage.

Geographical Variations

None recognized.

Field Notes

Cayley wrote: "The Gang-gang or 'Red-crowned' Cockatoo is becoming rare, even in districts where it was at one time fairly common. It is mostly recorded in the timbered districts lying westward of the Illawarra Ranges, and southwards into south-eastern Victoria—the present stronghold of the species. It also occurs at intervals at Moss Vale, Bundanoon, the Burragorang Valley and throughout the Blue Mountains, especially at Mount Victoria, where it is known to breed. During the autumn and winter months it congregates in small flocks, but in the breeding-season it is usually met with in pairs. As a youth I had many opportunities of observing these birds in the Illawarra district and at Bowral. In those days it was not uncommon to see flocks of from thirty to fifty birds feeding together on the seeds of eucalypts as well as different acacias. It has many quaint habits, different entirely from other cockatoos. For example, it delights to congregate in small parties (family groups most likely) close together on the topmost branch of a tall tree, and lazily preen one another's feathers. I have seen a bird lying along a branch with its wings spread, while its neighbour went carefully over its feathers as if seeking vermin in a monkey-like fashion. All its actions are droll and are generally accompanied with its wheezy notes. Another peculiar habit is for a party to take flight without any discernible cause, wheel and twist in all directions as if playing a game, or as an old bushman of my acquaintance once remarked—as if they had a touch of the sun—then settle again, often in the same tree, and either commence feeding or preening as if nothing had interrupted the proceeding.

"Some years ago, when on a visit to Mount Victoria, Blue Mountains, New South Wales, I was shown several nesting-sites where these birds had nested the previous season, also a young male that had been taken from the only nest accessible. My informant also told me that these cockatoos regularly visited the locality each year to breed. However, they were absent that year and the following one when I made another visit. The nesting-hollows were fully sixty to seventy feet from the ground in dead limbs of huge living trees growing on the sides of a steep spur and overlooking a deep gorge.

"From published accounts it appears more or less nomadic. Its flight is laboured and its peculiar wheezy cry is uttered while on the wing or when disturbed while feeding. The cry is quite unlike that of any other cockatoo, and often when feeding it utters a quaint growling sound. The food consists of the seeds of various trees, particularly eucalypts and acacias, generally eaten when green. Young birds I have handled smelt strongly of eucalyptus oil.

"Clutch: two, sometimes three, eggs; white, and rounded-oval in form; shell close-grained, thickly and finely pitted, and lustreless. Breeding-season: October to December or January."

My first meeting with this species in the wild state was at Marysville, Victoria, during World War I; since that time I have seen it on a number of occasions in various parts of Victoria and especially in and around the Healesville sanctuary.

I have always been impressed by their tameness and their curious, owl-like flight; they draw attention to their presence, both when feeding and on the wing, by their very unusual and quite unmistakable call-notes.

They feed to a great extent on the seeds of wattles and have developed a great liking for hawthorn berries, often coming into the suburbs of Melbourne and Canberra to feed on these.

In October 1969 I saw a few of this species at Mount Wilson, in the Blue Mountains of New South Wales. They were in wattle trees and a member of the party felt certain they were feeding on cicadas; admittedly, a number of the insects were falling to the ground but I could not convince myself of the accuracy of the observation. However, my younger son now informs me that he has observed Gang-gangs in Gippsland feeding on the grubs known as "spitfires".

Cayley's statement that this species was becoming rare has not been borne out over the last thirty years or so; it is in fact a common bird throughout most of the high country of eastern Australia.

Aviary Notes

Cayley wrote: "A most desirable aviary bird; although not so brilliantly coloured as some of the other cockatoos, it has many quaint and amusing mannerisms. It usually thrives well in captivity, soon becoming tame and devoted to its owner, and sometimes learning to say a few words. One my father possessed when I was a boy was taught to say, 'Poor Cocky has one eye.' It had been shot and wounded and lost an eye. When brought to him it was in a very sorry state, but lived for many years a cherished family pet.

"I can find no authentic record of its breeding in captivity in Australia."

Always a rare bird in captivity, this is one to which I have always been greatly attracted. Unfortunately it very frequently becomes addicted to feather-biting, and good specimens in captivity are quite exceptional.

The first specimen that I ever possessed was a cock in perfect plumage which A. Wachsmann, of the Sydney suburb of Beecroft, sent to me in October 1937. The following month I obtained the loan of a very tame hen that was in a deplorable state, not only as regards her body feathers but also her wings and tail. The two birds were placed in adjoining small parrot cages, and it was immediately apparent that it was a case of love at first sight. They were allowed together in a medium-sized parrot cage a few days later, and the plumage of the hen soon began to improve with the onset of a moult, the new feathers not being interfered with. By March of the following year she was in very good condition, only a few of the flight feathers not having been replaced, and in April the pair were released in an aviary. Within a few days her feathers were in almost as bad a state as they had been when I obtained her, and the breast feathers of the cock were also showing signs of unwelcome attention. I was so disgusted that I returned the hen forthwith to her owner, and let him have the cock as well. In 1950 this pair of birds were still in captivity in South Australia, and the cock remains in tolerably good feather most of the time, but the hen is always in a semi-nude and flightless condition.

In December 1948 I acquired another cock, a tame bird in very good condition, and capable of saying a couple of words. This bird I kept for nearly a year and it became very friendly, enjoying having its crest scratched and always performing its quaint display, consisting of a purposeful advance along the perch, culminating in a hop with the crest erect, whenever spoken to. However, it was an inveterate shrieker in the early morning, and whenever alarmed, and I eventually parted with it with considerable regret.

In addition to the oft-quoted breedings by Lecallier in France and Tavistock in England, Gang-gangs have been bred in South Australia by Miss S. Merrifield, of Jamestown, a success which gained the bronze medal of the Avicultural Society of South Australia, and also the silver medal of the Society for the outstanding breeding achievement of the 1945 season. Miss Merrifield's birds were kept in a relatively small aviary, and two eggs were laid in a hollow log. Both parents incubated, and the young hatched on about 20th November, the incubation period not being known. The first young bird left the nest on 11th January, and the second six days later; both were cocks, and they were independent in about another three or four weeks, having been fed by both parents prior thereto. The parents were fed on sunflower seed, boiled maize, and sweetened bread and milk; in addition, green food, such as lucerne, was provided, also bunches of eucalyptus leaves and a little mutton suet occasionally. The birds showed a preference for the sunflower seed and bread and milk whilst rearing the young. I am given to understand that Miss Merrifield's birds have had further successes in subsequent years.

This species was bred, one might say accidentally, in the Hallstrom collection in Sydney in 1948; a pair was included in a mixed collection of cockatoos accommodated in a magnificent long aviary and they bred in a log which had been left lying on the ground.

CACATUA Vieillot
White Cockatoos

An article by Vane[24] in the *Avicultural Magazine* has clarified the classification of this genus to a great extent, but it seems preferable to retain all the "white" cockatoos in the one genus with four, possibly five, well-defined subgenera as follows:

1 *Cacatua* (formerly *Kakatoë*) of which the Sulphur-crested Cockatoo, *galerita*, is the only Australian representative. The other members are the Lesser Sulphur-crested, *sulphurea*, of the Celebes; the Dwarf, *parvula*, of Timor and adjacent islands; the Citron-crested, *citrinocristata*, of Sumba; and, belonging possibly to a different subgenus, the White, *alba*, of the Halmaheras, the Salmon-crested, *moluccensis*, of Ceram and Amboina and the Blue-eyed, *ophthalmica*, of New Britain.

2 *Lophochroa*, with the Pink Cockatoo, *leadbeateri*, the sole species.

3 *Eolophus*, with the Galah, *roseicapilla*, the only representative.

4 *Ducorpsius* (incorporating *Licmetis*), with the two Corellas, *sanguinea* and *tenuirostris*, as the Australian species and including Goffin's, *goffini*, of the Tenimber Islands; Ducorps's, *ducorpsi*, of the Solomons; and the Red-vented, *haematuropygia*, of the Philippine and Sulu islands.

Mutual preening is indulged in frequently by all members of this genus. The display varies somewhat between each species but basically consists of an erected crest and outspread wings, with some head-shaking, all of which is reciprocated by the female. Courtship feeding rarely if ever occurs and incubation lasting about four weeks is almost certainly shared by both sexes in all species, as is the feeding of the chicks whilst they remain in the nest for about eight weeks. After they leave the nest, the male undertakes almost all of the feeding, gradually diminishing in frequency over the next several weeks.

The down colour is white, and the bill colour is lighter in those that ultimately become black and slightly yellowish in those that ultimately become horn-coloured.

All cockatoos of this genus enjoy a bathe in a shower of rain, and in captivity appreciate a spray.

Food is held in the foot, and head-scratching is under the wing.

The "white" cockatoos all have a somewhat similar flight pattern, consisting of rapid, rather shallow wing-beats with brief glides interspersed; the Galah's flight is faster, with stronger beats and without any interspersed gliding.

H

17 Sulphur-crested Cockatoo

Cacatua galerita (Latham)

PLATE V

Synonyms

White Cockatoo, Greater Sulphur-crested Cockatoo.

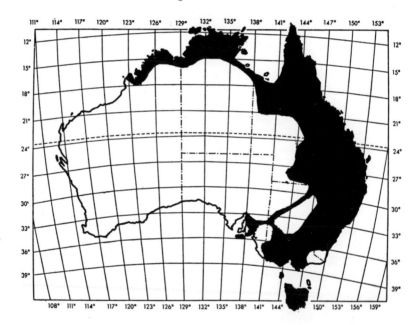

Distribution

The extralimital distribution given in the 1926 R.A.O.U. Checklist is grossly incorrect, the cockatoos of the Moluccas being *Cacatua alba* and *C. moluccensis*, which are not closely related.

In New Guinea the valid subspecies *triton*, with a larger crest and pale blue periorbital skin, occurs and this closely resembles *fitzroyi* of the north-west and Northern Territory. This subspecies occurs in Western Australia only as far south and west as the Fitzroy River.

In the Northern Territory it is widely distributed throughout the "Top End", coming as far south as Victoria River Downs in the west and the McArthur River in the east.

In Queensland the species may be said to occur in almost all localities, including Cape York, the islands of the Barrier Reef and the far south-west; it is probably relatively infrequent in the south-eastern corner of the State, though L. Nielsen states that it is common on the northern Darling Downs and increasing in numbers at Chinchilla.

In New South Wales it is again widely distributed both on the western plains and, to a lesser extent, to the east of the Divide. J. N. Hobbs qualifies this by saying, "Not general on the plains of western New South Wales, confined to the immediate area of the Murray and Darling but will foray up to thirty miles from the red gum timber fringe."

In Victoria the species occurs throughout most of the State, with the exception of the extreme eastern portion, although L. Robinson states that there are odd records from the Genoa River flats.

In South Australia it is found throughout the south-east, is scattered through the Mount Lofty Ranges, follows the Murray Valley and extends north at least as far as Wilmington. It also occurs on Kangaroo Island but does not spread west of Gulf St Vincent.

In Tasmania the species is widely but unevenly distributed and it also occurs on King Island, where M. McGarvie states it is no longer resident.

Description

SIZE. About 20 inches (508 mm).

ADULT MALE. General colour above and below white; inner webs of primary, secondary and tail-feathers except the central pair, sulphur yellow, as are also the elongated feathers of the nuchal crest; bill greyish-black; legs and feet mealy-black; iris blackish-brown.

ADULT FEMALE. Similar to the male but in some instances the iris is reddish-brown.

IMMATURE. Similar to the adult but with a lighter coloured bill.

Geographical Variations

As noted under DISTRIBUTION the race, *fitzroyi*, is recognized by virtue of its very pale blue periophthalmic skin and barely noticeable yellow ear-coverts; it probably intergrades with typical birds in north-western Queensland. Considerable variation in size occurs in different areas.

Field Notes

Cayley wrote: "The White (or Sulphur-crested) Cockatoo, next to the Galah, is perhaps the best known of our cockatoos. There can be few people in Australia who have not seen it either in its wild state or in captivity. Despite the many thousands trapped, destroyed, or taken from the nest annually, they are still extremely plentiful—far too many in certain agricultural districts for the farmers' peace of mind.

"Although its normal food consists of seeds and roots of various kinds, it is a great pest, causing considerable damage to newly-planted or growing crops; so a merciless warfare is constantly waged by farmers and agriculturists against it. A flock numbering many hundreds will settle on a newly-planted paddock or standing crop—only after the scouts sent in advance have reported everything clear—and in a remarkably short space of time will absolutely destroy the whole field. So wary and cunning are these birds that it is difficult to get within gun-range. When feasting, sentinels mount guard on the tops of high trees growing within sight and hearing of the raiders, and warn them with shrill discordant cries on the approach of danger. These sentinels are constantly relieved. It is only possible to get a shot at them by keeping well hidden amongst the crop and waiting for the birds to arrive. Scarecrows are useless. These birds are far too cunning to be misled by such devices. I remember seeing a scarecrow, in a field of ripening maize, used by a sentinel as an observation post. Apparently they know the difference between a gun and a stick.

"Though destructive, these birds are a striking and beautiful feature of the country-side as they wend their way in laboured, noisy flight, their white plumage contrasting with the dark green background of a timber-clad mountain range, or when resting among the tree-tops, or scattered in flocks over a plain digging for roots or bulbs.

"The nesting-place usually selected is in a hollow spout or trunk of a eucalypt, frequently in a dead tree, and often at a great height from the ground. Tall trees growing near rivers and creeks are favourite sites.

"Clutch: two, occasionally three, eggs; white, and varying from oval to elongate-oval in form; shell generally rough and lustreless. Breeding-season: August to December."

I cannot recall my first meeting with this species in the wild but I have certainly known it all my life. In recent years I have seen a great deal of the resident population of this species, which nests along the Gawler River at Buckland Park, some twenty-five miles north of Adelaide. There has always been some speculation as to the origin of these birds and the other two species of cockatoos found in the area, as it has been claimed that they were the result of introductions from station properties farther north. However, I feel sure this bird is a naturally occurring species there; it has become rare but is still found in small pockets throughout the Mount Lofty Ranges; it is much more plentiful in the south-east of the State and in the eastern States. It is an extremely noisy bird which gathers in large flocks and is notoriously destructive to crops.

In the "Top End" of the Northern Territory this cockatoo differs markedly in its habits; it is rarely seen other than in pairs or quite small parties and is much less noisy. These observations were made on three visits to the area during the dry season in 1964, 1967 and 1969; the birds were frequently noticed feeding on the fruit of the pandanus.

On a visit to Tasmania for the R.A.O.U. annual meeting in October 1969 I saw a small party of these birds not far south of Launceston on the main Hobart road; it is said not to be particularly plentiful on the island; however, J. R. Napier refutes this statement.

In the course of the bird-watchers' tour of eastern Queensland in May and June 1970, Sulphur-crested Cockatoos were observed in most areas visited. It was noted that they occurred with equal frequency in both open country and in rain-forest.

Aviary Notes

Cayley wrote: "One of the most popular of cage-birds; being easy to keep and often becoming an affectionate pet. Its longevity is remarkable; there are records of birds living one hundred years in captivity; so, presumably, they would live even longer in a state of nature. The late 'Cocky Bennett', of Tom Ugly's Point, near Sydney, was said to be well over one hundred years when it died a few years ago. This quaint old bird was quite a celebrity, with its few feathers—or was it only one?—its rather rude sayings, and its long bill, which had to be pared every few months. These parings, I believe, are still in existence; their owner had them joined and made into a bangle—a novelty, if nothing else.

" 'Cocky' is a bird gourmand, and a shameless waster of food. Watch one feeding. You will notice that it will not swallow its food whole, but grasps it in one of its feet—which are so formed that they act as hands—and with its bill it shells, peels, or slices away until only the sweetest part is left. Their bills are wonderfully powerful instruments—indeed, unique. In birds generally, the upper mandible is more or less joined to the skull, leaving only the lower jaw free to move; but in the cockatoo and parrot the upper mandible is also so hinged; so each is free to play upon the other. The tongue, thick, muscular, and very sensitive, is used to manipulate the food, placing it between the sharp cutting edge of the lower and the hooked and pointed upper mandible.

"Because of its numbers and cheapness in Australia, few attempt to breed it in captivity. The only records I have been able to gather are hearsay ones. Still, in the Adelaide Zoological Gardens is a beautiful hybrid between this species and the Galah that has been bred in Australia in captivity."

This species is very commonly kept as a cage bird in Australia, birds taken from the nest being always in demand as pets and usually making good talkers. Birds so treated are often very long-lived and are almost invariably remarkably tame and gentle, seldom exhibiting the desire to bite people which is only too evident with most of the other species. However, the bird has one great disadvantage, its raucous screech, and the number of these birds presented annually to the Adelaide Zoo is evidence of this failing, as many of them are talented talkers. In that institution they are all housed together in a large flight aviary, which usually contains between forty and fifty birds, and they agree quite amicably and constitute a great attraction to visitors. Several birds in this aviary have laid eggs, but they do not often remain in pairs as do most of the other members of the genus, and it is difficult to pick out a mated pair with a view to their segregation.

I have no record of this species having been bred in captivity in Australia, although I consider that it is highly probable that it has occurred. Abroad, it appears to have been bred on the Continent during the last century and in England by Whitley, in a state of semi-liberty, during World War I. There does not appear to be any record as to whether both sexes incubate, but I should consider it probable that they would.

I have owned a few of these birds for short periods, usually captured strays, but they have never been kept for long on account of their vocal propensities. There is no doubt that, apart from this failing, they make attractive and entertaining pets.

During the past twenty years or so I have still not been able to discover an Australian breeding success; however, in recent years, several eggs have been laid in the Adelaide Zoo in an aviary containing a number of this species, and on two occasions young have been hatched but complete success has not been achieved.

18 Pink Cockatoo

Cacatua (Lophochroa) leadbeateri (Vigors)

PLATE V

Synonyms

Major Mitchell Cockatoo, Leadbeater's Cockatoo, Wee Juggler, Cocklerina, Chockalott.

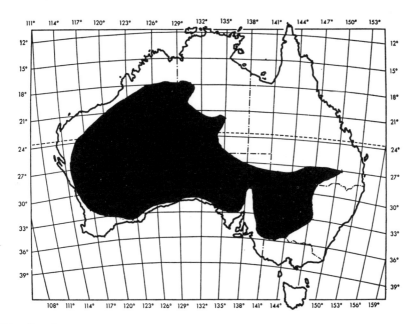

Distribution

For Western Australia, Serventy and Whittell[10] state that the species avoids the south-west corner—that is, south and west of a line through Jurien Bay, Toodyay and thence to Esperance. This accords with records from such places as Fitzroy River, Pilbara, Wiluna, Leonora, and east of Kalgoorlie.

The Northern Territory, though not mentioned in the 1926 R.A.O.U. Checklist, yields records from Tanami, Central Mount Stuart, Macdonald Downs, Alice Springs, Ayers Rock road and Finke.

In South Australia the species occurs almost everywhere north and

west of Spencer Gulf and the Flinders Ranges and also in the north-east
of the State as far south as the Murray River between Morgan and the
border and also in the Murray Mallee.

In Queensland it is confined to the south-west corner, extending as
far east as St George and also to Warra (L. Nielsen).

In New South Wales the species is scattered over most of the western
half of the State, extending as far east as about Forbes (A. R. McGill).

In Victoria it is confined to the north-western corner, apart from occasional records farther south.

Description

SIZE. About 16 inches (406 mm).

ADULT MALE. The entire back, wings, and tail white; inner webs of
primaries, secondaries and all but the central pair of tail-feathers, except
towards tips, rose colour; hind-neck, sides of face and entire under-
surface salmon-pink; crown of head and occiput pink at base and white
at tips of feathers; elongated nuchal crest white, crimson at base with a
yellow spot in centre; bill light horn colour; legs and feet dark mealy-
grey; iris black, orbits mealy red.

ADULT FEMALE. Duller than the male, with more yellow and less red in
the crest; iris reddish-brown.

IMMATURE. Generally paler and duller than the adult; the young males
are generally a little brighter on the underparts than the young females.

Geographical Variations

None of the described races appear to be valid, but it has been noticed
that Western Australian birds have longer crests.

Field Notes

Cayley wrote: "The Pink (also commonly called Major Mitchell, Wee
Juggler and Leadbeater's Cockatoo) is perhaps the most beautiful of all
known species; once fairly plentiful, it is now becoming scarce at an
alarming rate. If not more rigidly protected it will soon be exterminated.
Although its reputation as a talker is far behind that of all the other
cockatoos, its delicately coloured plumage makes it valuable as a cage-
bird. Usually it is met with in pairs or small flocks consisting of parents
and young; occasionally in larger numbers in association with other
species. Its food consists of various kinds of seeds of trees and herbaceous
plants, roots, and bulbs; it also eats the seeds of a small species of wild
melon—an inland weed-pest.

"Their habit of visiting water morning and evening to drink, made it
easy for the bird-trappers to net or snare them; until protected, hundreds
were caught and exported abroad.

"Kendall Bennett records that when its hunger is appeased it has a
habit of cutting off the smaller branches of the trees or shrubs in which
it may be resting. It also tears off the bark of the trunk and larger

branches, until the ground beneath is strewn with small branches, leaves and fragments of bark. This destruction is particularly noticeable in the vicinity of the trees in which they may be breeding. Bennett says he had frequently seen an old male bird engaged for hours at this pastime in the tree where his mate was engaged in the duties of incubation. The nesting-place is in a large roomy hollow, usually of a eucalypt, and at a height ranging from fifteen to sixty feet from the ground. Those stately Red River Gums that line the banks of the inland rivers, are favourite nesting-trees.

"Bennett also states that he once found a pair with their nest inside that of a Wedge-tailed Eagle. They had entered at the bottom of the huge nest and scooped out a cavity in the mould in the centre, the result of the decomposition of the successive linings of eucalypt leaves, placed there by the eagles each season.

"Clutch: three or four eggs; white, and oval or long oval in form; shell close-grained and almost lustreless. Breeding-season: September to November or December."

My first meeting with this species in the wild state is quite unforgettable: four pairs were seen on Carriewerloo station about fifty miles west of Port Augusta, in October 1952. The birds appeared at that time to be feeding mainly on the seeds of the native pine (*Callitris*), and their lovely plumage showed to great advantage against the dark background of the foliage of the trees. Two nesting hollows were located at that time in eucalypts in dry creek beds. The species was again seen in the course of a further visit to this station property in September 1963.

In the course of four visits with other members of the Adelaide Ornithologists' Club to the Renmark district, on the Upper Murray in South Australia, in the month of October of the years 1961 to 1964 inclusive, the species was observed in very small numbers (two or three birds only) on the first three occasions. However, in 1964 a party of about thirty-five birds feeding in open country close to the main Wentworth Road provided a most attractive sight; this being the only occasion that I have ever seen the birds in a flock of any size, and it bears out the statement of the late J. Neil McGilp to the same effect. His other interesting observation on the species was to the effect that it and the Little Corella were mutually exclusive, never occurring in his experience in the same area; subsequent observations have disproved this on several occasions, but as a generalization it is substantially correct and is supported by S. A. Parker's recent observations.[32]

Cayley's statement that this species was becoming scarce at an alarming rate and that it would soon become exterminated if not more rigidly protected have fortunately proved incorrect; however, it is not a common bird and in recent decades has faced serious competition, both for food and nesting sites, from the southward-spreading Galah, which appears to be a more aggressive and successful species.

Aviary Notes

Cayley wrote: "Unfortunately, this popular cage-bird is generally kept in single blessedness cooped up in a small cage. Has the reputation of being less easy to domesticate than other species, and by no means easy to teach to 'talk'. Some become exceedingly noisy, and all are most destructive to perches and any woodwork within their reach.

"The only authentic Australian successful breeding of this species in captivity I have been able to find, is the one achieved by R. F. Bellchambers, of Humbug Scrub, South Australia, in 1935, who reared three young ones. Four eggs were laid and incubation commenced before the laying finished. Both birds shared in the incubation, the male during most of the day, the female at night. Incubation began on 11th September, and the young birds hatched out on 11th October, three being hatched. Both parents fed the young. Six weeks after they were hatched the young were still in the nest, but not fully feathered. The food supplied consisted of wheat, peas, *green* broad beans, almonds, and thistles."

Since Bellchambers's success this species has been bred on a good many occasions in South Australia, notably by the Adelaide Zoo for several years in succession.

Always rather a rare bird in captivity and although extremely decorative, it is not as popular as the other cockatoos because it seldom becomes a talented speaker. It does not screech to any great extent but it has an extremely irritating, plaintive cry which it utters frequently when alarmed. I kept two of these birds during my avicultural career, both being hens, and the most recent example laid several times, but I never had suitable aviary accommodation to warrant trying to breed from them.

However, in 1954 my elder son procured a tame pair of these birds which had been kept for an indefinite period in small cages; they were very wing-stiff when first liberated in an aviary but soon recovered their powers of flight. Contrary to general belief, the male of this pair is an extremely talented and versatile talker, but, apart from a few commonplace remarks, reserves his talent for the breeding season. This pair have been remarkably successful as breeders; starting in 1954, they successfully reared thirteen young in thirteen consecutive seasons, the best result being three in their second year, in addition to two young on two other occasions. Furthermore, on two occasions a fertile egg was accidentally broken and it is remarkable that they have never failed to rear any young bird that has hatched. Since my move from the city to the Mount Lofty Ranges, they have been less successful; after rearing one young one in the first year, their eggs have, with one exception, been infertile in the last three seasons. Whether this failure is due to their increasing age or to the climatic difference, I am unable to say.

In their early years the cock bird was a most reluctant incubator, leaving the nest at the slightest provocation in the day-time and returning to it most unwillingly. However, in recent years he has become much more diligent in this regard. My records show that the incubation period is about twenty-eight days and that the young birds remain about eight weeks in the nest after hatching. Both parents feed the young in the nest; but immediately they leave, the cock bird seems to assume full responsibility and continues to feed them on demand, long after they appear to be self-supporting—for about a further six or eight weeks.

19 Little Corella

Cacatua (Ducorpsius) sanguinea (Gould)

PLATE V

Synonyms

Bare-eyed Cockatoo, Bloodstained Cockatoo, Short-billed Corella.

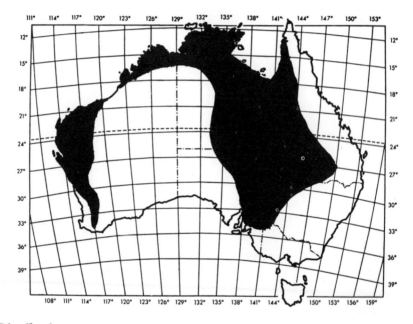

Distribution

Beginning with Queensland (not mentioned in the 1926 R.A.O.U. Checklist) the species extends as far north as the Archer River on Cape York Peninsula and is found throughout the western portion of the State, occasionally extending as far east as Jandowae, Kogan and Chinchilla, but apparently it does not transgress the Great Dividing Range.

Similarly, in New South Wales the species is confined to the western division; and in Victoria it is restricted to the north-west corner of the State, with a surprising record from the You Yangs, presumably of a nomadic flock.

In South Australia isolated populations occur as far south as Lang-horne Creek and Ashbourne and it appears to be extending slowly south-wards. Proceeding north it becomes more common and extends through-out the north-eastern part of the State but is infrequently found to the west of Spencer Gulf and in the north-west of the State.

In the Northern Territory the species is widespread from the South Australian border right up to the north coast and extending thence into and covering the whole of the north-west of Western Australia reaching as far south as a line drawn through Dongara, Mullewa and Morawa. Here it comes in contact with and slightly overlaps the range of *pastinator*, formerly considered the western race of the Corella, *Cacatua tenuirostris*, but better treated as a well-defined race of *sanguinea*. *C. s. pastinator* continues southward to roughly a line from the coast at Jurien Bay through Dandaragan, Moora, Wongan Hills and Kalannie, with isolated populations surviving in the far south-west, most notably that in the vicinity of Lake Muir.

Description

SIZE. About 15 inches (381 mm).

ADULT MALE. General colour white; bases of feathers of lores and head rose-red; basal portion of inner webs of primaries, and inner webs of all but the central pair of tail-feathers, sulphur-yellow; bill greyish horn colour; legs and feet mealy-grey; bare patches around eyes dark bluish-grey; eyes blackish-brown.

ADULT FEMALE. Similar in plumage to the male; usually slightly smaller, with a less massive head; no appreciable difference in eye colour.

IMMATURE. Resembles the adult but the bare skin round the eye is not as prominent inferiorly and is nearly circular when the young first leave the nest.

Geographical Variations

As noted under DISTRIBUTION, the long-billed form, *pastinator*, inhabiting the south-west of Western Australia, is very distinct, although some intergradation with the typical birds appears to be occurring. Elsewhere, over the extensive range, the only major variation is of size, *pastinator* being appreciably larger. Serventy and Whittell[10] state that there is no difference between the calls of the two races.

Field Notes

Cayley wrote: "The Little Corella (also known as the Bare-eyed and Bloodstained Cockatoo) is an inhabitant of the northern and inland portions of the continent. It is still fairly plentiful despite the fact that many hundreds of young birds are taken annually by bird-catchers. It is gregarious, the flocks often numbering many thousands—especially after the breeding-season is over; when resting or roosting on trees, or when feeding out on the plains, the trees or ground are whitened by the birds.

A ground-feeder, it lives chiefly on the seeds of various grasses and plants, roots and bulbs. A favourite food is the seed of the 'paddy-melon', a weed pest said to cause blindness and paralysis in horses—and another pest called 'double-gees' the seeds of which seriously lame sheep.

"The flocks visit the feeding-grounds just after sunrise, where they feed for several hours; then return to the trees and amuse themselves for most of the day, stripping off leaves, twigs and bark, often completely destroying them; towards evening they again fly to the plains to feed for an hour or so before returning to roost for the night. In good seasons these birds breed in great numbers; but if the season is a dry one few birds breed at all. Favourite nesting-sites are in hollows in those stately river gums; they seldom, if ever, breed far from water. Usually the entrance to the nesting-hollow is bitten round by the birds, and the eggs are laid on the decayed wood at the bottom, often three or more feet from the entrance.

"Clutch: usually three eggs; white, and oval or elongate-oval in form; shell close-grained, smooth, and slightly lustrous. Breeding-season: August to October; in parts of northern Australia, February to May."

My first meeting with this species in the wild was at Buckland Park, some twenty-five miles north of Adelaide, where it is moderately common and breeds in the red gums along the Gawler River. It is generally thought that this population has resulted from liberation of specimens brought by the former owners from station properties farther north; be that as it may, the species occurs in similar localities along the small rivers and creeks not so very much farther north and may well have done so always.

In more recent years I have seen this bird in other localities in the mid-north of South Australia, one very large flock of about a thousand birds being seen in the vicinity of Port Augusta and other smaller parties in many parts of the Flinders Range. Lately it has been turning up in small flocks in several places not far from Adelaide; perhaps the longest known of such populations is that in the vicinity of Langhorne Creek. I have a strong feeling that this species is following the pattern of the Galah and gradually extending its range southward as the country becomes cleared; it appears to be about fifty years behind the Galah in this movement.

In the Northern Territory this bird is very common in the vicinity of permanent water in such places as Fogg's Dam, near Humpty Doo and Knuckey's Lagoon on the outskirts of Darwin; at Kununurra in the Kimberleys it roosts in countless thousands near the Diversion Dam, and the sight and sound of the birds leaving the roosting place at dawn is unforgettable.

The Long-billed Cockatoo of south-western Australia, *pastinator*, is now widely thought to be a subspecies of the Little Corella; apart from its elongated bill, it differs very little in appearance and it probably interbreeds with the southward spreading population at the northern extremity of its range. My first meeting with this race was at Three Springs, about two hundred miles north of Perth. I cannot do better than quote Dr G. M. Storr's account as follows: "We did not see this species till we reached Three Springs, where a flock of 54 birds were feeding in the station yard. They were digging out corms of onion grass (*Romulea rosea*) from the heavy red soil: some of the holes were as deep as two inches. Most of the birds were dirty, especially on their under parts. They were quite tame, taking little notice of townspeople crossing the rail tracks. When flushed they flew up into nearby gimlets uttering soft quavering notes. On the following day, when returning to Perth, we saw two birds among a flock of Galahs, near Arrino. They were again seen at Three Springs; some birds flying over the town, others feeding as before. Near Coorow another three birds were seen. We had stopped to inspect a patch of salmon gum/gimlet woodland, where hollows in the salmon gums were tenanted by a dense population of breeding Port Lincoln and Regent Parrots and Galahs. Into this area three Corellas flew, screeching loudly, quite different notes to those of the large flock at Three Springs. Our last observation of the species was at Namban where a single bird was seen."

Aviary Notes

Cayley's brief notes read: "A favourite cage-bird, very hardy and, as a rule, more docile and tractable than most species. It makes a delightful and affectionate pet, and may easily be taught to say almost any word or sentence. So far as I know it has never been bred in captivity in Australia; but there is no reason why it should not be."

A very common bird in captivity and one which has a good reputation as a talker. I have never possessed an example of this species but have watched them on many occasions in a large flight aviary at the Adelaide Zoo, where they are kept together with several other species of cockatoos. The birds of this species usually keep in pairs and appear most devoted to their mates; I well remember one bird which, when given a peanut, would immediately fly back to its mate and allow it to take half of the nut.

The first Australian success that I am aware of occurred late in 1949 when two pairs nested at the Adelaide Zoo. The first pair, which were segregated, hatched their young but failed to rear them. The second pair nested in a log in the large flight aviary previously referred to, containing some thirty to forty various cockatoos, and successfully reared one young bird which left the nest in mid-January 1950. Owing to the similarity of the sexes it is difficult to, be certain whether both birds incubate; in the case of the segregated birds, both were frequently in the nest simultaneously. However, Blaauw[33] recorded that only the female incubated in the case of his pair of birds, but I consider that this statement requires verification.

A further successful breeding took place at the Adelaide Zoo in 1957 when two young were reared.

There have been several successes recorded outside Australia, notably at the San Diego Zoo where a vast number have been reared over the years.

There does not appear to be any record of the western long-billed race, *pastinator*, having bred in captivity.

20 Long-billed Corella

Cacatua (Licmetis) tenuirostris (Kuhl)

PLATE V

Synonyms

Slender-billed Cockatoo, Long-billed Cockatoo, Corella.

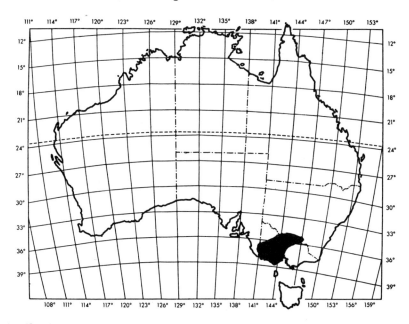

Distribution

As noted under *C. sanguinea*, the distribution of this species as Western Australia to North-western Australia, given by the 1926 R.A.O.U. Checklist, is accounted for by the relegation of *pastinator* (and the doubtful *derbyi*) to a subspecies of *sanguinea*.

The true Corella has consequently a comparatively restricted range in southern Australia from the south-east of South Australia in the vicinity of Naracoorte and Penola across the border into its main stronghold in the western district of Victoria, extending as far east as Port Phillip Bay on occasions.

Although New South Wales is not mentioned in the 1926 R.A.O.U. Checklist the species undoubtedly occurs in that State, mainly in the

I

Riverina district—for example, between Mathoura and Koondrook, between Moulamein and Deniliquin, at Euston and along the Lachlan and Murrumbidgee rivers. In the H. L. White collection there is a surprising skin from Byrock in northern New South Wales; this must surely have been from a cage bird. J. N. Hobbs writes: "I do not think this species occurs at Euston in the breeding sense; my record there was of a transitory flock. It is suspected that the Riverina population moves out in winter, possibly linking up with western Victorian mobs."

Description

SIZE. About 16 inches (406 mm).

ADULT MALE. General plumage colour above and below white; bases of feathers on head, hind-neck, sides of face, sides of neck and throat, lores, bases of feathers in front and below the eye rosy red; inner webs of primaries, secondaries and tail-feathers, except the central pair, sulphur-yellow; bill bluish-white; legs and feet dark mealy-grey; iris dark brown, the orbits leaden-blue.

ADULT FEMALE. Similar to the male but slightly smaller and with a less massive head. No appreciable difference in eye colour.

IMMATURE. Resembles the adult but the bill is not as long and the red crescent on the throat is not as marked.

Geographical Variations

With the treatment of *pastinator* as a race of the Little Corella, there is no recognizable variation in this species.

Field Notes

Cayley wrote: "The Corella (or Long-billed Cockatoo) is usually met with in pairs or flocks, frequenting plains or timber bordering water-courses. Seldom found far from permanent water and procures most of its food on the ground—chiefly roots and bulbs (which it is able to secure with the aid of its long upper bill that appears to have been specially made for such a service), but also various kinds of seeds. Unfortunately, the bird finds other work for its bill, and causes havoc in freshly planted grain-fields.

"This species is becoming rather rare, mainly because much of the country once the home of the bird, is now overrun with stock, thus depleting its food-supply. Another cause is its popularity as a cage-bird. The demand for young ones as pets was so great that, until placed on the protected lists, the bird-shops were crowded with them each season.

"It usually selects the most inaccessible hollows in trees in which to nest, the tall Red Gums that border most rivers and streams being favourite nesting-trees.

"Clutch: two to four eggs; white, and oval in form, somewhat pointed at the smaller end; shell close-grained, minutely pitted, and slightly lustreless. Breeding-season: August to November."

This species for a long time eluded me in the field, despite several searches in the south-east of South Australia, where it is relatively common. It was not until October 1951 that I first observed it, at Naracoorte, South Australia; since then I have never failed to see it in the course of numerous visits to the south-east of the State and to the western district of Victoria. It usually occurs in small flocks of up to fifty individuals, as distinct from the often much larger flocks of the White (Sulphur-crested) Cockatoo, but not infrequently it feeds in mixed flocks of both species. Not uncommonly it is disturbed from the roadsides where it feeds on the bulbs of nutweed (*Romulea rosea*); its elongated bill is obviously adapted for the purpose of digging but its plumage, especially around the face, often becomes very dirty in the process. Although capable of loud shrieks, its usual call is quite distinctive and is not as harsh or as unpleasant as that of many other cockatoos. Forshaw's statement[5] that all calls of the Little Corella are very similar to those of the Long-billed Corella is quite incorrect.

Aviary Notes

Cayley wrote: "There is no record of this cockatoo ever having bred in captivity. Exceptionally hardy in an aviary, it would probably breed if given the encouragement to do so. When in Adelaide recently I saw a pair in the collection of E. Baxter Cox; they were housed in a large open aviary and accommodated with a hollow log very much larger than usually seen in aviaries, and approximating natural conditions. In it they spend most of their time but without results so far. Both of these birds are exceptionally good talkers and have been pets for a long time.

"This species has the reputation of being the best talker of all Australian cockatoos; although of somewhat grotesque appearance it becomes remarkably tame and affectionate. Food suggested: a mixture of canary-seed, millet, and oats, with as many peanuts as it likes to eat, and any raw vegetables except potato and parsley. A good-sized turf should be kept in the cage to provide the bird with amusement and exercise for its digging propensities."

I had always been attracted to this somewhat odd-looking species but had never possessed a specimen, although it is not uncommon as a cage bird on account of its reputation as a talker.

In December 1967 my elder son arrived home with a pair of this species which he had obtained from a mixed collection of parrots and cockatoos exhibited at a service station, with the story that they had attempted to breed and had actually laid eggs during the previous season. A less likely breeding pair at first acquaintance could hardly be imagined; the cock being very timid and unable to fly on account of a damaged wing and the hen being obviously hand-reared, tame and with a strong tendency to human fixation, and a repertoire consisting of a monotonously repeated "Hullo, Cocky." However, they appeared to be well mated and they frequently indulged in mutual preening.

They were released in an aviary with a flight 12½ feet long, 3½ feet wide and 7 feet high covered with one-inch chain wire, the shelter at the rear being 5½ feet long, 3½ feet wide and 8 feet high. The cock was provided with a perch which enabled him to clamber into the shelter.

In August 1968 they were supplied with a hollow log about 5 feet long and with an internal diameter of about 6 inches and an inspection hole near the lower end. This was suspended obliquely in the shelter and in close proximity to a perch to enable easy access on the part of the cock. An immediate interest was evinced and the hen spent a considerable amount of time in the log from the start.

From this time onward, mating was frequently observed and the first egg was seen on 22nd September and the second the next day; it was not until four days later that an opportunity to inspect the nest revealed a third egg; it is to be presumed that they were laid with either two- or three-day intervals between each. Incubation appeared to commence with the laying of the second egg, and as is the case with most cockatoos (excluding the "blacks") the cock bird carried out the task for most of the day and the hen in the early morning, late afternoon and at night.

Two of the eggs were fertile and the first hatched on 16th October and the second the following day after an incubation period of approximately twenty-four days. One of the chicks, presumably the younger, died after about a week but the other flourished and ultimately left the nest on 10th December, approximately seven weeks after hatching. It flew well from the start, but was appreciably smaller than the parents and with a considerably shorter upper mandible and a slightly less obvious red crescent on the upper chest.

Although both parents fed the young bird whilst it was in the nest, after it emerged the hen rarely did so and the cock continued on demand for several weeks, although the youngster fed itself and was deemed independent after about three weeks.

The food supplied consisted of a mixture of sunflower seed, hulled oats and canary seed and in addition a plentiful supply of nutweed, thistle and seeding grasses.

Soon after the young bird became independent, the cock developed an aversion to the hen and pursued her relentlessly around the aviary although, fortunately for her, he was unable to catch up with her on account of his flightlessness.

The young bird soon became very tame and would accept peanuts from the fingers, as the hen had always done. About this time it became very noisy and the parents, who had always indulged in a pre-roosting screeching session, somewhat increased their vocal propensities so I presented them to the Adelaide Zoo, where they were satisfactorily housed and I had hoped they would continue to breed and thus add to that institution's already long list of psittacine successes. However, although eggs were laid in 1969, no success was obtained until 1970 when two young were reared.

At this time I borrowed a tame bird of unknown sex as a companion for the young bird, but it proved ill at ease in an aviary and unwilling to fly, in addition to appearing terrified of the youngster. This condition lessened slightly after a time but they never became really friendly and after several weeks, the young bird still being very noisy, I sent them both to the owner of the tame bird, and they now occupy an aviary with several others of the species.

For a long time I was quite unable to sex the young bird with any certainty; at first I thought it was probably a hen; later I was quite undecided. However, as it has matured, it seems likely that my first impression was correct.

I had thought that this breeding might have been a world first; although I was aware of successes at San Diego Zoo, I thought it likely that the young there had been partly hand-reared; however, K. C. Lint informs me that they reared one young one in both 1959 and 1960. Following publication of my success[34] a correspondent mentioned the successful breeding of the species by Mrs C. Pullen of Wellington, New Zealand, eight young having been reared in the four seasons 1965-68.

21 Galah

Cacatua (Eolophus) roseicapilla (Vieillot)

PLATE V

Synonyms

Rose-breasted Cockatoo, Roseate Cockatoo, Willock.

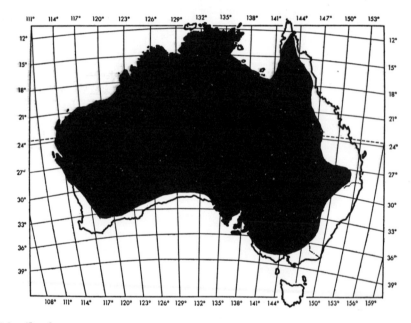

Distribution

This species is rapidly increasing its range and tending to become more southern and more coastal.

In Western Australia it occurs throughout the State except south and west of a line through Dongara, Moora and Kellerberrin (Serventy and Whittell[10]), though intrusions beyond this line are not infrequently recorded. The Western Australian race is distinguished by its larger crest, which is of a deeper pink shade than that of the eastern birds.

In the Northern Territory and in South Australia the Galah is widely distributed, although in the latter State it has only come south in the last forty years or so and is now rapidly increasing in the south-east.

In Victoria the species has rapidly extended southward and eastward to cover most of the State, whilst in New South Wales and Queensland it is widely distributed west of the Great Dividing Range and seems to be spreading east of this in many places, though possibly to a lesser extent in Queensland than in New South Wales. It also occurs over much of Cape York Peninsula.

The Galah appears to have been introduced to Tasmania in the Huon River district but with what success is uncertain. There is fairly recent information of the presence of a small flock on the outskirts of Launceston. M. McGarvie stated in 1968: "Five years ago a flock of over thirty appeared on King Island; since then numbers have dwindled but odd birds are still present."

Description

SIZE. About 14 inches (356 mm).

ADULT MALE. General colour above, including back, wings, and tail, hoary-grey, lighter on rump and upper tail-coverts; outer webs of wing-coverts and secondaries, crown of head, hind-neck, and feathers below eye rosy-white, deeper at bases; throat, sides of face, breast, abdomen, axillaries and under wing-coverts deep rose-red; lower flanks and under tail-coverts light grey; bill greenish-white, paler at tip; legs and feet mealy-grey; iris black; naked skin round eye dull red.

ADULT FEMALE. Similar to the male but the iris is reddish-brown.

IMMATURE. Similar to the adult but duller and with the under-parts appreciably greyer.

Geographical Variations

Western Australian birds, *assimilis*, are readily distinguishable by their larger crests, which are much pinker than those of the typical birds, and by the much paler, almost white, periophthalmic skin. Considerable size variation occurs over the very extensive range.

Field Notes

Cayley wrote: "The Galah (or Rose-breasted Cockatoo) is essentially a bird of the inland areas. During the winter months it congregates in large flocks, and in pairs in the spring. I have often seen these birds in flocks of many thousands, and gloried in the sight they made when perched in the branches of trees, giving the effect of masses of pink and white blossom, or when on the wing with the alternating flashes of grey and pink, and again as they feed on the plains, a living carpet of the same colours. On one occasion I saw telegraph lines lying on the ground, torn from the insulators by the weight of these birds as they rested or clung to the wires in their hundreds.

"A ground-feeder, it lives chiefly on seeds (many of which are those of well-known weed-pests) roots, bulbs, etc. Very destructive at times in grain fields, farmers consider it one of our worst bird pests.

"Unlike most species of cockatoos, it lines its nesting-hollow with freshly-gathered gum-leaves; and any suitable hollow limb or hole in a tree is selected for breeding purposes, either high up or low down. The birds usually bite off and clear away all rotten wood or bark around the entrance to the nesting hollow. Sometimes a tree is ring-barked for quite some distance down—as a precaution, some observers contend, against an attack by iguanas, which prey upon their eggs and young. By tearing off the bark, they say, the trunk is left bare and devoid of toe-holds for these large lizards. Possibly. Still, I have seen an iguana climb with amazing speed to the topmost limb of a tall dead gum-tree absolutely bare of bark.

"Clutch: four, sometimes five, eggs; white, and varying in shape from oval to thick oval, sharply pointed at the smaller end, and in size; shell smooth-grained, with minute pittings, and as a rule lustreless. Breeding-season: in eastern Australia, September and October; in northern Australia, February and March."

I had never seen this species in the field until I returned to Australia early in 1932 after three years' absence; I was greatly surprised to find a party of a dozen or so birds on a back road near Victor Harbour, not having realized that the species had become common in the vicinity of Adelaide during the previous decade. Since that date it has continued its spread in a southerly and easterly direction and is now a common bird in areas where it was previously quite unknown; it is now always present in considerable numbers in the parklands surrounding the city of Adelaide and in the suburbs.

Apparently a population existed along the Gawler River, in the vicinity of Buckland Park, long before being engulfed in the southerly invasion, and it seems certain that this, at least, was the result of introduction.

There are few more beautiful sights than a flock of Galahs in flight, with their delicately contrasting colouring of pink and grey; although now commonplace to Australians, the spectacle never fails to evoke admiration on the part of overseas visitors whether they be bird-lovers or not. Unfortunately the Galah with its vast increase in numbers is proving a menace in agricultural areas and also takes a heavy toll in almond orchards. It has been claimed that its abundance in areas where it was previously rare or unknown has made it a serious competitor of the Pink Cockatoo in regard to the availability of nesting sites.

In Central Australia the Galah is plentiful and in the far north and in the Kimberleys it is also widespread; these birds are noticeably smaller and paler in coloration.

In eastern Queensland in June 1970 the Galah was quite uncommon; a pair were seen near the Belyando River, about midway between Charters Towers and Clermont, and a small flock south of the latter place.

Aviary Notes

Cayley's notes were brief, as follows: "Perhaps the commonest cage-bird among cockatoos; is exceptionally hardy, and if obtained when young, will soon become a proficient talker.

"They have been bred and reared in captivity on several occasions in Australia. One pair that had been reared from the nest and liberated, nested near the homestead of a friend of mine living in the north-west of New South Wales; they were great pets and talkers, visiting the house each day for food and petting, and bringing along their families to share the food."

This is a very common cage bird throughout Australia, although it seldom makes a very good talker. It is, however, the least offensive of the genus as regards screaming. I have possessed several birds of this species at different times but have never attempted to breed them.

The first breedings of this cockatoo appear to have occurred in 1922 in both England and France; since that date it has been bred on a number of occasions abroad. The Avicultural Society of South Australia deemed the Galah ineligible for its bronze medal, presumably because it was known to have been bred in that State. In October 1937 a lady who was not a member of the Society wrote to the Secretary stating that a pair in her possession had hatched four young birds, but there is no record as to whether they were reared. Both parents incubated in this case.

Galahs were successfully reared at the Adelaide Zoo in 1940 in a large flight aviary containing a number of cockatoos of several species, and they have been bred there subsequently. They do well in communities in association with other members of the family.

NYMPHICUS Wagler
Cockatiel

This genus, comprising a single species, has caused considerable speculation in regard to its correct taxonomic relationship, and no unanimity of thought exists. I have a leaning towards its association with the cockatoos, possibly in a subfamily of its own. It is crested, and although the crest is usually held erect it can be lowered. In its plumage pattern it is somewhat reminiscent of some features of the cockatoos of the genera *Callocephalon* and *Calyptorhynchus*.

In its ecology it resembles the Budgerigar, being a nomadic and opportunist breeder.

Cockatiels indulge frequently in mutual preening. The display is rarely performed and I have seen it given only by a male when a female is first introduced into the aviary; it consists of a series of rather absurd-looking hops whilst following the female along the ground, and accompanied by a low, warbling variant of the usual shrill call-note. Courtship feeding of the female by the male apparently does not occur, but both sexes incubate and feed the young, both before and after fledging. The down of the chicks is a cream colour and the bill of the young is pale yellow.

Cockatiels exhibit a variation of the wing-stripe of the broadtails. It consists of four or five yellowish spots on the inner webs of both the primaries and secondaries and is present in the adult female and in the immature of both sexes but is lost in the adult male.

The Cockatiel enjoys bathing in rain or under a spray.

It rarely holds food in the foot, and head-scratching is over the wing.

The flight is swift, with a deliberate, regular motion of the backward-swept wings. The slim, streamlined silhouette is very similar to that of the genus *Polytelis*, and the white wing-patches are very obvious.

22 Cockatiel

Nymphicus hollandicus (Kerr)

PLATE VI

Synonyms

Cockatoo Parrot, Crested Parrot, Quarrion, Weero.

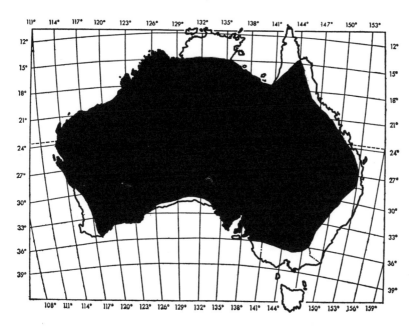

Distribution

This species is widely distributed over much of the continent, although mainly inland and only occasionally coastal.

In Western Australia, according to Serventy and Whittell[10] it occurs all over the State except the south-west jarrah forest area, with wandering birds occasionally penetrating as far as Bridgetown.

In South Australia the species is widely distributed, but hitherto there have been only a few records, from Kingston and Penola in the south-east. However, A. R. Attiwell informs me that it is common around Keith and Bordertown and is slowly coming south and that it is now a regular breeder in the upper south-east.

In Victoria the species has seldom been recorded south or east of the Wimmera, but L. Robinson states that it is not uncommon along the Murray and its tributaries north and north-east of Melbourne and that it is a regular visitor to, if not resident in, the Nagambie, Wangaratta, Cobram and Yarrawonga districts, where it breeds.

In New South Wales the Cockatiel is rarely coastal but is widely distributed over the inland parts of the State west of the Dividing Range.

In Queensland it is found in almost all parts with still some preference for the inland areas. Brigadier H. R. Officer observed it as far north as Princess Charlotte Bay.

In the Northern Territory it has been recorded in all parts.

Description

SIZE. About 12 inches (305 mm).

ADULT MALE. General colour above and below dark greyish-brown, passing into grey on rump and upper tail-coverts, and more greyish-brown on under-surface; wings dark grey, blackish towards tips of quills, the primary coverts darker, almost black; outer series of median and greater wing-coverts white, forming an oblong patch down centre of wing; central pair of tail-feathers grey, remainder blackish-brown, the next pair on either side to the central ones greyish on their outer webs; forehead, basal portion of crest feathers, cheeks and throat lemon-yellow; ear-coverts orange-red; bill grey; legs and feet dark grey; iris brown.

ADULT FEMALE. Duller in coloration than the male; head and crest brown washed with yellow, except on apical portion of latter; ear-coverts dull orange-red; lower back, rump and upper tail-coverts grey with narrow transverse yellowish-white bands; central pair of tail-feathers greyish-brown speckled with white, the lateral feathers darker, and the two outermost pairs, on each side, lemon-yellow mottled and barred with dark brown; back and lesser wing-coverts grey, some of the latter white on the outer webs, like the median and greater coverts and secondary quills, which form a conspicuous white patch on the wing; inner webs of quills with four or five yellowish-white spots or bars, smaller on outer ones; lower portion of abdomen dull greyish-brown crossed with yellowish bars; under tail-coverts distinctly darker especially on the longer ones, and with similar yellowish cross-bars.

IMMATURE. Resembles the female but the young male usually shows a slightly brighter yellow colouring on the face; it usually assumes the adult facial colouring when about five or six months old but retains the speckled tail-feathers until the first complete moult.

Geographical Variations

As would be expected in a species with such pronounced nomadic habits, geographical variation is negligible. However, it has been observed that birds derived from Queensland are of a noticeably darker shade of grey, especially the males.

Field Notes

Cayley wrote: "Quaint and unique, the Cockatiel is fortunately still fairly numerous, chiefly over the inland portions of New South Wales where I have met with it on many occasions. It is more or less nomadic, although a few may stay in a district throughout the year; only on rare occasions do they visit the coastal districts, driven there, most likely, by drought conditions inland. Generally it is met with in flocks of from four to a dozen in number, sometimes in far greater numbers, and nearly always in the vicinity of water. The species is a ground-feeder, its food being chiefly of the seeds of grasses and herbaceous plants; although it sometimes visits wheatfields and does a certain amount of damage, it cannot be included among the pests. It breeds in the hollow spouts of dead trees, and on account of its plumage being much the same colour as the dead limbs it is rather difficult to see. Both birds share in the duties of incubation and the rearing of the young.

"Clutch: usually five eggs, although as many as seven are not uncommon in good seasons; white, and oval to elongate-oval in form; shell close-grained, smooth and lustreless. Breeding-season: August to December."

I had not met with this species in the field until I was stationed on the outskirts of Brisbane late in 1942; there they were not infrequently seen either in pairs or in what were presumably family parties of six or eight birds, judging by the presence of a single adult male in the group.

Since that time I have seen them on very many occasions in South Australia and there is evidence that the species is gradually extending its range in a southerly direction as it is only in recent years that it has been noted as a breeding species in the upper south-east. It is nearly always to be seen along the upper Murray River in South Australia, and in October 1963 it was present there in vast numbers and breeding freely; in the spring of 1969 not infrequently it was seen flying over some of the suburbs of Adelaide, and there appears to have been a considerable irruption into the southern parts of the State.

In the Northern Territory the Cockatiel was common between the Adelaide River and Newcastle Waters in July and August 1964, and in July and August of the years 1967, 1968 and 1969 it was plentiful in the vicinity of Alice Springs. In 1967 and 1969 it was seen throughout much of the "Top End" and in the latter year was also found some miles east of Kununurra near the border of Western Australia and the Northern Territory.

In north-eastern New South Wales these birds were plentiful in the vicinity of Inverell in May 1960 and 1961, and in May 1965, in the course of a trip through south-eastern Queensland, we found them widely dispersed.

In May and June 1970 I saw more Cockatiels in eastern Queensland than I had ever seen anywhere before; they were plentiful everywhere from Gin Gin to north of Ayr, and hundreds were feeding on sorghum crops near Gumlu. Farther inland they were in thousands from Charters Towers southwards, and were extraordinarily numerous in the sorghum in the Clermont area; when disturbed, they perched on nearby telephone wires and their weight caused an appreciable sagging of the wires.

Aviary Notes

Cockatiels have long been favourite aviary birds and are bred so freely in so many parts of the world that they can be considered almost as domesticated as are Budgerigars. They have unusual natures inasmuch as they are relatively peaceful inhabitants of a mixed collection and yet can appropriate a nesting site and defend it successfully against some of the most aggressive broadtails. They will breed well in a colony, provided there is not an excess of cock birds and that there is reasonable space and plenty of nests provided.

My first success with this species was when a pair went to nest in a mixed collection in November 1935 and a single young bird fledged in the following January. In the following two seasons this pair proved very prolific, rearing five in the spring of 1936 and two broods of four and six respectively in 1937. Since that time I have bred a fair number of them, but strangely enough never more than two or three in a clutch; in fairness to the birds it must be acknowledged that they were never accorded the special privilege of an aviary to themselves.

Cockatiels resemble some of the cockatoos in that the male shares the duties of incubation, sitting from early morning to late afternoon while the female carries on for the remainder of the twenty-four hours.

POLYTELIS Wagler
Long-tailed Parrots

This genus comprises three species confined to the mainland of Australia. None are particularly closely related. The Superb Parrot exhibits marked sexual dimorphism and is confined to a comparatively restricted area of the eastern part of the continent. The Regent Parrot, with less —but nevertheless an obvious—difference between the sexes, is common in the south of Western Australia. A relatively small, isolated population is centred on the Murray River, principally in eastern South Australia and north-western Victoria and apparently barely overlapping the range of the first species. The third member, the Princess Parrot, for which the subgenus *Spathopterus* was created on the slender evidence of the spatulate elongation of the third primary in the male, exhibits only slight sexual differences and is a nomadic desert form inhabiting the centre of the continent; very few observers have had the good fortune to see this bird in the wild.

Polytelis parrots do not indulge in mutual preening. The courtship display is quite elaborate and differs somewhat from species to species, and is consequently described separately under each. Courtship feeding occurs, and the female persistently begs the male to feed her for some time before eggs are actually laid. Incubation, lasting three weeks, is performed only by the female, and the chicks are fed solely by the female for the first two weeks or so after hatching; thereafter the male usually participates in the task and continues to do so after fledging, which takes place about five weeks after hatching. The down is white and the bills of the young birds are duller than those of the adult females.

There is no wing-stripe present in this genus; bathing takes place only in rain or under a spray, never in surface water or, in captivity, in water receptacles.

Food is rarely held in the foot, occasionally by some individuals and certainly not as freely as by the larger broadtailed parrots. Head-scratching is over the wing.

The flight is swift and direct, the backswept wings producing an effortless impression. The silhouette is quite characteristic, with the very long, pointed tail and narrow pointed wings giving a streamlined appearance.

23 Superb Parrot

Polytelis swainsonii (Desmarest)

PLATE VI

Synonyms

Barraband's Parrot, Green Leek, Scarlet-breasted Parrot (erroneous).

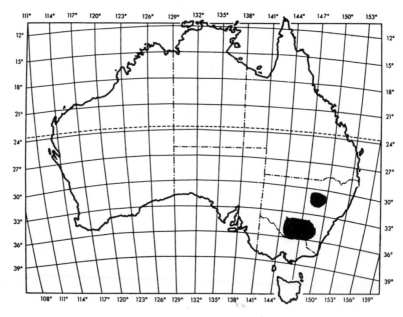

Distribution

Frith and Calaby[35] have elaborated on the range of this species in New South Wales and others have extended it somewhat. It may be summarized as the Murrumbidgee River from Hay in the west to the northern part of the Australian Capital Territory in the east. To the north, it is unusual along the lower Lachlan but is well known along the upper reaches of this river—at Cowra, for example. Southward in New South Wales there are records from the vicinities of Mathoura, Deniliquin, Jerilderie and Finley. Recently, the existence of what may well be an isolated northern population has been described as occurring along the Castlereagh River and its tributaries between Coonamble and

Gilgandra and extending to Gunnedah on the Namoi in the east and westward to Warren on the Macquarie River. Even so, it is difficult to accept old records from the Warrego and Condamine rivers.

In Victoria all records apart from a few along the Murray Valley seem to belong to a past era and include such places as Wangaratta, Mooroopna, Black Rock, Pine Plains (in the mallee and therefore highly suspect), Keilor and Heidelberg on the Yarra River.

Description

SIZE. About 16 inches (406 mm).

ADULT MALE. General colour above and below bright grass-green; occiput washed with bluish-green; forepart of head, throat, entire cheeks, reaching on to sides of neck, bright yellow; a crescent of scarlet across foreneck; lores, orbital region and ear-coverts grass-green; outer webs of primaries blue washed with green, black on their inner webs; primary coverts blue slightly tinged with green; tail grass-green, central feathers tinged with blue near their shafts, and lateral feathers washed with blue on their outer webs; under-surface of tail-feathers black, lighter at tips; bill red; legs and feet mealy-brown; eyes rich yellow.

ADULT FEMALE. General colour above and below dull grass-green; wings and tail as in the male but having inner webs of primaries narrowly edged with yellowish-white, and inner webs of lateral tail-feathers broadly margined with rose and tipped with dull yellow; face and ear-coverts pale greenish-grey washed with blue on the latter and cheeks; margins of feathers on lower throat tinged with dull rose; thighs scarlet; under tail-coverts yellowish-green.

IMMATURE. Young on leaving nest are exactly like the adult female except that most young cocks show a slightly brighter green body colour and a suspicion (very variable) of the eventual yellow and red areas. At about three months they undergo a partial moult and the young cocks then assume a noticeably brighter green dress. When nine to ten months old they show a mottled red and yellow appearance, but they do not assume full adult plumage until about fifteen months old.

Geographical Variations

None recognized.

Field Notes

Cayley wrote: "The Superb (more commonly called Barraband's Parrot or Green Leek) is becoming exceedingly rare. If property owners in the localities where it is found do not assist by giving them sanctuary the species will soon pass right out. Its present habitat is practically confined to the lightly-timbered plains in the neighbourhood of the mid-south-eastern inland portions of New South Wales. The Riverina and the area lying between Yass and Temora is now, perhaps, its stronghold. It is seldom found far from water, and spends most of its time on the ground,

K

where it procures its food, consisting chiefly of the seeds of grasses and herbaceous plants. Besides seeds, this parrot is partial to the blossoms of box-trees, from which it extracts the nectar. During the breeding-season the males congregate in flocks; from a dozen to as many as twenty may be seen together. Hence the one-time erroneous idea that the sexes were alike in plumage.

"The nesting-places are almost invariably in hollow branches and holes of the largest trees the birds can find, and the most difficult of access. The male bird does not sit, but feeds its mate, visiting her frequently throughout the day.

"Clutch: four to six eggs; white, and nearly oval in form; shell close-grained and lustreless. Breeding-season: September to December."

Until recently my personal experience of this species in the field was limited to a glimpse of a pair which flushed from the roadside in southern New South Wales in November 1933 and a single male seen on the outskirts of Canberra in October 1967. In October 1969, in the course of a daylight rail journey from Melbourne to Sydney, I saw large numbers of this species flushing from the side of the track between Cootamundra and Yass in southern New South Wales; they were mainly in small parties but on one occasion a flock of about thirty birds was disturbed. The brilliant green of the plumage of the males and their streamlined shape and long tails render them quite unmistakable in the field.

Cayley's statement that this bird was becoming exceedingly rare and his fear that the species "would soon pass right out" have fortunately proved incorrect, the species being quite common in its relatively restricted habitat.

The most authoritative article on this species is that published in the *Emu* by Frith and Calaby.[35] The authors point out that at the western extremity of its range it is restricted to river frontage and as one proceeds eastward the species spreads out more widely; it seems obvious that it prefers a wooded watercourse or at least well-watered savannah wood-land as a general habitat; in this respect it resembles the Yellow Rosella.

In their remarks on general habits Frith and Calaby note that, in addition to feeding on seeds and the green heads of various plants, an addition to the diet in spring is provided by the flowers of various eucalypts, especially the yellow box (*Eucalyptus melliodora*) and the sugar gum (*E. cladocalyx*), the latter being an introduction to the area. Drinking takes place mainly in the morning and late afternoon, unlike the associated species, the Yellow Rosella, which waters frequently during the day.

The birds appear to congregate in small flocks throughout the whole year and these comprise adults of both sexes and immature birds during late summer, autumn and winter. In spring the females disappear, presumably to nest, and the flocks, which are then considerably larger, consist entirely of males; there is some evidence to suggest that there is naturally a preponderance of males in the population. The breeding season is from September to November and the nests are almost invariably high and inaccessible.

Aviary Notes

This bird, which is almost always called the Barraband Parrot in avicultural circles, both in Australia and abroad, is one of my favourites on account of its beauty and its pleasant disposition.

My first breeding pair of this species consisted of a cock in adult plumage and of uncertain age which I acquired early in 1937 and a hen which was bred in captivity in Melbourne in 1937 and obtained in 1939. Although this pair were kept in an aviary to themselves from the time of acquisition of the hen, it was not until six years later, in 1945, that breeding eventuated. In October a clutch of five eggs was laid; young were first heard on 10th November and five could be counted by 19th November. The first two left the nest rather prematurely on 13th December, the temperature on that day being well over the century. On the following day, which was equally hot, a third youngster was out of the nest on the ground and the remaining two, although almost fully feathered, were dead in the log. The third young bird was dead the following day but the two eldest were reared, and appeared from the first to be a true pair; this was subsequently confirmed.

In 1946 five young were reared from the same pair, but in 1947, although three eggs were laid, no results were obtained and both of the adult birds died before the next winter.

In 1948 one of the young hens bred in the 1946 season was mated to an unrelated cock and this pair successfully reared three young birds that spring and five more in each of the two following seasons. In 1951 the cock bird died unexpectedly just as the clutch was hatching but the hen succeeded in rearing four perfect specimens single-handed.

For the following season, 1952, the hen was provided with a new mate in the shape of a young wild-caught cock who had only just attained adult plumage. When first introduced he displayed almost non-stop for several weeks and then proceeded to drive his mate, in a manner reminiscent of the worst type of bullying Crimson-wing cock, for weeks before she was ready to go to nest; ultimately, however, she hatched four young ones and reared three successfully. I disposed of this pair of birds before leaving on a trip abroad in 1953 but they continued to breed prolifically for their new owner for many years thereafter.

Tavistock[3] wrote: "The courtship display of the Barraband is of a lively and varied character; sometimes he will fly in a very slow and laboured fashion around the hen, bowing as he alights with contracting pupils and uttering a great variety of calls. When very excited he will puff his head feathers, draw his body plumage tight, partly spread his wings and race to and fro round the hen in a series of rapid hops, 'scroogling' at the top of his voice. If the object of these attentions is favourably impressed she crouches motionless with puffed head feathers and partly spread wings. It is noteworthy that the full courtship display is not in any sense a preliminary to actual pairing. It takes place months before the birds are in full breeding condition and is not repeated later; hens in breeding condition invite their mates to feed them with monotonous calls and up and down movements of the head."

24 Regent Parrot

Polytelis anthopeplus (Lear)

PLATE VI

Synonyms

Black-tailed Parrot, Plaide-wing Parrot, Rock Pebbler, Rock Peplar, Marlock, Smoker.

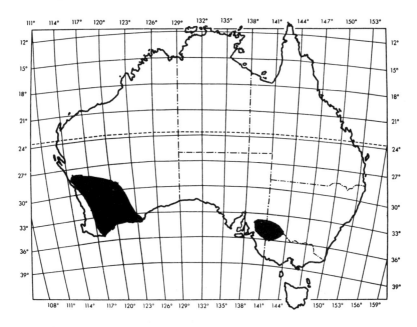

Distribution

This species is found only in the north-western corner of the State of Victoria as the records include the area west of Euston and Lake Albacutya and thence towards the South Australian border. J. N. Hobbs states categorically that the records for north-eastern Victoria must refer to the Yellow Rosella; he adds that the Regent Parrot is relatively common in north-western Victoria and extends a short distance over the Murray in the vicinity of Euston and twenty miles west thereof: he has seen it in mallee ten miles north of the river. The only other New South Wales record is that for Lake Victoria; however, C. E. Rix has informed me that he has recently observed this species in the country between Hay and Narrandera and also as far east as the town of Narrandera itself.

The Victorian range is continued directly into South Australia, forming a roughly triangular area of which the corners are Renmark, Morgan and Pinnaroo; records of extensions southward are few and irregular. It will be appreciated that this species, in the east, has a relatively limited range, like the previous one, and the two do not appear to overlap appreciably.

In Western Australia it is a much commoner and more widely spread bird. Serventy and Whittell[10] give its distribution as "the south-west portion of the State, north to Ajana, east to the Kalgoorlie area, the Dundas district, Esperance and Israelite Bay. It does not usually occur in the jarrah forest area and the extreme south-west corner." The recent records from Laverton, Leonora and 243 miles east of Norseman must raise the suspicion of mistaken identification of *P. alexandrae*.

Description

SIZE. About 17 inches (432 mm).

ADULT MALE. General colour above and below jonquil-yellow; head, nape and upper tail-coverts washed with yellow; interscapular region olive; scapulars blackish, olive in centre, and on inner webs of feathers; primaries and secondaries black, dark blue on their outer webs, apical half of outer primaries washed with bluish-green; outer webs of inner-most secondaries pale salmon-red; greater wing-coverts black, centre webs of outer series dark blue, median series washed with green (in very old birds jonquil-yellow) and tinged with dull crimson, innermost series crimson margined with jonquil-yellow; median and lesser wing-coverts jonquil-yellow; tail black tinged with blue; under-surface of tail black, lateral feathers narrowly edged with rose on their inner webs, and tipped with yellow tinged with rose; bill coral-red; legs and feet olive; eyes hazel.

ADULT FEMALE. General colour above and below olive-green, brighter on rump, breast and abdomen; inner series of lesser and median wing-coverts greenish-yellow; greater wing-coverts blue washed with olive-green, outer webs of inner series dull red towards tips; primaries blackish-brown, their outer webs dark blue externally washed with olive-yellow; outer webs of inner secondaries dull red near tips; tail dull greenish-blue, inner webs of lateral feathers black tinged with blue, those of the three outermost being broadly margined and tipped with rose-red.

IMMATURE. Resembles the female on leaving the nest, but the young male can usually be identified by the slightly yellower tinge in the green colouring, particularly on the head. A slow moult begins at about the age of six months, when the bright yellow feathers begin to appear on the head and breast. Full adult plumage is usually reached when the bird is about fourteen or fifteen months old.

Geographical Variations

Males of the Western Australian population, *westralis*, seldom, if ever, are of as bright a shade of yellow; females tend to be a little brighter, less olive, shade of green. It must be stressed that, contrary to Cayley's statement, the two populations are completely isolated.

Field Notes

Cayley wrote: "The Regent (also known as Black-tailed, Rock-pebbler, Smoker, and Marlock Parrakeet) is another comparatively rare species. Its present stronghold is in the Mallee belt of north-western Victoria and adjoining areas of similar country of South Australia and south-western New South Wales, although its range extends right across southern Australia to the Moore River, near the coast of Western Australia, where it has been observed breeding.

"In habits it is somewhat similar to the Superb. And, like that species, is in grave danger of extermination. Nests in hollows in trees, usually growing on river-banks; but has also been observed to breed in holes in the cliffs bordering the Murray River. The flight is swift and straight, usually at a great height. It often travels great distances to the feeding-grounds. The call is a succession of soft warbling notes; when on the wing it utters a loud high-pitched note that can be heard a considerable distance away.

"Clutch: four to six eggs; white, and varying in form from elliptical to rounded-oval; shell close-grained and smooth, but very minutely pitted and lustreless. Breeding-season: September to December."

I had not met with this species in the field until August 1948 when I saw three birds from the window of a train near Southern Cross, Western Australia: in flight they certainly give the impression of being predominantly yellow birds and are very striking.

Since that date I have frequently seen the species in the Renmark district but never in large numbers, a party of ten birds being the largest that I can recall in that area. However, in July 1954, in the course of a hurried weekend trip extending from Perth to Dongara in Western Australia, I found the species widely distributed, apart from the jarrah forest area; it was particularly common in the vicinity of Waddington. It is a strange, unexplained fact that the Western Australian population of this species has increased with development whilst the eastern population has apparently declined considerably.

In January 1966 I encountered these birds at Hattah, in north-western Victoria. A party of about a dozen birds were resting in the midday heat in small mallees and were extraordinarily fearless and only flushed on close approach.

As with the Superb Parrot, Cayley's fears as to the Regent being in grave danger of extermination have fortunately proved incorrect. In point of fact, the western segment of the population has increased in abundance and range of distribution since the settlement of the wheatbelt, in marked contrast to the response to similar development in the east, where it has undoubtedly decreased.

Aviary Notes

This bird is commonly known to aviculturists by the apparently meaningless name of Rock Pebbler, the origin of which has never been satisfactorily determined. It is an attractive aviary bird, although of a rather more sedate disposition than either of the other two members of its genus.

My earliest success in the breeding of this species was with a pair consisting of a cock which was in adult plumage when obtained in 1938 from a local bird-shop and a hen obtained for me during 1940. This pair made no attempts to breed for the first four years that they were mated but in 1944, whilst I was stationed near home, a clutch of four eggs was laid late in September and three young birds were seen on 22nd October, the fourth egg having disappeared. One of the young died during the first week but the remaining two survived and both emerged from the nest on 27th November, one being a little more mature than the other; these birds proved ultimately to be two cocks, as had been thought likely when they first fledged.

For the next three seasons, three, three, and four young were successfully reared but the old hen died during the winter of 1948 after an unsatisfactory moult. A new hen was obtained and mated to the old cock bird; she readily went to nest and successfully reared six fine young birds late in the same spring. This hen died before the following breeding season and although eggs were produced by subsequent pairs, no further results were obtained.

The display of this species somewhat resembles that of its relative, the Superb Parrot; it is, however, not nearly as elaborate and ostentatious. Hens in breeding condition persistently implore their mates to feed them, by monotonously calling and up-and-down movements of the head.

25 Princess Parrot

Polytelis (Spathopterus) alexandrae Gould

PLATE VI

Synonyms

Rose-throated Parrot, Princess of Wales Parrot, Queen Alexandra's Parrot, Spinifex Parrot.

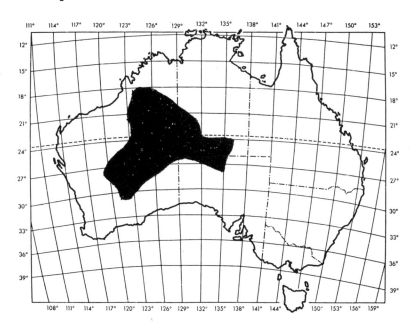

Distribution

There have been so few observations of this species that its range is extremely difficult to determine as, like many other desert forms, it is presumably nomadic.

In Central Australia the records are all from places on or about the 24th parallel (Ellery Creek, Todd, Hugh and Hale rivers) extending southward to places near the South Australian border (for example, Tomkinson Ranges, Finke, Abminga and Lambinna) and farther south to the vicinity of Alberga and Oodnadatta. More recent records are from the Bonython Ranges and half-way to the Petermann Ranges, and on Ringwood and Numery east of Alice Springs.

For Western Australia, Serventy and Whittell[10] state: "An inhabitant of the arid interior, occurring north almost to the Fitzroy River and south to Wiluna, Sandstone and occasionally Menzies. It occurs eastwards through the Great Victoria and Gibson Deserts to the central Australian range country." There is, however, a specimen in the H. L. White collection from Coolgardie, which is still farther south; the record from Three Springs, not far from the coast, is difficult to accept.

For Northern Australia, as distinct from Central Australia, there is the record from the type locality at Howell's Ponds near Newcastle Waters.

Description

SIZE. About 20 inches (508 mm).

ADULT MALE. Forehead, crown of head and nape light blue; hind-neck, upper portion of back, scapulars and innermost secondaries light olive-green, some feathers of the upper back indistinctly margined with green at the tips; lower back and rump violet; upper tail-coverts light olive-green; two central tail-feathers olive-green passing into a dull bluish-green towards tips, their basal half narrowly edged with greenish-yellow, the next on either side similar but having the basal half of their inner webs narrowly edged with rose-pink; remainder pale bluish-grey on their outer webs, dusky bluish-grey on their inner webs next the shaft, broadly margined with rose-pink and indistinctly tipped with greenish-yellow which decreases in extent towards the central pair; upper wing-coverts yellowish-green; primary coverts indigo-blue, outer ones nearly black; quills dark brown, innermost secondaries pale olive-green like the scapulars, remainder green on their outer webs tinged with blue near tips, and externally edged with greenish-yellow, the primaries alike but without the bluish tinge, except on the outer series; feathers in front and below eye dull yellowish-green; chin, cheeks and throat rose-pink, becoming much paler on basal portion of ear-coverts; remainder of under-surface pale olive-green with a pale ashy-blue shade on abdomen; thighs dull rose-red; sides of flanks deep blue and lilac; under tail-coverts olive-green; under wing-coverts bright grass-green; bill coral-red, fleshy-white at tip; legs and feet dark grey; eyes rich orange; the third primary has a peculiar spatulate elongation.

ADULT FEMALE. The spatula is never present and the tail is never as long as that of the male. In addition, the rump is always rather slaty in colour, the blue on the head of the male is replaced by greyish-mauve and the wing-coverts are greener and the bill is darker.

IMMATURE. Tends to resemble the female but the forehead is pinkish and the colouring of the throat is brighter, tending to a puce shade. They are not very easy to sex, but young males have larger and flatter heads and tend to be a little brighter on the crown. Adult plumage is acquired rather slowly and more or less imperceptibly between the age of twelve and fifteen months; the age at which young males attain the spatula does not appear to be recorded.

Geographical Variations

None recognized.

Field Notes

Cayley wrote: "According to some observers fortunate enough to have seen this beautiful bird in its native haunts, the Princess Parrakeet usually makes its appearance in some locality where it has seldom, if ever, been seen before. There it remains to breed, leaving again as soon as the young ones are reared. These observers also state that it is almost invariably found amongst the spinifex, the seeds of which constitute its chief food. Usually it breeds about the time the seeds of this grass are ripening, and generally in the vicinity of water. Another singular habit this bird is said to have is that, instead of perching on a twig or thin branch, it lies along a stout limb, like a lizard.

"Like the *Polytelis* parrakeets it breeds in holes in trees. Said to be extremely tame, showing little fear of people, cattle, or horses.

"Clutch: four to six eggs; white, and varying in form from elliptical to rounded-oval; shell close-grained, smooth, and lustrous. Breeding-season: in Central Australia, November to January. Owing to its 'will-o'-the-wisp' movements, it is difficult to estimate its numbers. As it is only recorded occasionally, it must be classed as very rare."

My son and I visited Hermannsburg in August 1968 in the hope of finding this species but were unsuccessful; we learnt from the mission station that when it last appeared and bred on the Finke River some four or five years earlier, it was quite unknown to any of the aborigines who were less than about thirty-five years old.

The following notes, published by Gee,[36] are worthy of being reprinted here:

"THE PRINCESS ALEXANDRA PARRAKEETS—
FOUND ONLY IN CENTRAL AUSTRALIA

"My knowledge of these rare and interesting birds was gained during my residence of nearly a year in the Macdonnell Ranges a good many years ago. Throughout the Commonwealth, attention is now being turned to the vast, almost unoccupied, spaces of Central Australia, and information concerning them is eagerly sought. Therefore, I am glad to say something about these beautiful and rare birds whose sole habitat is Central Australia.

"They were first seen by that genial old Burnside resident, the late Mr F. G. Waterhouse, F.Z.S., when passing through the Macdonnell Ranges as a member of Stuart's expedition in 1862, when that intrepid explorer finally succeeded in crossing the continent from south to north.

They are not large birds, about the size of grass parrots, with red bills and eyes; the feathers of the head and body give a most beautiful colour effect in delicate shades of pink, salmon, blue, and green; the tail is long. The inside feathers of one of my birds measured 17 inches, were darkish green on the outside, and rosy salmon on the inside. When they fly, the tail-feathers are spread out fanwise. They are strong and rapid in flight, and the only thing one sees of them in the wilds is something like a flash of colour passing swiftly from tree to tree. They generally perch along the branch, not across it, as birds generally do, and it is, therefore, difficult to see them in the trees.

"In the Macdonnell Ranges at certain irregular times they appear from nowhere, and then, after a stay of a few months, go back to nowhere, and where that nowhere is no one exactly knows; but I fancy it is in the immense solitudes southward from Tanami. I have never seen or heard anything of them at Tanami (latitude 19°S.) or for about 100 miles south of that place, and that would be about 800 miles south from Port Darwin, and 300 miles west of the telegraph line, but there is plenty of country southward again of that.

"I saw them first at Claraville, on the Hale River, about 70 miles east from Alice Springs. Claraville consisted of a jumbled-up galvanized-iron building with sheds and stockyards adjacent, and a well of good water in the sandy bed of the Hale nearby. The boss of the place used to be a coltbreaker at Norwood, and I remembered, as a boy, having greatly admired his feats of horsemanship. He gave me some particulars about these birds. Their visits are irregular, as they only come in good seasons, when water and seeds are plentiful. They do not nest in the Hale itself, but on the big gum-lined tributaries coming in from the north: the Maude, the Florence, and other 'Rivers of Rubies', from which came the abundance of 'Australian' rubies which caused visions of unbounded wealth to flit across the minds of some enthusiasts a good many years ago. The Hale is the main water channel of the eastern part of the Ranges, and breaks through the wall-like southern front of Ruby Gap.

"The birds arrive in early September, and by the middle of December they have gone—young and old, out on to nowhere. One year they were seen in considerable numbers on the Finke and the Alberga. The blacks at Claraville told me that plenty of the birds were about, but it was difficult for a white man to see them, a fact which I afterwards verified."

Aviary Notes

This species has always been highly sought after by aviculturists on account of its initial rarity, its pleasing pastel colouring and its almost invariable tameness. Although it has a reputation for being an erratic breeder in captivity, many thousands must have been bred in Australia alone without any significant introduction of wild-caught birds since the species first became established in captivity in this country.

My early experiences with the species were extremely disappointing. Eggs were laid by two successive hens in 1935 and 1936 without any results and for the next four years nothing whatever eventuated. However, in 1941 during my absence on service, five good young were reared and it was thought that the tide had turned. This proved not to be the case, as for the next four seasons, no young were reared although clutches were laid on several occasions and at least one young hatched.

In 1946 a new hen, bred in captivity in 1944, was tried; she laid a clutch of five eggs early in September but only two were fertile, of which one chick hatched and was successfully reared. It was hoped that this was a break-through but in 1947 the hen became egg-bound with her fifth egg and although she incubated after this, none were hatched. In 1948 one young bird was successfully reared from a clutch of four laid in September and of a second clutch of six laid in November, four were fertile and duly hatched and three of these young were successfully reared. This pair proved, by its subsequent results, to be the most satisfactory that I have possessed, as in 1949 four chicks were reared from the first clutch and one from the second; in 1950 four young were reared and a second clutch deserted, and in 1951 two chicks were reared from each of two clutches. Thereafter the hen failed to moult satisfactorily and two clutches laid in 1952 were infertile and she succumbed soon after that.

Boosey[37] described the display as follows: "The cock bird's display is the most spirited and amusing performance, during which he rushes about, uttering excited cries, and periodically jerking his head up and down, as though it were controlled by an invisible wire from above. At the same time, he erects a tiny opalescent shield of feathers on his forehead, and rapidly expands and contracts the pupils of his tawny-orange eyes. All this is, of course, usually done for the benefit of his mate, but most cocks are equally willing to display in order to welcome and entertain their human friends."

APROSMICTUS Gould
Square-tailed Parrots

It seems more appropriate that the two Australian species listed in the 1926 R.A.O.U. Checklist under this genus should be treated as belonging to separate genera. Under that arrangement the genus *Aprosmictus* would comprise the two Red-winged Parrots—namely, the well-known Australian bird *erythropterus* which extends to the south coast of New Guinea and which exhibits marked sexual dimorphism, and the little-known *jonquillaceus* which inhabits Timor and some adjacent islands in which sexual differences are less marked. The genus *Alisterus* would then contain the King Parrots with three well-marked species: *scapularis*, the well-known Australian bird; *chloropterus*, the fairly closely related Green-winged King Parrot occurring over most of Papua and New Guinea (in these two species sexual dimorphism is marked); and *amboinensis*, the Amboina King Parrot (in which the sexes are said to be alike), inhabiting the Moluccas and north-western New Guinea.

Quite apart from the obvious external differences between the two groups it is worthy of note that the Red-winged Parrots are relatively short-tailed compared with the King Parrots, and the flight patterns are also noticeably different in the two groups.

The Red-winged and King Parrots do not preen their mates. The courtship display is interesting, and differs considerably in the two groups and is described in detail under each. Courtship feeding occurs and, as in the preceding genus, the female begs the male for food for some time before egg-laying occurs. Incubation lasting three weeks is performed entirely by the female and she alone feeds the young in the early stages, but later the male participates and continues to do so after fledging, which occurs after about five weeks, often playing a greater part than the female at this stage.

The down of the young is white and the bills of young King Parrots are dark, but somewhat lighter in the young males and very slowly acquire the adult colour. In young Red-winged Parrots the bill colour is similar to that of the adult female. There is no wing-stripe in either subgenus.

Bathing occurs only in rain or under an artificial spray.

Food is held in the foot, and head-scratching is over the wing in the King but is stated to be under in the Red-winged; this requires further observation as to its invariability.

The flight of the Red-winged Parrot is flapping and erratic with rather slow wing-beats; that of the King Parrot is more direct and often gives an impression of heaviness.

26 Red-winged Parrot

Aprosmictus erythropterus (Gmelin)

PLATE VII

Synonyms

Crimson-winged Parrot, Blood-winged Parrot.

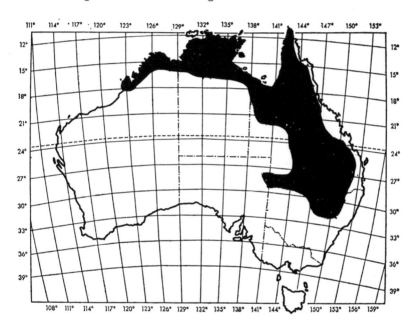

Distribution

The range, which extends as far west as Broome in the Kimberley division of Western Australia and over the whole of the northern part of the Northern Territory at least as far south as the latitude of Elliott, is that of the doubtfully distinct subspecies *coccineopterus* which is smaller and has the red coloration a more scarlet shade than the crimson of the eastern birds.

The typical bird extends over practically the whole of Queensland from Cape York Peninsula to the New South Wales border, being absent from only some of the east coast, especially in the south. It extends into the interior of northern New South Wales, where the vicinity of Oakwood may be its eastern limit, and reaches as far south as Scone, Dunedoo and Narromine.

The species also reaches the north-eastern corner of South Australia and extends southward along the eastern border as far as Mutooroo. When the 1926 R.A.O.U. Checklist was published this bird's occurrence in the Merauke district of West Irian was not known.

Description

SIZE. About 13 inches (330 mm).

ADULT MALE. Crown of head, nape and hind-neck bluish-green; inter-scapular region black; lower back and rump ultramarine blue; upper wing-coverts rich crimson-red; quills black, the primaries having their outer webs and apical portion dark green, and the secondaries edged externally with dark green, some being tinged with red near the tip; tail-feathers dark green tipped with pale yellowish-green, all but the central pair margined with dark brown on their inner webs; forehead and sides of head light green; all the under-surface, under wing, and under tail-coverts yellowish-green; bill orange-red; legs and feet brown; eyes red.

ADULT FEMALE. General colour above and below green; rump blue; upper tail-coverts yellowish-green; wings dull green, the outer series of the median upper wing-coverts red, some being externally margined with dull green; tail-feathers green tipped with yellowish-green, the lateral ones edged with rose-red on their inner webs; under-surface pale yellow-ish-green.

IMMATURE. Resembles the female and defies any attempts to be sexed by plumage differences. Adult plumage is not attained by the young male until it is over two years old; frequently, however, the sex is first revealed by the appearance of a few dark feathers on the mantle or extra red ones on the wing when the bird is between fifteen and eighteen months of age.

Geographical Variations

As noted under DISTRIBUTION, birds occurring in the Kimberleys and in the Northern Territory, *coccineopterus*, are genuinely red-winged where-as the nominate race from eastern Australia is crimson-winged in accord-ance with the earlier vernacular name. Intergradation between the two forms probably occurs in north-western Queensland.

Field Notes

Cayley wrote: "The Red-winged (more commonly Crimson-winged) Parra-keet is still very plentiful in the districts where Gould made his observa-tions so long ago. I have observed the species on numerous occasions in the north-western portion of New South Wales. Usually it was met with in pairs or family parties, according to the season of the year, and generally was exceedingly wary. It nests in hollow trunks of tall trees, mostly those growing on the banks of rivers and creeks; frequently the entrance to the nesting-place is in a hollow limb often thirty feet or more above the cavity itself, which is almost invariably situated in debris at the bottom of the main trunk. It would be interesting to know how the parents manage to get their young out. Do they carry them up the perpendicular walls on their backs, or do the young scramble out themselves?

"A well-known ornithologist, the late F. C. Morse, for many years a resident of Garah, New South Wales, had these birds breeding quite close to his home, and over a period of several years carried out a series of observations on their breeding-habits. Mr Morse exposed several of their nesting-chambers by cutting a scarf in the tree-trunks. These openings were covered again by nailing pieces of tin over them; thus, by removing the covers, he was able to watch and note developments. Interference with their nesting-places did not appear to scare the birds, for they returned each year to the same sites.

"This parrakeet appears to obtain most of its food from flowering and seeding trees; rarely is it seen feeding upon the ground like most parrakeets. A party of these birds when feeding upon honey-laden flowers or berries, or when flying erratically from one clump of trees to another, is a really beautiful sight; the brilliant plumage of the adult males offers a striking contrast to the less gaily-plumaged females and immature males, and to the surrounding objects.

"Clutch: four to six eggs; white, and rounded-oval in form; shell close-grained, smooth and lustreless. Breeding-season: in southern Queensland and New South Wales, September to December; Cape York Peninsula, April to July."

My first encounter with this bird in the wild state was in Darwin in November 1945 during a short period spent in a staging camp when a single bird flew over. In May 1960 two immature birds were constantly in the vicinity of A. C. Hunt's aviaries at Inverell, New South Wales, and a party of five birds, including an adult male, was disturbed whilst feeding on a sorghum crop in the vicinity of Moree; a year later a pair and an odd bird were seen in the course of an overnight stop at a station property near Inglewood in southern Queensland.

In the Northern Territory during the winter of the years 1964, 1967 and 1969 this species was found to be plentiful and widely dispersed throughout all areas north of Dunmarra. It was plentiful eastwards towards Arnhem Land and in 1969 was found to be very common at Victoria River Downs and also in the Ord River area.

This species was not seen near the coast in eastern Queensland in the course of the bird-watchers' tour of May and June 1970. It was first encountered near Dimbulah, west of Mareeba, and later was frequently seen on the inland road from Cape River southward through Clermont, Emerald, and Moura to as far south as the vicinity of Eidsvold.

Aviary Notes

Almost invariably called the Crimson-wing by aviculturists, this has always been a somewhat tricky bird in captivity, for although many are

L

very long lived once properly settled down, they have a reputation for dying suddenly and quite unexpectedly.

After a number of unsuccessful attempts to acclimatize wild-caught birds, a cock obtained in 1937 and a hen the following year settled down well and in 1941 reared two young; the following two seasons eggs were laid but no results obtained. Thereafter, it was not until late in 1948 that I obtained another satisfactory pair and although they did nothing in the subsequent spring, in 1950 three eggs were laid and hatched but only one young survived and fledged in mid-December. The following year four eggs were laid and hatched, rather later than the previous season. Of these, three chicks were reared; however, all these young birds, together with their male parent, died suddenly some weeks later. Another mate was provided for the surviving hen and late in November 1952 three eggs were laid; these all hatched and the young were reared, leaving the nest late in January.

Like King Parrots, Crimson-wings are notoriously difficult to accommodate with a suitable nesting-site; in most instances they seem to prefer a very long hollow, placed almost vertically; strangely enough, my best results were obtained in a very short log, with a large open mouth, hung in an oblique position.

Writing of the courtship of the Crimson-wing, Tavistock[3] said: "You can never tell what will happen when you introduce a healthy cock to a hen. Sometimes he will pursue her furiously about the aviary with open beak and torrents of Billingsgate. In more hopeful cases he will mingle the pursuit and abuse with a certain amount of display and if really in love with the lady he will do more showing off than cursing, though he will never entirely forgo the latter exhibition of masculine talent. The display of the Crimson-wing is curious and is of two kinds. Sometimes he will slightly depress his shoulders so as to show the blue patch on his back, draw his plumage very tight and with contracted pupils and blazing eyes take two or three long strides in a rather drunken and uncertain gait. At other times he will fly to and fro, uttering a kind of song, repeatedly gathering and chewing up bits of green stuff. On very rare occasions during the early days of their married life a cock Crimson-wing may feed his hen, but he never perseveres sufficiently to be of any real service to her when she is actually engaged in domestic duties. In some cases the hen will stop in the middle of pursuit and invite the cock to pair with her. He will do so after first pulling out some of her feathers and he may then become moderately quiet and amiable. The usual call-note resembles the word 'Crillik!' and when startled and on the wing they make a noise like 'Etz! Etz! Etz!' "

27 King Parrot

Aprosmictus (Alisterus) scapularis (Lichtenstein)

PLATE VII

Synonyms

Australian King Parrot, Scarlet and Green Parrot, Spud Parrot, Blood Rosella.

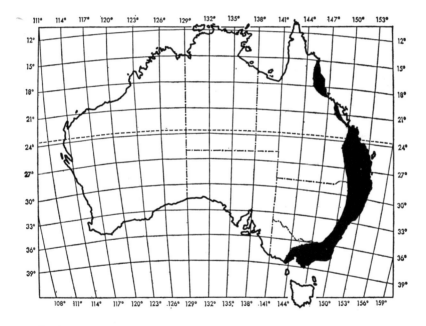

Distribution

Dr G. M. Storr found the species at Helenvale, south of Cooktown, which is the northernmost recording. From this point it probably extends along most of the high country of the Great Dividing Range, throughout Queensland, New South Wales and eastern Victoria and with occasional, rather surprising, extensions down the western slopes—for example, Condamine in Queensland and Bingara and the Warrumbungles in New South Wales. One also suspects that there may be considerable gaps in parts of this range—for example, between Cardwell and the Eungella

Range west of Mackay and again between this area and the Tropic of Capricorn.

In Victoria there is a further extension into the Otway Ranges.

Description

SIZE. About 17 inches (432 mm).

ADULT MALE. General colour above, including wings, green; inner series of upper wing-coverts pale turquoise-green; lower back and rump blue; upper tail-coverts black washed with olive; tail-feathers black, glossed with olive on their margins; head, neck, and all the under-surface scarlet, a narrow line of dark blue feathers separating the hind-neck from the interscapular region; under tail-coverts scarlet, with black centres to feathers; under wing-coverts green margined with blue at their tips; edge of wing green; bill scarlet, paler at tip; legs and feet mealy-grey; eyes yellow.

ADULT FEMALE. Head, wings and upper-surface green; rump-feathers green largely tipped with blue; tail-feathers green, lateral ones washed on their outer webs with blue and tipped with light red; throat and chest dull green, feathers of chin and upper throat washed with dull red; lower portion of breast and abdomen scarlet; under tail-coverts green, broadly margined with scarlet; bill black.

IMMATURE. Resembles the female but can be sexed soon after leaving the nest as the bills of the females quickly darken whilst those of the males are of a yellowish colour; in addition, young hens have much less red on the abdomen and lower breast. Adult male plumage is acquired by a slow moult, which starts when the bird is something over fifteen months of age and is not completed for a further twelve months or so.

Geographical Variations

Birds from the northern extremity of the range are claimed to be considerably smaller (*minor*); this is not apparent in the field.

Field Notes

Cayley wrote: "The King Parrakeet is an inhabitant of the heavily timbered ranges and dense scrubs of eastern Australia; its range extending from as far north as Cairns in northern Queensland right down throughout the coastal districts of New South Wales into Victoria. Still fairly plentiful, it is almost exclusively confined to the dense scrub lands and heavily-timbered ranges. Usually met with in pairs and can often be seen and heard in National Park and similar districts close to Sydney. As in Gould's time, it congregates in flocks during the non-breeding season and visits ripening crops, causing considerable damage. Its nesting-places are difficult to find as it shows a liking for some isolated locality in which to breed. As with the Red-winged Parrakeet, a hollow trunk of a large tree is used for breeding-purposes, and usually the nesting-cavity is placed at a considerable distance down the trunk from the entrance hole. Its call is loud and shrill, and easily distinguished from the cries of other species.

"Clutch: three to five eggs; white, and rounded-oval in form; shell close-grained, smooth and lustreless. Breeding-season: October to January."

I have frequently seen this species at the Sir Colin Mackenzie Sanctuary, near Healesville, Victoria, where a number of birds obtain an easy living from some of the food provided for the inmates of the sanctuary; the flock, which is extraordinarily tame, tends to follow the keepers on their rounds.

In May 1961 I encountered the species on the MacIntyre River in northern New South Wales and again in May 1965 on the Boyne River near Gayndah in Queensland.

In eastern Queensland during the bird-watchers' tour of May and June 1970 this species was observed in small numbers at Gin Gin and, farther north, in the Eungella Range, west of Mackay. Later, it was found to be fairly plentiful in the rain-forest around Lake Barrine, on the Atherton Tableland.

It is interesting to reflect that the range of the King Parrot, from North Queensland to Victoria, is almost identical with that of the Crimson Rosella except for the extension of the latter species farther to the west into south-eastern South Australia; both tend to prefer the same type of high rainfall mountainous country. Confusion between the two species may conceivably occur and it should be remembered that in the case of the larger King Parrot, the male is scarlet with green wings whilst the female and immatures are predominantly green with red underparts. On the other hand, both sexes of the adult Crimson Rosella are largely crimson, relieved with blue areas; however, the immatures, in the southern part of the range, are mostly dark green, with some red and blue areas.

Aviary Notes

For many years I was unsuccessful in my efforts to breed King Parrots; a hen which I had for ten seasons from 1936 onward with two different mates, invariably raised my hopes by coming into breeding condition each November but, as far as I know, never produced a single egg. A new hen obtained in 1947 did nothing that year, but laid four eggs from the perch late in the following spring.

In 1951 I considered myself fortunate to obtain a pair which had bred regularly for several seasons when in the possession of their previous owner. The hen laid two eggs on the ground late that spring, and in the following season, although provided with the original massive log in which they had previously bred, did not even lay.

When I moved to the Mount Lofty Ranges in 1966 I acquired a pair of Kings which were believed to have bred in captivity; however, the hen of this pair died egg-bound and I could not obtain a replacement for some time. Late in 1967 a sub-adult cock bird—obviously an escapee, for the species does not occur in the wild state in South Australia—began to visit my pair at frequent intervals, and when another hen was obtained he was obviously delighted. We proceeded to train him to enter the aviary next to the hen by means of a funnel, releasing him every morning and later putting the hen in the same aviary. In 1968 this pair had an unsuccessful first clutch and then laid again in December and successfully reared three young birds which emerged from the nest early in February 1969. In the following spring a second successful breeding took place by this semi-liberated pair, two further young being fledged in December of that year.

Meanwhile, the other pair of reputed breeders succeeded in hatching one young one, in both 1968 and 1969, but in each case it only survived about a fortnight; I assume the hen stopped brooding at night too soon, for the crop in each case was full.

King Parrots in Australia have not proved free breeders in captivity, largely because of the difficulty in supplying them with suitable nesting sites. They seem to like a very long log in an almost vertical position; frequently they will lay on the ground or in a seed receptacle, and have even been known to breed successfully under such apparently adverse conditions.

Tavistock[3] wrote: "The courtship of the King Parrot is elaborate and amusing. When a pair in good condition are introduced to one another they show great excitement. The cock puffs the feathers on his head, draws his body plumage tight, displays his green wing bar to the fullest extent, shakes his head, gives his wings a quick, shivering flip, makes a nibbling motion with his beak and after uttering his 'Crashak!' call loudly goes off into a singular kind of song in a minor key interspersed by sounds not unlike a hen announcing the arrival of her egg. All the while his eyes blaze, with contracting pupils, and from time to time he scratches his head violently, the access of the tender passion apparently sending blood to his brain to such an extent as to cause irritation! The hen responds by also puffing her head feathers, drawing tight her body plumage, contracting the pupils of her eyes and joining her cries to those of her lover. When courting a hen confined in an aviary a cock at liberty will sometimes indulge in an aerial form of display,. flying about in a figure of eight with his plumage set as when displaying on a perch and keeping up his chirruping song as he goes. When in breeding condition and about to lay, the hen King invites the cock to feed her by a noise and up and down motion of the head similar to that of the other close relatives. In addition to the calls already mentioned both sexes of the King Parrot have a long-drawn whistle, 'Eeng, eeng, eeng' repeatedly, many times in succession at short intervals."

ECLECTUS Wagler
Eclectus Parrots

This genus exhibits one of the most unusual examples of sexual dimorphism known, inasmuch as the female is equally as brilliantly plumaged as the male, if not more so, and the sexes are so dissimilar that for a considerable time they were believed to belong to different species, and possibly to different genera. Eclectus Parrots range widely through the islands to the north of Australia, from the Moluccas in the west to the Solomons in the east and with a southward extension to Cape York Peninsula, Queensland. Although there has been a recent tendency to consider them all as races of one species, there are good grounds for retaining two species—namely, the Grand Eclectus, *roratus*, of the west and the Red-sided, *pectoralis*, of the east, each of which has several not very well-defined subspecies.

I am informed that Eclectus Parrots do indulge in mutual preening on occasions; the display consists of slow bobbing and head-dipping by the male. Courtship feeding occurs, and the incubation, lasting thirty days, is performed entirely by the female, as is the feeding of the chicks in the early stages; later the male assists, and continues to do so after the chicks emerge from the nesting hollow some eight or nine weeks after hatching.

The down of the young is sooty-grey in colour; the bill of the young male is at first a dusky orange, that of the young female a dingy black. There is no wing-stripe.

Eclectus Parrots bathe in rain and, in captivity, enjoy a spray. Food is held in the foot and head-scratching is under the wing.

Flight is slow and heavy, with short periods of gliding.

28 Eclectus Parrot

Eclectus pectoralis (P. L. S. Müller)

PLATE VII

Synonyms

Rocky Parrot, Red-sided Parrot.

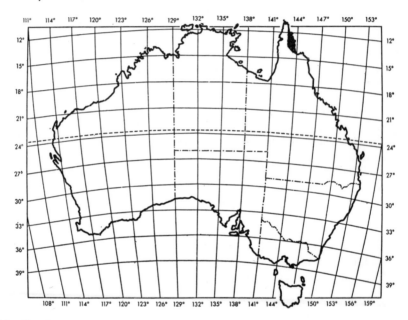

Distribution

The extralimital range of *pectoralis*, as opposed to *roratus*, comprises New Guinea, New Britain, the Solomons and adjacent islands.

The limited Australian distribution is given by Thomson[19] as "in the Pascoe, Claudie, Lockhart, Hayes, Nesbit and Rocky Rivers and in the Massey Creek districts—the last named is apparently its southern limit". However, Austin[38] has dramatically extended its range by his observations in the vicinity of Lake Barrine.

Description

SIZE. About 16 inches (406 mm).

ADULT MALE. General colour above and below green, brighter and somewhat paler on head, hind-neck, mantle, and sides of face, duller on wings and central tail-feathers; bastard wing, primary coverts, primary and secondary quills deep ultramarine blue, inclining to black on inner webs of feathers, the outer edges of some of the feathers paler blue, outer margin of wing brighter and inclining to cobalt-blue; secondary quills green on greater portion of outer webs, the green increasing in extent towards the innermost which are almost entirely green; outermost tail-feathers deep blue, broadly margined with dark brown on the inner webs, the next pair slightly edged with green on the outer webs, which colour increases in extent towards the middle ones which are green with blue towards the tips, all the tips whitish; centre of throat blackish-green; under wing-coverts, axillaries, and a large patch on sides of body red; under tail-coverts yellowish-green at tips of feathers; lower aspect of under wing-coverts and primaries glossy black, and of the tail glossy black with yellow at the tips; bill, upper mandible, red with yellowish tip, lower mandible black; legs and feet mealy-black; eyes brown.

ADULT FEMALE. General colour above and below red inclining to crimson on back, wings and upper tail-coverts; a band of blue across mantle; a narrow blue circle round eye; abdomen and sides of body purplish-blue, brighter on under wing-coverts, axillaries, and edge of wing both above and below; bastard wing, primary coverts, outer portions of primaries and tips of secondaries deep blue; tail orange-red at tip and more or less blue on basal portion of outer feathers; bill black; legs and feet mealy-black; eyes brown.

IMMATURE. Closely resembles the adult of each sex, but the plumage is less brilliant and the female shows greenish margins on some feathers; bill of young male very dusky orange with the red tip; bill of young female very dingy black.

Geographical Variations

None within Australia.

Field Notes

Cayley had no personal experience of this bird in the wild state and merely quoted as follows from Thomson's little-known *Birds of Cape York Peninsula*.[19] "A New Guinea bird, restricted, in North Queensland, to the heavy jungle country of the east coast. Numerous in suitable habitats. . . . It is a wary bird, frequenting the tree-tops of the jungle and generally congregating in small flocks. It is a noisy bird, and utters a loud call 'Kar! Kar! Kar!' as it flies."

I observed the closely allied, but probably specifically distinct, Grand Eclectus on Morotai, N.E.I., in 1945; they were usually seen singly, had a slow flapping flight and uttered their harsh call-note at intervals while flying.

Forshaw[5] found this species particularly numerous in the Iron Range area; there were three roosting sites within walking distance of his camp, one being occupied by more than eighty birds! He noted that they mainly frequent rain-forest but occasionally rested in tall eucalypts in open country. He further observed that in the early morning pairs and small parties leave the roosting tree and move out into the nearby forest to feed. They are wary, and when disturbed fly off or circle overhead, screeching loudly. The return flights to the roosting tree begin towards dusk in parties of three or four, males generally flying in front of females. As each group reaches the tree it joins in the noise, which continues unabated until after nightfall.

The nesting season on Cape York Peninsula appears to be towards the end of the year, and an interesting observation is that many nests seem to be attended by groups of up to eight birds of both sexes; four males and two females were in attendance at a nest found by Forshaw in November 1963.

Forshaw is convinced that reports of "a large black parrot on the Peninsula" refer to this bird, which when seen under difficult conditions of light appears to be black.

Aviary Notes

This species has proved very hardy in captivity and in many instances a free breeder; they are, however, not ideal aviary birds from most fanciers' viewpoint, as they require heavy netting and are very noisy at times.

For a short time in 1945 I was the nominal owner of a pair of these birds, but having no suitable accommodation for them at that time I exchanged them without ever actually taking delivery of them. Late in 1950 the late Sir Edward Hallstrom was kind enough to give me a pair of these birds which proved rather dull and stolid. They were, however, very noisy and as their aviary was close to the house, four months proved long enough to put up with them and I presented them to the Adelaide Zoo, where they successfully reared a young female in both 1954 and 1955. Although they are still at the Zoo, they have been unsuccessful since then, despite the hen having been provided with another mate in recent years.

GEOFFROYUS Bonaparte
Geoffroyus Parrots

Like *Eclectus* this genus is widely ranging in islands to the north of Australia, extending from the Moluccas through Timor and New Guinea east to the Solomons and south to Cape York Peninsula in Queensland. The Australian bird, *geoffroyi*, is only one race of the most widely spread species, all of which differ only slightly from one another. There are, however, two other very distinct species: the Yellow-headed, *heteroclitus*, of the Solomon Islands, New Britain and New Ireland, and the Blue-collared, *simplex*, of New Guinea.

Very little has been recorded of the habits of this genus, largely because of the infrequency with which its members have been kept in captivity. Mutual preening probably does not occur; the display, as I have recorded under field notes, consists of a purposeful walk by the male towards the female, culminating in a rather ridiculous-looking hop with outspread tail. Courtship feeding is to be presumed, and it is thought that only the female incubates and that the male assists with the feeding of the young as they near the stage of fledging and thereafter.

The colour of the down is not recorded, nor have I any note or recollection of the colour of the bill in the young that I handled briefly. There is no wing-stripe.

It seems unlikely that the genus would bathe other than in rain; Forshaw states that food is not held in the foot; and the head-scratching pattern is unknown.

The flight is swift and direct, with rapid wing-beats.

29 Red-cheeked Parrot

Geoffroyus geoffroyi (Bechstein)

PLATE VII

Synonym

Geoffroy's Parrot.

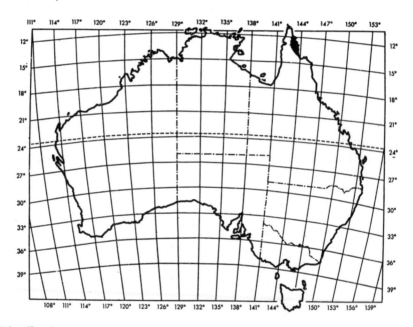

Distribution

This species has a wide extralimital range, extending from the Moluccas to Timor and New Guinea, with only slight racial variation.

For Australia, Thomson[19] has recorded it as "numerous in its special and restricted habitat in dense tropical jungles of the Lockhart, Hayes, Nesbit and Rocky Rivers, but never seen in open forest". The late G. Mack stated that it was confined to rainforest north-east of Coen in the Iron Range and Peach River area. Forshaw[5] states that "it is restricted to that area on the east coast of Cape York Peninsula bounded by the Pascoe River in the north and the Rocky River in the south. It does not occur west of the Dividing Range."

Description

SIZE. About 10 inches (254 mm).

ADULT MALE. General colour above and below green, lighter on under-parts, where many of the feathers have yellow bases; some inner upper wing-coverts tipped with bronze; inner webs of primary and secondary quills dark brown; tail-feathers yellowish-green, the under-surface lighter; crown of head and nape lavender-blue; forehead, sides of face, and throat scarlet; under wing-coverts and axillaries turquoise-blue, more or less mixed with green on edge of wing, the greater series mixed with greyish-brown and blue; bill, upper mandible red with olive-yellow tip, lower dark brown; cere olive-green; legs and feet olive-green; eyes, outer circle silvery cream, inner circle greenish; skin round eye pale olive, eyelid darker.

ADULT FEMALE. General colour above and below dull green, lighter on under-parts; entire head, nape and ear-coverts cinnamon-brown, the forehead, lores, cheeks, and throat washed with pale dull green; bill olive-brown; legs and feet olive-green; eyes silvery cream, inner circle greenish.

IMMATURE. Resembles the female except that the brown head is replaced by green. Young males show a slight pinkish suffusion on the face. Forshaw[5] believes that adult plumage is not acquired until the male is at least two years old and that the male probably assumes the brownish head colour of the female before acquiring the red and blue coloration. If this is the case, it is analogous to some of the parrots of the Asiatic genus *Psittacula*—for example, *rosa* and *cyanocephala*, where the immatures leave the nest with green heads and later have an intermediate plumage with grey heads like the adult females before the males ultimately acquire the pink heads.

Geographical Variations

None within Australia.

Field Notes

Once again, Cayley had no personal experience but quotes from Thomson's *Birds of Cape York Peninsula*[19] as follows: "Numerous in its special and restricted habitat in dense tropical jungles but never seen in the open forest. This species, like *Lorius pectoralis*, is also a Papuan bird. New Guinea forms are numerous in this east coast jungle. Occurs in small flocks in riverside scrubs. It has a swift flight, screeching noisily as it flies. Frequents big trees, and as soon as it settles is almost invisible among the green foliage."

As with *E. pectoralis*, my field experience is derived from observation of the closely allied, if not identical, bird which I found plentiful on Morotai in 1945. In the early months of my sojourn there, these birds were always seen in pairs and attracted attention by their rapid flight and harsh monotonous call, given both in flight and when perched. In

June and July I observed females investigating hollows in dead coconut palms and also saw the males feeding and displaying to the females; the display consisted of a purposeful walk by the male along a palm frond towards the female and culminated in a rather absurd-looking hop with outspread tail. I think they must have laid about the middle of August as for about a month thereafter females were not often seen and were very silent in flight. I do not know what this species feeds on but presume that it is a fruit eater; it is certainly not a nectar feeder. Late in October I saw a female, calling loudly, fly to a hole in a dead coconut and, hanging to the edge, proceed to feed two practically full-grown young. I persuaded a native to climb the tree and obtain the young for me but my efforts to hand-rear them on chopped apple, the only fruit obtainable, were proving difficult so I released them in the vicinity of their nest and was gratified to find within a few hours that their parents had found them and were feeding them. I kept them under observation for a few days and they appeared to thrive.

Aviary Notes

Virtually nothing is known of this bird in captivity in Australia. Cayley stated: "Rarely kept in captivity; the few I have seen were in Taronga Park Zoological Gardens and came from New Guinea. They were short-lived, succumbing during the cold winter months. So far as I am aware, there is no record of it ever having bred in captivity. Have only been able to gather that it is exceedingly delicate when kept in confinement."

To the best of my knowledge not even the late Sir Edward Hallstrom—who, in his heyday, was prone to equip expeditions to procure species that he especially desired—ever had a living specimen of this bird. However, he once showed me a spirit specimen of a female which had been obtained by one of his collectors, possibly in New Guinea, and he seemed surprised when I knew what it was!

PURPUREICEPHALUS Bonaparte
Red-capped Parrot

This genus, which consists solely of the handsome species *P. spurius*, has been the subject of considerable discussion in regard to its correct relationships. Although it has undoubted platycercine affinities, it is felt that these are not very close; its behaviour and calls and particularly its form of display are quite unlike those of *Platycercus, Barnardius* and *Psephotus*. Serventy[39] thought it may well be a relict form which once extended more widely, but this seems to be pure speculation. A fantastic suggestion was that of Cain,[2] who sought to relate it to *Eunymphicus* of the New Caledonia group of islands; anyone seeing both genera in life would find this theory untenable in a few seconds; *Eunymphicus* is obviously a close relative of the New Zealand and Pacific Islands genus *Cyanoramphus*.

Like most of the broadtails *Purpureicephalus* does not indulge in mutual preening. Its display is, however, quite unlike that of any other parrot. The male alights near the female, erects the red feathers of the cap, droops the wings slightly, thereby making the yellow rump more obvious, and slowly raises the fanned-out tail-feathers; there is none of the shoulder-squaring or tail-wagging which is characteristic of most broadtails. During the display the harsh, rattling call is given.

Courtship feeding and feeding of the female by the male during the three weeks' incubation period and for about a fortnight after the young hatch is the usual pattern; thereafter the male feeds the young directly in the nesting hollow and continues to do so for a few weeks after they fledge some five weeks after hatching. Incubation is performed only by the female.

The newly hatched young are clothed in white down and when they emerge the bill is yellowish and its strange shape seems accentuated; the colour changes to horn in a few weeks.

As would be expected in a species in which the immature plumage differs so markedly from that of the adult, the wing-stripe in immatures is constant. Also, because the adult female is appreciably duller than the male, there is a practically invariable retention of the stripe in the female and its loss in the male at the first moult, as noted in my article on the wing-stripe in broadtailed parrots.[40]

Purpureicephalus bathes freely in the wild state and in captivity.

The foot is used for holding food and the strange bill shape is an adaptation for extracting the seeds of some of the eucalypts, notably the marri (*Eucalyptus calophylla*), from the hard seed capsule. It has been noted that immature birds are not nearly as adept at the process and frequently chew away the margins of the capsules to get at the seeds.

Head-scratching is performed from behind the wing.

The flight of this parrot is more direct than that of the Rosellas and Ringnecks; there is only slight gliding and, consequently, very slight undulation.

30 Red-capped Parrot

Purpureicephalus spurius (Kuhl)

PLATES IX, X

Synonyms

Pileated Parrot, King Parrot (W.A.), Hookbill, Western King Parrot.

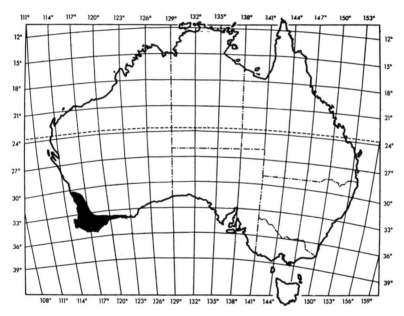

Distribution

This species is confined to a relatively small area of Western Australia and stated by Serventy and Whittell[10] to be found "in the south-west corner north to Dandaragan, Gingin and Mooliabeenee and generally west of the Great Southern Railway but in the south extending eastward to Lake Grace (rare) and along the coast to Esperance". There do not appear to be any records which extend the foregoing range.

Description

SIZE. About 14 inches (356 mm).

ADULT MALE. General colour above, including hind-neck, back, scapulars, innermost secondaries and upper wing-coverts, dull green; outer

M

edge of wing and under wing-coverts, outer webs of bastard wing, primary coverts, and primary quills dark blue; outer webs of secondaries pale blue; inner webs of bastard wing, primary coverts, primary and secondary quills blackish-brown; rump and upper tail-coverts yellowish-green shading to green towards base of tail-feathers; central tail-feathers green, darkening towards tips, the remainder blackish at base, blue on middle portion, and whitish at tips; crown of head and nape deep red; short feathers in front and over eyes green with blackish bases; sides of face and sides of throat pale green shading to yellow on sides of neck; breast, abdomen, and sides of body purplish-blue; centre of lower abdomen, thighs, and under tail-coverts red; bill dark bluish-horn, the upper mandible long and narrow; legs and feet fleshy-grey; eyes hazel.

ADULT FEMALE. Similar to the adult male but appreciably duller as regards the red cap which may be tinged with green, the under-parts which are not as deep a purple, and the subcaudals which have some green mixed with the red.

IMMATURE. Head and upper parts a dull dark green; rump greenish-yellow; middle tail-feathers olive-green; a narrow frontal band of red on forehead; throat and fore-neck greyish shading to a vinous tinge on breast, abdomen pale purplish-blue; feathers on flanks and thighs light green margined with red; under tail-coverts light red mixed with green. Young males have larger and flatter heads and show more red on the under tail-coverts. Adult plumage is acquired, in the case of males, by the first complete moult when the birds are from twelve to fifteen months old; however, young females often appear not to acquire full plumage, especially as regards the red cap, till the next moult.

Geographical Variations

None recognized.

Field Notes

Cayley wrote: "Although by no means plentiful, not an uncommon bird. Usually met with in small parties, probably families, amongst the gum-trees, especially the Red Gum (*E. calophylla*), the seeds of which it is very fond; or upon the ground, feeding on various seeds of grasses and plants. Commonly called the King Parrot in Western Australia. The native name for the bird is said to be Chelyup, a rendering, no doubt, of its call-note.

"Recent reports state that this parrakeet is becoming very troublesome in orchards and in the wheat areas, and heavy toll is taken to keep the species in check.

"It breeds in hollow limbs and holes in eucalypts; often the nesting-cavity is several feet from the entrance.

"Clutch: five or six eggs; white, and rounded-oval in form; shell close-grained and lustreless. Breeding-season: August to November."

In the course of a hurried trip through the south-west of Western Australia in August 1948 I observed a number of these birds but never obtained a good view of an adult. Further views were obtained in the vicinity of Perth in 1957 and it was not until October 1964 that a really satisfactory view of an adult was achieved near Dwarda where the rarely seen Western Shrike-tit was also encountered.

This species is quite unmistakable in the field, even in immature plumage, on account of the distinctive, rattling call-note and the tell-tale yellowish rump, well seen in flight, which distinguishes it immediately from the *Barnardius* parrots.

Aviary Notes

Ever since 1936 when I first saw a magnificent specimen in the collection of the late Dr R. N. Thomson of the Sydney suburb of Bankstown, this bird has been one of my favourites; I have always felt that its gorgeous coloration more than compensates for the somewhat strange shape of its bill. Soon after seeing the above-mentioned bird I was able to arrange, through the kindness of a colleague practising in Bunbury, Western Australia, for a small consignment to be sent to South Australia; most of these birds went to the Adelaide Zoo where the species had not been previously exhibited.

My first pair of these birds, like all newly caught examples of this species, were extremely timid and took a long time to steady down. No breeding was attempted in the first two seasons that they were in my possession but in 1939 a clutch of five eggs was laid in mid-October and four young were seen in mid-November; all went well for about a week thereafter but then the parents apparently ceased feeding the chicks and immediately started to moult.

The hen of this pair, which was in adult plumage when obtained, died early in the following year and it was not until the spring of 1942 that a suitable replacement was obtained. I was overseas at the time, but it appears from the records that some eggs were laid the same season though nothing eventuated, nor were any eggs laid in the following two seasons. In 1945 three eggs were laid from the perch and broken, and again in 1946 nothing happened.

In 1947 a clutch of five eggs was produced, most of them being laid on the ground but two of them, unbroken, in a nesting log. For a few days it looked as if incubation would follow, but the task was abandoned and a moult immediately followed. I was so certain by then that this hen would never do any good that I would have disposed of her had a substitute been available. It was fortunate that I did not do so, for in 1948 a clutch of six eggs was produced in mid-October: four of these proved to be fertile and all of them had hatched by 19th November. All these birds flourished and left the nest at daily intervals from 19th December onwards, being fine specimens and reasonably steady. This success gained the bronze medal of the Avicultural Society of South Australia.

Thereafter this pair of birds had a very good record, for in 1949 four were reared from five hatched. Although, for some unexplained reason, no eggs were laid in 1950, in 1951 five were fledged from six hatched and in 1952 three young left the nest out of four hatched.

BARNARDIUS Bonaparte
Ringneck Parrots

This genus comprises the Australian Ringneck Parrots, and the four species listed in the 1926 edition of the R.A.O.U. Checklist before its subsequent amendments are recognized. Some authors have placed these birds in the genus *Platycercus* to which they are obviously closely related, but their plumage patterns are quite distinct from those of the Rosellas and in addition there are osteological differences which Condon[41] has demonstrated, further substantiating their generic status.

The species form eastern and western pairs, the eastern forms being predominantly green-headed and the western black-headed. Of the eastern birds the Ringneck Parrot, *barnardi*, has a wide range and appears to be separated by a relatively treeless belt of country from the very distinct northern isolate, the Cloncurry Parrot, *macgillivrayi*. In the west, the Yellow-banded Parrot, *zonarius*, has a very extensive range from Eyre Peninsula in South Australia northwards into the Northern Territory and westward over a large part of Western Australia. In the south-western corner of Western Australia there occurs the green-bellied Twenty-eight, *semitorquatus*, and there is an intermediate hybrid population extending over a wide zone where the two species make contact. Claims regarding extensive hybridization between *zonarius* and *barnardi* in the western Flinders Range appear, as yet, to be unsubstantiated.

The remarks made in regard to the Rosellas apply, almost without exception, to the Ringnecks. There is no mutual preening, the display is identical, and the incubation and feeding pattern is the same. The down of the young is white and the bill of the immatures is pale yellow, rapidly changing to horn coloured.

The wing-stripe is not invariably present in the immatures of some species; particularly is this so in the young males. The retention of the stripe by the adult female is variable and is particularly marked in *barnardi*, the species which exhibits the most difference generally between the plumage of the adult male and female.

Bathing habits, use of feet for feeding, and head-scratching are the same as in the Rosellas.

The flight of the Ringneck Parrots is practically identical with that of the Rosellas, consisting of a series of wing-beats followed by short glides, producing an undulating pattern.

31 Ringneck Parrot

Barnardius barnardi (Vigors and Horsfield)

PLATE X

Synonyms

Barnard's Parrakeet, Scrub Parrot, Buln-buln, Mallee Parrot.

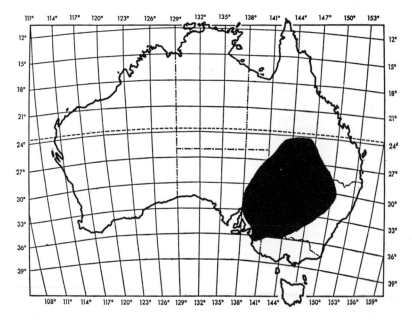

Distribution

In South Australia the range is best defined by saying that this species does not occur west of the Flinders Ranges and Spencer Gulf and that it avoids the high rainfall areas of the Mount Lofty Ranges and the south-east of the State, where it extends as far south as Kingston and about midway between Keith and Naracoorte.

In Victoria it is confined to the north-western portion, the southern-most recordings being Kaniva and Kerang.

In New South Wales the species occurs over most of the western two-thirds of the State, extending as far east as Garah, Warialda, and Pilliga in the north and such places as Dubbo, Dunedoo, West Wyalong and Temora in the central portion, but apparently avoiding most of the

Riverina in the south, although L. Robinson reports having seen a pair at Tocumwal.

In Queensland it is widely spread in the south-western corner, being roughly enclosed by a line running through Goondiwindi, St George, Mitchell, Augathella, Blackall and Windorah and probably becoming continuous with the South Australian population in the north-eastern corner of that State.

Records from Barcaldine, Longreach and Winton appear to be well beyond the accepted distribution and raise the possibility of an extension of *B. macgillivrayi* in this direction.

Description

SIZE. About 14 inches (356 mm).

ADULT MALE. Forehead red; crown of head, ear-coverts and cheeks verditer-green and anterior of latter blue; dull bluish-brown band on nape; a yellow band around hind-neck, broader at sides; back and scapulars dark blue; a yellowish-green band down centre of upper wing-coverts; rump and upper tail-coverts verditer-green washed with yellow; lesser median upper wing-coverts, primary coverts, and outer webs of primaries rich deep blue; outer webs of outer secondaries blue, all the remainder of innermost series green, inner webs of quills blackish; central pair of tail-feathers green passing into blue towards tips, the next on either side green, dark blue on outer webs towards tips, which are pale blue, the remainder dark blue at their bases, pale blue on their apical half; all under-surface and under tail-coverts verditer-green, with a variable and irregular band of orange-yellow across breast; bill whitish-horn colour, bluish-horn colour on lower mandible; legs and feet greyish-black; eyes blackish-brown.

ADULT FEMALE. Differs from the male in its duller coloration and slightly smaller size; the back is greenish-blue; the head and bill are also smaller.

IMMATURE. Resembles the female but all markings are less clearly defined and the coloration is duskier in all respects. The sexes can be distinguished in most cases by the size and shape of the head and bill. Adult plumage is attained by the first complete moult which occurs when the bird is between twelve and eighteen months old.

Geographical Variations

Birds occurring in the Flinders Range, *whitei*, are undoubtedly darker on the head, the abdominal band is wider and more yellow than orange and the males have not the obvious blue back of the typical birds; it has been suggested that this is the result of hybridization with *zonarius*, which is found to the west of the Range.

Field Notes

Cayley wrote: "The Mallee Parrakeet (also commonly called Barnard's Parrakeet, Ringneck Parrot, and Buln Buln) is widely distributed over the inland portions of the eastern and southern States, its range extending from southern Queensland to South Australia. It is fairly plentiful in the Moree district, New South Wales, and is usually met with in pairs, or after the breeding-season in small family parties, either feeding on the ground on the seeds of various grasses and herbaceous plants, or on the seeds of acacias and other trees.

"It mostly breeds in hollow limbs or holes in trees growing on river-banks or on the margins of watercourses, and in coolabah-trees dotted over the plains. During a recent 'Camp' of members of the Royal Australasian Ornithologists' Union held at the Moree Watercourse, many nesting-hollows containing young were found in dead trees standing in the watercourse. In Boodgeree Swamp, in the same district, one dead tree had two hollows containing young; two others were occupied by Blue Bonnets, one containing eggs, the other young; a pair of Galahs had young in another, while several pairs of Budgerigars were flushed from other small hollows. In a nearby dead tree, also in the swamp, Red-rumps, Blue Bonnets and Galahs were breeding. In fact, from nearly every dead tree-trunk knocked upon with sticks parrots—especially Budgerigars which were very plentiful—were flushed from their nesting-hollows.

"Clutch: four to six eggs; white, and varying from oval to rounded-oval and an ellipse in form; shell close-grained, dull, and lustreless. Breeding-season: July to December."

My experience of this species in the wild is almost entirely confined to observations in South Australia. It has always been plentiful in the area of mallee country known as Chauncey's Line, about forty miles south-east of Adelaide to the north of Lake Alexandrina; unfortunately much of this country has been cleared in recent years, apart from a relatively small reserve.

It also occurs in the country along the main road to Melbourne south of Tailem Bend, extending nearly as far south as Naracoorte and Kingston; in fact it seems likely that it may well be extending its range in this direction. It is still plentiful in the flat country between the eastern slopes of the Mount Lofty Ranges and the Murray River and also along the upper Murray between Morgan and Renmark and in the country both north and south of the river. Whether it has a continuous distribution farther north is not certain, but it is met with in the Lower Flinders Range and I have seen it as far north in the Range as Arkaroola; these northern birds, *whitei*, are said to be darker on the head, and it is claimed that there is some hybridization with the Yellow-banded Parrot which occurs to the west of the range; to my knowledge this is as yet unproved.

Outside South Australia I had met with the species only at Hattah and Kiata in western Victoria, but only recently I was fortunate enough to see it at the northern extremity of its range in southern Queensland and northern New South Wales.

Aviary Notes

Cayley's notes were scanty, as follows: "A popular aviary bird, being hardy and a free breeder. Quite unsuited to cage-life, although it makes an interesting pet. If taken when young it will soon learn to whistle and talk.

"Said to resemble the Rosella in its general disposition and needs; is double-brooded; its nesting-habits do not differ from the other Broadtails."

Hand-reared birds of this species are always in demand as they frequently make good whistlers; they are, however, most unattractive pets as they almost invariably become aggressive and anxious to bite anyone who takes any notice of them. Like all its near relatives, this bird is unsuitable for a mixed collection on account of its pugnacity.

I had several birds of this species between 1937 and 1944 without ever getting them to go to nest. Then, in May 1944, I acquired an elderly hen that had bred a considerable number of unattractive hybrids with various other broadtail mates in previous years. She proved to be a temperamental lady, and although terrified of the first mate I provided for her she was extremely rude to the substitute provided in July. Notwithstanding her disapproval of her mate, she went to nest early that season, laying the first of a clutch of five eggs on 14th August and incubating steadily. However, as I had expected, these eggs were all infertile and I removed them early in September. By this time the cock had got over some of his early nervousness and fed the old lady occasionally in an apologetic sort of way and consequently I was more hopeful when a second clutch was commenced on 19th September. On 11th October one young bird had hatched, and a week later there were three large and one small young in the log; the little one only survived a few days, however, and a fifth egg contained a dead embryo. The three larger chicks did well and the first, a hen, left the log on 14th November and the other two, a pair, four days later. This success, being the first recorded breeding of the species in South Australia, gained the bronze medal of the Avicultural Society of South Australia.

The following season, 1945, a clutch of four was laid early in September and all were successfully hatched and reared, proving to be two of each sex. A second clutch was not laid that year. In 1946 a clutch of six was laid early in August, but the cock bird, who had not looked very well during the winter, was found dead soon after incubation had started and the eggs proved to be clear and were thereupon removed. A new mate obtained almost immediately was very badly received and a period of introduction in the adjoining cage was necessary. By mid-September the old lady seemed reconciled to her new mate and laid a further clutch of five before the end of that month; however, these were again infertile as were a third clutch laid late in October.

In 1947 a clutch of three was laid early in September and although these again proved infertile the hen was allowed to continue incubating until late in the month, when four fertile Red-rump eggs, taken in the bush, were substituted. Two of these hatched three days later, and a fortnight later three young Blue-bonnets, a little more than half-grown, were also put in the nest. Quite undeterred, the old lady proceeded to rear the lot with a minimum of assistance from her mate. I disposed of her before the 1948 breeding season because she was becoming progressively more difficult to satisfy as regards a mate, a characteristic not uncommon in broadtail hens as they get old, and especially in those that are inclined to be tame.

PLATES

Scale

one foot

PLATE I LORIKEETS

1. Rainbow Lorikeet (*Trichoglossus moluccanus*); 2. Red-collared Lorikeet (*Trichoglossus rubritorquis*); 3. Scaly-breasted Lorikeet (*Trichoglossus chlorolepidotus*); 4. Red-capped Lorikeet (*Psitteuteles versicolor*); 5. Musk Lorikeet (*Glossopsitta concinna*); 6. Purple-crowned Lorikeet (*Glossopsitta porphyrocephala*); 7. Little Lorikeet (*Glossopsitta pusilla*).

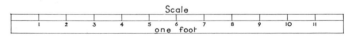

Scale
one foot

PLATE II FIG-PARROTS

8. Southern Fig-parrot (*Opopsitta coxeni*); 8a. Female Southern Fig-parrot; 9. Northern Fig-parrot (*Opopsitta macleayana*); 9a. Female Northern Fig-parrot; 10. Cape York Fig-parrot (*Opopsitta diophthalma*); 10a. Female Cape York Fig-parrot.

PLATE III PALM COCKATOO AND WHITE-TAILED AND YELLOW-TAILED BLACK COCKATOOS

11. Palm Cockatoo (*Probosciger aterrimus*); 12. White-tailed Black Cockatoo (*Calyptorhynchus baudini*); 13. Yellow-tailed Black Cockatoo (*Calyptorhynchus funereus*).

14a

15a

15

14

Scale

| 1 | 2 | 3 | 4 | 5 | 6 | 7 | 8 | 9 | 10 | 11 |

one foot

PLATE IV RED-TAILED AND CASUARINA BLACK COCKATOOS

14. Red-tailed Black Cockatoo (*Calyptorhynchus magnificus*); 14a. Female Red-tailed Black Cockatoo; 15. Casuarina Black Cockatoo (*Calyptorhynchus lathami*); 15a. Female Casuarina Black Cockatoo.

PLATE V   GANG-GANG, SULPHUR-CRESTED AND PINK COCKATOOS, LITTLE
AND LONG-BILLED CORELLAS, AND GALAH

16. Gang-gang Cockatoo (*Callocephalon fimbriatum*); 16a. Female Gang-gang Cockatoo;
17. Sulphur-crested Cockatoo (*Cacatua galerita*); 18. Pink Cockatoo (*Cacatua lead-beateri*); 19. Little Corella (*Cacatua sanguinea*); 20. Long-billed Corella (*Cacatua tenuirostris*); 21. Galah (*Cacatua roseicapilla*).

PLATE VI COCKATIEL AND SUPERB, REGENT AND PRINCESS PARROTS

22. Cockatiel (*Nymphicus hollandicus*); 22a. Female Cockatiel; 23. Superb Parrot (*Polytelis swainsonii*); 23a. Female Superb Parrot; 24. Regent Parrot (*Polytelis anthopeplus*); 24a. Female Regent Parrot; 25. Princess Parrot (*Polytelis alexandrae*).

PLATE VII RED-WINGED, KING, ECLECTUS AND RED-CHEEKED PARROTS

26. Red-winged Parrot (*Aprosmictus erythropterus*); 26a. Female Red-winged Parrot;
27. King Parrot (*Aprosmictus scapularis*); 27a. Female King Parrot; 28. Eclectus Parrot
(*Eclectus pectoralis*); 28a. Female Eclectus Parrot; 29. Red-cheeked Parrot (*Geoffroyus
geoffroyi*); 29a. Female Red-cheeked Parrot.

Scale
one foot

PLATE VIII ROSELLAS

35. Crimson Rosella (*Platycercus elegans*); 36. Adelaide Rosella (*Platycercus adelaidae*);
37. Yellow Rosella (*Platycercus flaveolus*); 38. Green Rosella (*Platycercus caledonicus*);
39. Northern Rosella (*Platycercus venustus*); 40. Pale-headed Rosella (*Platycercus
adscitus*); 41. Eastern Rosella (*Platycercus eximius*); 42. Western Rosella (*Platycercus
icterotis*).

42b

35b

38b

40c

30b

Scale

1 2 3 4 5 one 6 foot 7 8 9 10 11

PLATE IX IMMATURE RED-CAPPED PARROT, CRIMSON, GREEN AND WESTERN ROSELLAS AND NORTHERN RACE OF PALE-HEADED ROSELLA

30b. Immature Red-capped Parrot (*Purpureicephalus spurius*); 35b. Immature Crimson Rosella (*Platycercus elegans*); 38b. Immature Green Rosella (*Platycercus caledonicus*); 40c. Northern race of Pale-headed Rosella (*Platycercus adscitus*); 42b. Immature Western Rosella (*Platycercus icterotis*).

(The paintings reproduced in this plate, previously unpublished, have been extracted from original Neville Cayley paintings of groups of parrots. The tails of some of the birds still show where the tails of other birds in the originals crossed them.)

Scale

| 1 | 2 | 3 | 4 | 5 | 6 | 7 | 8 | 9 | 10 | 11 |
one foot

PLATE X RED-CAPPED, RED-RUMPED AND MANY-COLOURED PARROTS
AND AUSTRALIAN RINGNECKS

30. Red-capped Parrot (*Purpureicephalus spurius*); 31. Ringneck Parrot (*Barnardius barnardi*); 32. Cloncurry Parrot (*Barnardius macgillivrayi*); 33. Yellow-banded Parrot (*Barnardius zonarius*); 34. Twenty-eight Parrot (*Barnardius semitorquatus*. 43. Red-rumped Parrot (*Psephotus haematonotus*); 43a. Female Red-rumped Parrot; 44. Many-coloured Parrot (*Psephotus varius*); 44a. Female Many-coloured Parrot.

Scale
| 1 | 2 | 3 | 4 | 5 one 6 foot | 7 | 8 | 9 | 10 | 11 |

PLATE XI BLUE BONNETS AND PARADISE, GOLDEN-SHOULDERED AND
HOODED PARROTS

45. Blue Bonnet (*Psephotus haematogaster*); 46. Little Blue Bonnet (*Psephotus narethae*); 47. Paradise Parrot (*Psephotus pulcherrimus*); 47a. Female Paradise Parrot; 48. Golden-shouldered Parrot (*Psephotus chrysopterygius*); 48a. Female Golden-shouldered Parrot; 49. Hooded Parrot (*Psephotus dissimilis*); 49a. Female Hooded Parrot.

PLATE XII GRASS PARROTS

50. Bourke Parrot (*Neophema bourkii*); 51. Orange-bellied Parrot (*Neophema chryso-gaster*); 52. Rock Parrot (*Neophema petrophila*); 53. Blue-winged Parrot (*Neophema chrysostoma*); 54. Elegant Parrot (*Neophema elegans*); 55. Turquoise Parrot (*Neophema pulchella*); 55a. Female Turquoise Parrot; 56. Scarlet-chested Parrot (*Neophema splendida*); 56a. Female Scarlet-chested Parrot.

Scale

| 1 | 2 | 3 | 4 | 5 | 6 | 7 | 8 | 9 | 10 | 11 |

one foot

PLATE XIII BUDGERIGAR AND SWIFT, SWAMP AND NIGHT PARROTS

57. Swift Parrot (*Lathamus discolor*); 58. Budgerigar (*Melopsittacus undulatus*);
59. Swamp Parrot (*Pezoporus wallicus*); 60. Night Parrot (*Geopsittacus occidentalis*).

32 Cloncurry Parrot

Barnardius macgillivrayi (North)

PLATE X

Synonyms

Cloncurry Buln-buln, Northern Buln-buln.

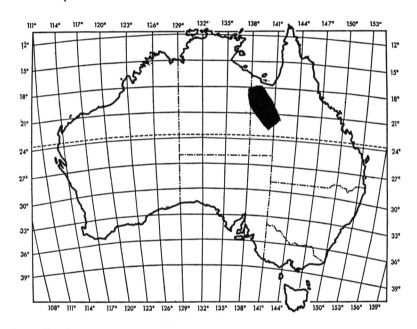

Distribution

The sparse records available suggest that this species is confined to the Selwyn Range of north-western Queensland and to the creeks and rivers emerging therefrom. Bearing this in mind, the distribution would be a roughly diamond-shaped area bounded by Burketown in the north, Camooweal to the west, Boulia to the south and Kynuna to the east, all records falling within the foregoing boundaries.

A specimen has recently been collected in the Nicholson River area, in the far eastern portion of the Northern Territory, thereby extending the range a little to the westward.

Description

SIZE. About 13 inches (330 mm).

ADULT MALE. General colour bright bluish-green with an infusion of yellow including crown of the head, upper wing-coverts, lower back, rump and upper tail-coverts, sides of face, throat, breast, lower flanks, under tail-coverts and under wing-coverts; lesser upper wing-coverts and bend of wing turquoise-blue; outer median and greater coverts cobalt blue; outer webs of bastard wing, primary coverts and primary quills deep blue, inner webs blackish becoming paler at tips of the last, on which position the outer webs are bluish-grey including entire outer web of first primary; middle tail-feathers bronze-green, becoming darker and more or less blue at tips, outer feathers green at base, dark brown on inner webs, followed by dark blue and cobalt blue on apical portions; a collar on hind-neck lemon-yellow; nape and behind the eye somewhat darker than crown; forepart of cheeks, feathers on sides of throat, axillaries and under wing-coverts turquoise blue; lower breast, abdomen and sides of body bright yellow; greater series of under wing-coverts and quills below dark brown; lower aspect of tail dark brown on middle feathers and pale iridescent blue on outer ones. Bill bluish-white; eyes dark brown.

ADULT FEMALE. Resembles the male very closely, usually slightly duller, with a smaller, more rounded head and a smaller bill; however, individual birds can be very difficult to sex with certainty.

IMMATURE. Plumage only slightly duller than that of the adult; surprisingly, an indistinct orange-coloured frontal band is present which is lost after a few months; thereafter the transition to mature plumage is practically imperceptible.

Geographical Variations

None recognized.

Field Notes

Cayley wrote of this species: "The late Dr W. Macgillivray, a brother of its discoverer, told me that he met with it in pairs and small family parties, frequenting open forest country, scrublands, and belts of timber bordering watercourses; also that its habits and economy were similar to the Ringneck or Mallee parrakeets. Nesting-places in hollow limbs containing young have been found, but the eggs have not yet been described. A correspondent, resident in Cloncurry, advised me he had hand-reared young parrots of a species not figured in *What Bird Is That?* The description of the birds forwarded was undoubtedly of an immature of this form which is represented by a coloured figure of an adult in that book."

Very few ornithologists have seen this bird in the field and as yet I have not been one of the fortunate few. It appears to favour trees growing along the margins of rivers and creeks and to be relatively common in this somewhat restricted habitat. It may well extend considerably farther than its recorded range, but it seems certain that it is separated from the northern extremity of the range of the Ringneck Parrot by a considerable distance of almost treeless grassland.

One of the few recorded observations of this species in the wild state is that of Lovell,[42] who actually saw a bird feeding its young in a nesting hollow near Mary Kathleen, in Queensland.

Aviary Notes

Obviously Cayley had never seen this species in life nor was he able to provide any aviary notes. It was practically unknown to aviculturists before 1939; a few birds were kept as pets in Townsville, North Queensland, and it is probable that others were kept in the districts where the bird is found.

Through the kindness of Oscar Seppelt I obtained my first example of the species, a young male, in April 1939. In August of the same year, while on holiday in North Queensland, I succeeded in obtaining a pair of these birds in Townsville. These appeared anxious to nest as soon as they arrived in Adelaide, and a clutch of five eggs was laid towards the end of September. Of this clutch one disappeared, two proved infertile, a fourth contained a fully developed embryo which failed to hatch and the fifth hatched on 20th October but the young bird survived only three days. After this initial disappointment, a second clutch of four was laid in the middle of November and although two of the eggs were again infertile, the other two hatched early in December. One of these died a few days later and the other was successfully reared and left the nest on 9th January 1940 and proved to be a hen. This first recorded breeding of the species anywhere in the world gained the bronze medal of the Avicultural Society of South Australia; it is described in more detail in an article I published in the *Avicultural Magazine* in 1940.[43]

Not satisfied with this record, the hen laid another clutch of four almost immediately and hatched them all, but unfortunately three died during a spell of very hot weather when almost fully fledged, and the sole survivor left the nest on 19th March.

Thereafter this pair of birds had a remarkably consistent record, rearing two nests of three young each in 1940, 1941 and 1942. Early in 1943 the cock died as a result of injuries sustained in a fight with a pair of Mealy Rosellas into whose cage he had accidentally found his way, but I was fortunate enough to again be able to obtain Mr Seppelt's original cock bird. With this new mate the old hen again reared three young from the first nest in 1943, but the second clutch were all infertile. In 1944 three were reared from the first clutch and two from the second and in 1945 two were reared from the first and none from the second.

The beginning of the end came early in 1946 when the second mate died, for although one of her sons, bred in 1944, was obtained the old hen obviously did not like him much and a solitary egg, laid in September, was infertile. I exchanged her mate for one of her 1942 sons without any improvement, as two more eggs laid in December were also clear. In 1947 the first clutch consisted of two eggs, one of which surprisingly was fertile and hatched on 7th October. This bird was reared and left the nest on 15th November but was never a very robust specimen. A second clutch of two was laid but both were clear. The year 1948 saw what I think is the usual end of an old hen's breeding career, namely diminishing clutches, most of which are infertile. In this year a single egg was laid and, although incubated steadily, was clear.

33 Yellow-banded Parrot

Barnardius zonarius (Shaw)

PLATE X

Synonyms

Port Lincoln Parrot, Bauer's Parrakeet, Banded Parrot, North's Parrot (subspecies *occidentalis*).

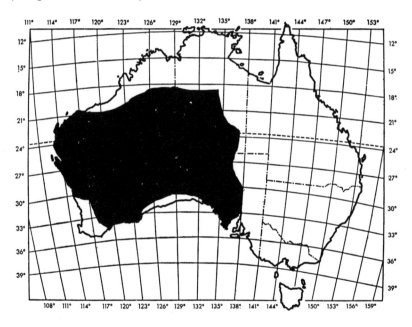

Distribution

This species has an extremely wide range. In South Australia it occurs over practically all of the western two-thirds of the State—that is, over the whole of Eyre Peninsula and the west coast and everywhere that suitable habitat occurs west of the Flinders Ranges and the north-south railway line. Similarly, in the Northern Territory, it has been recorded as far north as Banka Banka and in many areas to the west of the Stuart Highway, and also to the east thereof, according to S. A. Parker, at Tarlton Downs, Ammaroo and Elkedra.

In Western Australia the species is extremely widespread and is presumably continued from the South Australian population westward as far as a line running from Moora, through Goomalling, Wickepin and Nyabing, (Serventy and Whittell[10]). West of this line, the hybrid population of the wheatbelt, mentioned under *B. semitorquatus*, is encountered. Elsewhere in Western Australia *zonarius* is probably indistinguishable from the birds occurring on Eyre Peninsula or in Central Australia with the exception of the northernmost pale race, *occidentalis*, which occurs as far north as the Pilbara district.

Description

SIZE. About 15 inches (381 mm).

ADULT MALE. General colour above, including back, scapulars, upper wing-coverts and innermost secondaries green; rump and upper tail-coverts bluish-green; outer wing-coverts yellowish-green, most of the lesser series bluish-green; bastard wing, primary coverts and quills dark brown becoming paler at the tips of the primaries, the outer webs dark blue; central pair of tail-feathers green shading to blue at tips, the remainder with the outer webs dark blue at their basal portion shading to pale blue at their tips, the inner webs greenish-brown; head and nape dull black; cheeks blue, shading to black on ear-coverts; a yellow band on hind-neck; foreneck and breast bluish-green, abdomen yellow, under tail-coverts yellowish-green; bill bluish-white; legs and feet grey; eyes brown.

ADULT FEMALE. Similar to the male, but slightly smaller; the head and bill are also slightly smaller. However, individual birds are particularly difficult to sex with any degree of certainty; the black coloration of the head is generally less intense than on the male.

IMMATURE. Duller than the adult, particularly as regards the head which has an almost brownish hue; the difference in the size of the bill seems to be more apparent in young birds and makes them easier to sex than adults. The assumption of full adult plumage is gradual and not particularly noticeable; it is not completed till the bird is over a year old.

Geographical Variations

Remarkably little variation occurs over the extremely wide range; however, the birds occurring in the north-west of Western Australia, *occidentalis*, are of an appreciably lighter shade of green with slaty-black heads; there seems to be a gradual transition between these and the typical birds.

Field Notes

Cayley wrote: "The Port Lincoln Parrakeet (also known as Bauer's Parrakeet and the Banded Parrot) is an inhabitant of South, Central and Western Australia. As its name suggests, this parrakeet was once very plentiful in the neighbourhood of Port Lincoln. Now, it is not nearly so numerous in that locality, although still found all over Eyre Peninsula. Very little is known of its life-history. We have only the usual casual observations recorded about parrakeets generally.

"Usually found in pairs or small flocks, inhabiting open forest, scrub-lands, or belts of timber bordering watercourses. Its call is somewhat like that of the rosella—several sharp whistling notes. Mellor records that it is very pugnacious, especially during the breeding-season; seldom do more than one pair of birds occupy the same area for nesting-purposes. When nesting, the pair will keep constantly on the alert, and if another of their kind trespass near their haunts will furiously attack and drive it away.

"Like the Mallee Parrakeet, it spends much of its time on the ground feeding on the seeds of various grasses and other plants; is said to be very fond of berries and fruits.

"It nests in hollow limbs and holes in trees, usually eucalypts—both living and dead.

"Clutch: four or five eggs; white, and rounded-oval in form; shell close-grained, dull and lustreless. Breeding-season: August to November generally, but varies according to seasonal conditions in different localities."

One of my most vivid recollections is my first meeting with this species in the vicinity of Port Lincoln in January 1948; in the afternoon sun-light the colouring appeared extraordinarily brilliant, and since then the species has appealed to me as being one of the most attractive Australian parrots. On subsequent visits to areas of the west coast of South Australia, I have found the bird to be quite common, notably on Carriewerloo station, some forty miles west of Port Augusta, in October 1952 and September 1963, and in the vicinity of Iron Knob in October 1966.

In Western Australia one sees some birds in the vicinity of Perth which could be considered pure *zonarius*, but the majority show evidence of intergradation with *semitorquatus*. Travelling north from Perth in July 1954, the hybrid population was evident as far as Coorow; north of this point all birds seen, and they were plentiful, were typical *zonarius*, indistinguishable in the field from birds in the type locality of Port Lincoln. Again, in October 1964 birds seen near Cunderdin all seemed to be hybrid stock.

In the Centre in July 1964, my colleagues and I found the Port Lincoln Parrot quite common in the immediate vicinity of Alice Springs but we did not meet with it farther north. However, during July and August 1967 members of the R.A.O.U. field outing observed it also at Barrow Creek and between Renner Springs and Banka Banka. In August 1968, following on a very good season, we found the species to be extremely common everywhere in and around Alice Springs, and in July 1969 the bird-watchers' party again found the species plentiful in

N

the Centre and observed it along the Stuart Highway as far as several miles north of Banka Banka.

Aviary Notes

Cayley's very sparse notes were as follows: "A hardy species in captivity; but, owing to its uncertain temper, an unpopular bird in mixed collections. Said to resemble the rosella in general character and needs, and that under favourable conditions it is double-brooded.

"I have no authentic Australian records of breeding in captivity, but as it is fairly common and easily procured, doubtless there are many aviarists who have been successful. Although not really suited to cage life, it is long-lived under such conditions."

This is a very popular cage bird on the west coast of South Australia, with the reputation of being an accomplished whistler. Most specimens seen in captivity have been hand-reared and are consequently fearless and aggressive and not very suitable for breeding purposes.

I obtained a nice young hen of this species in 1935, and since she was not too tame I always regarded her as a potential breeder. For some time I had considerable trouble in finding a suitable mate for her and it was not until August 1937 that I secured what appeared to be a good specimen. Nothing eventuated that season, but the following year a clutch of four eggs was laid early in September; of these, the first was broken and the rest were incubated steadily but proved to be infertile. Early in 1939 I exchanged the cock for a very fine specimen which exhibited the almost silvery sheen which is sometimes noticeable in the green of the upper surface. This season a clutch of four was commenced on 10th September, all the eggs proved fertile and duly hatched, young being first seen in the nest on 3rd October. All four young, two of each sex, were successfully reared, the first leaving the nest on 9th November and the last on the 15th. This being the first breeding recorded by a member of the Avicultural Society of South Australia gained the bronze medal award, but there is also a doubtful record of an earlier breeding in South Australia by a person who was not a member of the Society.

This pair of birds had a gloomy record following their success, as the hen did not lay in 1940, laid and broke all the eggs in 1941, and again did not lay in 1942. The hen died early in 1943 and was not replaced until August of the following year. The newcomer soon appeared anxious to nest, and the first egg of a clutch of five was laid on 15th September. All the eggs were fertile, and young were first seen on 13th October. All five eventually hatched and were successfully reared, leaving the nest between 20th and 23rd November. The following year two clutches of six were laid, but on each occasion all the eggs disappeared; in view of a previous similar occurrence the cock was suspected of being the culprit. In 1946 clutches of six and four were laid, but again the eggs gradually disappeared; this time it was thought more likely that the hen was to blame. A new pair was tried in 1947, but they did not go to nest and I did not have any of the species during the following season.

I have seen the pale race, *occidentalis*, in captivity on only two occasions: a single bird being in the Hallstrom collection in Sydney early in 1948 and several birds in the possession of Eric Lindgren in Perth in 1966.

34 Twenty-eight Parrot

Barnardius semitorquatus (Quoy and Gaimard)

PLATE X

Synonyms

Yellow-naped Parrakeet, Yellow-collared Parrakeet.

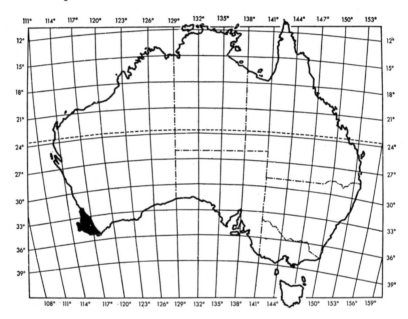

Distribution

Serventy and Whittell[10] write of this species: "In the wetter areas of the south-west corner occurs the all-green form with a prominent red forehead. Almost all birds south-west of a line from just north of Perth, through the Darling Range country to just west of Albany belong to this colour type." To the east of this line and occupying most of the wheatbelt, there occurs a hybrid population which comprises various stages intermediate between the true *semitorquatus* and *B. zonarius*.

Description

SIZE. About 16 inches (406 mm).

ADULT MALE. General colour above, including back, scapulars, upper wing-coverts and innermost secondaries green; rump and upper tail-coverts bluish-green; outer wing-coverts yellowish-green, most of the lesser series bluish-green; bastard wing, primary coverts and quills dark brown becoming paler at the tips of the primaries, the outer webs dark blue; central pair of tail-feathers green shading to blue at tips, the remainder have the outer webs dark blue at their basal portion shading to pale blue at their tips, the inner webs greenish-brown; head and nape dull black, frontal band crimson red; cheeks blue, shading to black on the ear-coverts; yellow band on hind-neck; foreneck and breast bluish-green; abdomen paler green; under tail-coverts yellowish-green; bill bluish-white; legs and feet grey; eyes brown. The shade of green generally has a less bluish tinge than that of the Yellow-banded (Port Lincoln) Parrot.

ADULT FEMALE. Smaller generally, with smaller rounded head and much smaller bill: the black of the head is less intense and the red frontal band is much narrower and sometimes quite inconspicuous.

IMMATURE. Resembles the female but quite easily sexed by the size of the bill. The head, in addition to being dull black, sometimes has a greenish suffusion and the frontal band is quite small and of a dull orange shade. Adult plumage is not attained till the birds are a little over a year old, and its assumption is gradual and not very noticeable.

Geographical Variations

None recognized, unless the large, yellow-bellied birds, generally considered to be a hybrid population, are regarded as a race.

Field Notes

Cayley wrote: "The Twenty-eight Parrot or Yellow-naped Parrot, known as a distinct species for many years, is an inhabitant of the coastal districts of south-western Australia. This form is the largest, being about sixteen inches in length; it has the forehead a crimson red, and, although it resembles *B. zonarius*, is much more brightly coloured, and the yellow collar is broader. Its popular name is derived from its call which is said to resemble the words twenty-eight."

The sight of a small flock of these magnificent large birds early one morning in an orchard near Bridgetown during a trip to the south-west corner of Western Australia in August 1948 was unforgettable. Another pair was seen investigating a nesting hollow in a tall eucalypt, and several other small parties were seen. All these south-western birds gave the typical "Twenty-eight" call-note which I have not heard given by the hybrid population of the wheatbelt or by the typical *zonarius* farther north; it is said that the pale race of the latter (*occidentalis*) possesses a call somewhat resembling "twenty-eight".

On a visit to Dwarda in October 1964 I again saw typical Twenty-eights and was once again impressed by their large size and brilliant plumage.

Aviary Notes

Cayley did not differentiate this bird specifically from *B. zonarius* and consequently had no special remarks under this heading.

Like *zonarius* hand-reared specimens are in considerable demand as pets and are as aggressive as most other broadtails similarly treated; the size of the beak should certainly engender caution in any would-be fondler! Trapped birds of this species are more commonly available than is the case with Port Lincolns.

I obtained my first specimen, a very fine old male, from a bird-shop in Sydney in January 1936, but it was not until May of the following year that I obtained a young hen, an extremely wild bird that never really became quiet in captivity. From 1938 onwards this bird used to spend a considerable amount of time in the log every spring, and feeding and mating were often observed. However, nothing ever eventuated as far as is known, and in 1943 the cock died. A replacement was not obtained until July 1944, and that season saw a repetition of previous performances. In 1945, however, a clutch of four eggs was commenced on 25th October and three young were seen on 26th November. These flourished: two of them, both hens, left the nest on 2nd January 1946, and the third, imperfectly fledged, three days later. This bird, a cock, had always been smaller than the others and was neglected by the parents after leaving the log; an attempt made to hand-rear it was not successful. This breeding was the first recorded for South Australia and gained the bronze medal of the Avicultural Society of South Australia.

In 1946 the same pair repeated their success, although the first egg of a clutch of four did not appear until 23rd November. All the eggs were fertile, young were first seen on 16th December, and all had hatched four days later. Two of this clutch perished during some very hot weather about Christmas time, but the other two survived and a cock left the nest on 24th January 1947, and a hen the following day. Both old birds died in the autumn of 1947, and although I was able to secure a new pair they did not attempt to breed that year and I disposed of them before the next breeding season.

PLATYCERCUS Vigors
Rosella Parrots

This genus comprises one of the most typical of the Australian psittacines and its members are generally known as the Rosellas. The characteristic distinguishing feature of the plumage is the scalloped pattern of the scapulars. The 1926 R.A.O.U. Checklist recognized eight species; not even Mathews,[23] with his predilection for the creation of subgenera, took any action in this direction and yet there is an easy separation of this genus into three groups. The first group contains the four species with close affinities—namely, the Crimson, Adelaide, Yellow and Green Rosellas—all, with the possible exception of the last-named, being closely related and all exhibiting a very distinct, predominantly green, immature plumage; this group inhabits the eastern and south-eastern portion of the continent and Tasmania. The second group consists of three species, the Northern, Pale-headed and Eastern Rosellas, inhabiting the northern, eastern and south-eastern parts of the mainland with again one species extending to Tasmania; in this group there is no distinct immature plumage, the juveniles merely being duller than the adults. The Western Rosella, the smallest of the genus and isolated in Western Australia, is alone in the last group; it is the only one showing marked sexual dimorphism and the only one with yellow, as opposed to blue or blue and white, cheek-patches; the immature plumage is predominantly green and the cheek-patches are notably absent. As subsequently pointed out, this species may well form a link with the genus *Psephotus*, occupying, as it does, a niche where no representative of that genus occurs.

The behaviour pattern of the Rosellas is identical in all species. None of the genus ever indulges in mutual preening and the display is a fairly simple one, the male squaring his shoulders, waggling his out-spread tail from side to side, and occasionally jerking his head up and down, and the female responding similarly but to a lesser extent. Court-ship feeding occurs, particularly immediately prior to egg-laying; incubation, which lasts for twenty-one days, is performed by the female only and she continues to be fed whenever she leaves the nest. After the chicks hatch, the male continues to feed the female frequently for about the first two weeks. Thereafter he enters the nesting hollow and feeds the chicks directly and continues to do so for two or three weeks after fledging, which occurs about five weeks after hatching; the amount of feeding performed by the female usually decreases at this stage.

The young are covered with a white down when they first hatch, and the bill is a pale yellow colour when they first fledge, changing to horn colour within the first couple of months.

The wing-stripe is, to a variable degree, a prominent feature of the Rosellas. Immature birds almost always exhibit this feature to a marked degree, the Northern Rosella, *venustus*, being an occasional exception. The retention of the stripe by the adult female varies, being generally absent or slight in those species in which the adult plumage differs markedly from the immature (for example, *elegans, adelaidae, flaveolus* and *caledonicus*), and being markedly retained in those females in which the immatures are merely duller editions of the adults (for example, *eximius, adscitus* and, to a lesser degree, *venustus*). In the eighth species, *icterotis*, where there is well-marked sexual dimorphism, the adult female retains the stripe to a marked degree. In this species the plumage of the immature does not differ very greatly from that of the adult female.

All Rosellas bathe freely and frequently, either in permanent water or in puddles left after rain and, in captivity, they readily bathe in drinking vessels.

Food is held in the foot while the bird is eating, and head-scratching is performed from behind the wing.

The flight of the Rosellas is characteristic; it is relatively swift, with interspersed short glides, during which altitude is lost, with the production of undulations. The Western Rosella is the only member of the genus whose flight differs appreciably from the standard pattern; Forshaw[5] describes it as more buoyant and fluttering, with less undulation and closely resembling that of the Many-coloured Parrot.

In captivity, all species are hardy and long-lived once acclimatized, although there is invariably some mortality amongst recently trapped birds if they are badly fed and handled. They are pugnacious towards other broadtails, and are best kept one pair to an aviary. They thrive on a seed mixture consisting of sunflower seed, canary seed, panicum or other millets, and some birds appreciate hulled oats. Apple is relished, and other fruits such as pears and grapes are appreciated; large quantities of green food, both seeding grasses and lettuce or silver beet, are consumed.

35 Crimson Rosella

Platycercus elegans (Gmelin)

PLATES VIII, IX

Synonyms

Pennant's Parrakeet, Lowry, Red Lowry, Campbell Parrakeet.

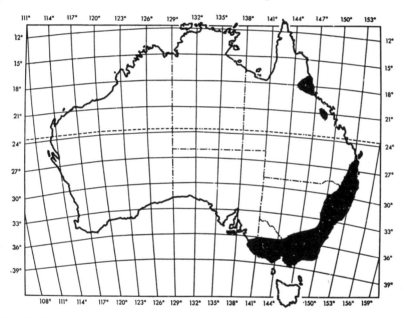

Distribution

The widely assumed continuous distribution of this species from north Queensland to Victoria is almost certainly incorrect. The well-marked northern subspecies, *nigrescens*, is recorded from such places as Cairns, the Bellenden-Ker Range, Cardwell, Lake Barrine, Herberton, and Georgetown but is not documented as occurring farther north on Cape York proper. Moving southward, there are records from near Townsville and of an apparently isolated population in the Eungella Ranges west of Mackay; thereafter the species is not recorded again until southern Queensland is reached where it occurs from such places as Nambour, Tamborine Mountain, Cunningham's Gap and the Macpherson Range.

There would then appear to be an unbroken distribution southward in New South Wales along the Great Dividing Range and to the east thereof as well as the lower slopes to the west and throughout suitable habitat in most of Victoria, the north-western corner being excepted.

South Australia, with the exception of Kangaroo Island, was not included in the 1926 R.A.O.U. Checklist distribution and yet the species is plentiful throughout much of the south-east of the State, extending as far north as Bordertown and as far west as the vicinity of Kingston. The subspecies *melanoptera*, occurring on Kangaroo Island, particularly at the western end, is not very common.

There seems no doubt that the species is on Norfolk Island, and the authority for its alleged introduction there is Salvadori.[7]

The original authority for the occurrence of Crimson Rosellas on King Island is not manifest, but J. Courtney informs me that this is correct and that they are mainly found in the north-eastern corner of the island, although M. McGarvie states he has never seen them there.

Description

SIZE. About 14 inches (356 mm).

ADULT MALE. General colour above and below crimson-red; cheeks blue; scapulars and feathers of back black, margined with crimson-red; quills black, dark blue on their outer webs, except apical half of outer primaries; median series of secondaries edged externally with light blue, the innermost ones margined and tipped with dull crimson-red; upper wing-coverts blue, darker on lesser wing-coverts, and having a conspicuous patch of black feathers on the inner coverts; four middle tail-feathers dark blue, central pair washed with green on their webs, remainder pale blue on their apical half, whitish at tips, dark blue on basal portion of their outer webs, inner webs dark brown; bill horn colour; legs and feet blackish-brown; eyes dark brown.

ADULT FEMALE. Similar to the male, but has a decidedly smaller head and bill.

IMMATURE. General colour dark green; forehead, crown, throat, lower abdomen and under tail-coverts crimson; cheeks blue; the blue on the wings is of the same extent as in the adult but there is no black on the inner wing-coverts; tail greenish-blue. The young of both sexes assume full adult plumage with the first complete moult, which takes place when the birds are a little over a year old.

Geographical Variations

The northern birds, *nigrescens*, which extend as far south as the vicinity of Townsville, are smaller and the crimson colouring is of an appreciably darker shade. There are no obvious differences between the birds occurring in south-eastern South Australia, Victoria, New South Wales and southern Queensland, and my observations suggest that the apparently isolated population in the Eungella Ranges, west of Mackay, are also indistinguishable. The Kangaroo Island population, *melanop-tera*, appears darker, due to the narrower crimson margins of the mantle feathers; it is doubtfully separable from the mainland birds.

Although this is not properly substantiated, it seems certain that immature *nigrescens* are not green and that a dull red juvenile plumage occurs in the northern parts of the range of the typical bird.

Field Notes

Cayley wrote: "The Crimson Rosella (more commonly called Lowry or Pennant's Parrakeet) favours the more heavily timbered ranges, gullies, and scrubs; it is very plentiful even in localities quite close to cities and towns. Its range extends from Cape York to Victoria; it also occurs on Kangaroo and King Islands. The species is well named *'elegans'*. Its crimson livery, strikingly marked with black on the back, with its dark blue tail, blue cheeks and shoulders, and graceful shape, affords a pleasing contrast to the green foliage of the trees. Although native fruits and seeds, especially the seeds of the different acacias, constitute its chief diet, it has acquired a taste for certain fruits, being very troublesome to orchardists in some districts. Immature birds keep much to themselves, and appear to be less wary than when fully-coloured adults.

"Like all the members of the genus *Platycercus* this species nests in a hollow limb or spout of a tree, depositing the eggs on the decaying wood or dust in these cavities. The nesting-place may be within a few feet of the ground, or so high up in a tall tree as to be almost inaccessible.

"Clutch: five to eight eggs; white, and rounded-oval in form; shell close-grained, smooth and slightly lustrous. Breeding-season: in eastern Australia, October until the end of January or the middle of February.

"A. J. Elliott of Cambewarra, New South Wales, sends me the following interesting note: 'While at Nerriga, south-west of Nowra, in October 1936, my brother and I located a nest which interested us because of the unexpected behaviour of the sitting bird. A rifle had been fired, and, immediately following the report, we happened to notice a Crimson Rosella's head protruding from a hollow twenty-five feet from the ground in a dry tree. It, however, was withdrawn so quickly that we could not be sure if it was a parrot's head we had seen. We threw sticks and stones at the hollow but no bird would show itself even though a fair-sized hole was knocked in the limb midway between the "nest" and the entrance, the detached piece falling down the hollow on to the sitting rosella. Mystified, we decided to climb the tree to investigate. I had scarcely begun to climb before the parrot left the hollow hurriedly, thus showing that it must have had an instinctive fear of goannas and was too wary to remain sitting until any reptile could reach the entrance to the nesting-hollow. The eggs rested on decayed wood about four feet down the hollow from the entrance.' "

My first meeting with this species was as a schoolboy during World War I when it was not uncommon in Sherbrooke Forest and at Marysville,

Victoria. Subsequent visits to the Dandenong Ranges and to Healesville have invariably resulted in further sightings, and it is plentiful around the Sir Colin Mackenzie Sanctuary at the latter place, where, like the King Parrot, it feeds happily on the food provided for the sanctuary inmates.

It is plentiful in the south-east of South Australia and the adjacent western district of Victoria and I have always observed it in the course of visits to these areas; although it is characteristically a bird of the more forested areas, it is not uncommon to find it in more open country where it mixes with the Eastern Rosella. A surprising association, which has not often been recorded, is its occurrence in the same country as the Ringneck Parrot (*Barnardius barnardi*), a typical mallee form. In October 1965 a party of Adelaide Ornithologists' Club members were surprised to find the two species associating a few miles inland from Kingston in the south-east of South Australia and in October 1968 we again found them together at the Mallee Fowl Reserve at Kiata in western Victoria; here both species were nesting a short distance from one another in the same tree and a photograph was taken showing the two male birds in the same frame.

Other areas where I have encountered the species are in the Dividing Range to the east of Inverell in northern New South Wales in May 1960; at Binnaburra in the Macpherson Range, southern Queensland, in May 1961; at Mallacoota in eastern Victoria in December 1968; and in National Park, Sydney, and in the Blue Mountains of New South Wales in October 1969.

The species occurs on Kangaroo Island, South Australia, where I first saw it in April 1954 and again on each of several subsequent visits; it does not appear to be particularly common on the island and is rather more plentiful at the western end. The island birds have been accorded subspecific rank (*melanoptera*); Forshaw's statement[5] that it is said that many young birds leave the nest with an almost completely red plumage (referring to the Kangaroo Island population) is quite incorrect.

Observations of this species in eastern Queensland in May and June 1970 were of considerable interest. Before this bird-watchers' tour commenced, I saw a few examples in the ranges inland from Southport. In the Eungella Ranges, west of Mackay, the species was observed in both rain-forest and on cleared land and I felt certain that these birds were indistinguishable from the southern birds. On the Atherton Tableland we found the species in rain-forest near Lake Eacham and in similar country between Ravenshoe and Innisfail; these birds were small and dark and obviously belonged to the race *nigrescens*. No birds exhibiting any trace of green immature plumage were seen on any occasion.

Aviary Notes

Cayley wrote: "Quite a common aviary bird, so much so that few in Australia attempt to breed it in captivity. Undoubtedly, there are many aviarists who have done so, but I have been unable to collect authentic data of such successes.

"As a rule less pugnacious than the other members of its genus. One of the hardiest of parrakeets, the Crimson Rosella would breed more readily if a pair had an aviary to themselves, and were provided with two or three large hollow logs."

This is a favourite aviary bird on account of its hardiness and gaudy colouring, but on account of its pugnacious nature it is no more suitable for a mixed collection than any of the other larger broadtails are.

I was seldom without one or more examples of this species in my collection, but it was only in later years that I had sufficient suitable aviaries to enable me to segregate a pair with a view to breeding. A very fine cock bird, obtained in 1938, lost his mate as a result of a brawl in 1940, and lived a bachelor existence in a mixed collection, no mate being provided for him until December 1944. Then he, too, succumbed after a fight in the spring of 1945, and I did not replace him till the beginning of 1946. In that year I attempted to breed the species for the first time, but although the hen spent a considerable time in the nesting log during September and October, no eggs were laid as far as is known.

In January 1947 I obtained two birds from Sydney, which were reputed to be a breeding pair. In October of that year they began to take an interest in the log provided, and on 22nd of the month the first egg of a clutch of five was laid. The hen sat very closely, and it was not until 17th November that two young were observed, the remaining eggs being infertile. By the end of the month one of the young birds had died, but the remaining one, a male, survived, and left the nest on 20th December, in the almost mature crimson plumage previously described. When disposed of in June 1948 this bird was in mature plumage except for some green feathers on the wings in the areas which ultimately become black.

In 1948 the hen of the same pair laid the first egg of a clutch of six on 24th October, three only being fertile. Two young had hatched on 19th November, and the third the following day. The parents on this occasion proved to be very indifferent feeders, and several times one or more of the young birds were found out of the nest and had to be replaced. The most advanced young bird continued to leave the nest very prematurely, and ultimately died on 24th December; the other two left the nest the following day, and although practically never fed thereafter by the parents, they appeared to thrive for a while, but both died about the middle of January. All three of this clutch left the nest in the crimson plumage, the youngest, a hen, being a little greener on the margins of the mantle feathers than the other two, which were a pair.

This species was not represented in my collection in either 1949 or 1950, and a pair obtained before the 1951 season did nothing, nor did another pair in 1952.

36 Adelaide Rosella

Platycercus adelaidae **Gould**

PLATE VIII

Synonym

Pheasant Parrot.

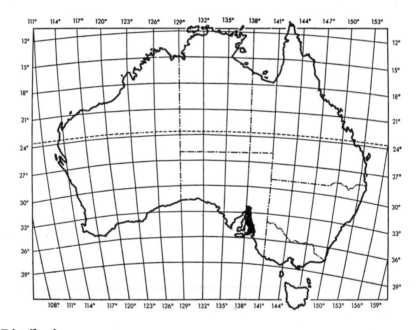

Distribution

Confined to South Australia, this species extends continuously, in suitable habitat, from Cape Jervis in the south to the vicinity of Bungaree, Clare and Burra in the north. The subspecies, *fleurieuensis*, is almost certainly unworthy of retention because pale birds occur frequently amongst the predominantly brighter coloured population of Fleurieu Peninsula. On the eastern limits of its range the species straggles down along some of the creeks towards the River Murray where it meets *flaveolus*—for example, on the River Marne near Wongulla, but apparently does not interbreed. The subspecies *subadelaidae,* which was confused with *flaveolus* by authorities in the past, occurs in the southern Flinders Range with a gap between its southern limit somewhere about Caltowie and Gladstone and the northernmost typical *adelaidae*. The northern limit has not been accurately defined but it is probably in the vicinity of Warren Gorge and Partacoona. This race is characterized by the paler coloration, especially of the males, which superficially resemble *flaveolus*; in addition, the call-note is materially different.

Description

SIZE. About 14 inches (356 mm).

ADULT MALE. General colour above and below varies from scarlet through pinkish brick to tawny yellow; cheeks blue; scapulars and feathers of back black, margined with varying shades from scarlet to yellowish green; quills black, dark blue on their outer webs, except apical half of outer primaries; median series of secondaries edged externally with light blue, innermost ones margined and tipped with varying shades between dull red and yellow; upper wing-coverts blue, darker on lesser wing-coverts; the four middle tail-feathers dark blue, the central pair washed with green on their webs, remainder pale blue on their apical half, whitish at tips, dark blue on basal portion of their outer webs, inner webs dark brown; bill horn colour; legs and feet blackish-brown; eyes dark brown.

ADULT FEMALE. Generally similar to the male but with a smaller head and bill; the mantle feathers often show a greenish tinge on their margins and the rump is not infrequently redder than that of the males.

IMMATURE. General colour olive-green; the forehead, crown, throat, lower abdomen and under tail-coverts vary from dull scarlet to orange-yellow; cheeks blue, the blue on the wings is of the same extent as in the adult but there is no black on the inner wing-coverts; tail greenish-blue. The young of both sexes assume full adult plumage with the first complete moult, which takes place when the birds are a little over a year old.

Geographical Variations

As noted under DISTRIBUTION, the Flinders Range population, *sub-adelaidae*, is considerably paler and approaches the Yellow Rosella, *flaveolus*, in appearance. Although some of the birds at the southern extremity of the range are appreciably brighter red in colouring, this is not universal and retention of *fleurieuensis* is not warranted.

Field Notes

Cayley noted: "Writing under date 22 March 1937, F. E. Parsons, of Adelaide, South Australia, contributes the following: '*Platycercus adelaidae*: The *Platycercus* found in the ranges from sixty miles south of

Adelaide to the Flinders Range near Port Augusta is exceedingly difficult to classify. I have spent much time on this subject and collected
specimens from one extreme of its range to the other. The feature that
first impresses one on examination of a series of skins is that there is
a gradual merging (transition) from birds in the southern extremity of
dark red under-surface, backs with black feathers margined dark red,
and all red rump, to birds in the extreme northern limit with under-
surface yellow splashed very sparsely with red, backs with black feathers
margined yellow, and yellow rumps. Whilst specimens taken from these
two extremes are so very distinct in colour (not shade of colour as is
often found in geographical races of a species, but a change in the colour
itself from red to yellow) yet a series of skins will show a very gradual
merging from this red form to the yellow, there being no abrupt change.
One thing is certain, the yellow form in the north is quite a distinct
species from *Pl. flaveolus*. In my opinion Ashby (*Emu*, vol. xxv) is in
error in stating that *Pl. flaveolus* extends through the Flinders Range.
Pl. flaveolus in South Australia is only found along the River Murray.
It is much more difficult when examining the birds in the southern
limits to decide whether or not there is a merging from *Pl. elegans*.

" 'I am convinced that *Pl. adelaidae* is a valid and definite species with
a range from Flinders Range in the north to the southern end of the
Mount Lofty Ranges about the latitude of the Murray mouth. At this
southern end of its habitat it is in contact with the very stable species
Pl. elegans, and by contamination we get here some birds undoubtedly
Pl. adelaidae, but showing a predominance of exceptionally red birds.
This contamination with *Pl. elegans* in my opinion is the cause of all
the confusion and doubt as to the validity of *Pl. adelaidae*. I feel sure
that the original *Platycercus* in the Mount Lofty Ranges and north of it
was a bird with yellow under-surface, possibly splashed with a little red,
with black feathers margined yellow on the back and yellowish rump,
being a more robust bird than *Pl. flaveolus* and brighter in colouring;
and it was not until comparatively recently that contact was made with
Pl. elegans in the south. There is no doubt that *Pl. elegans* is quickly
extending its range, as of quite recent years the species has appeared
within ten miles of Adelaide and the red of *Pl. elegans* being a very
dominant colour, shows very distinctly on the yellow of *Pl. adelaidae*,
and further contamination quite obliterated the yellow in the extreme
southern birds. The further we get north from the junction of *Pl. elegans*
and *Pl. adelaidae* the less colouring has been introduced to the latter
species until in the northern limits we get the genuinely typical *Pl.
adelaidae*.' '

The latter half of Parsons's contribution is unquestionably wrong;
adelaidae does *not* make contact with *elegans* in the vicinity of the
Murray mouth; in point of fact the nearest *elegans* to this area would
be in the region of Kingston, some one hundred miles to the south-east.

The species is certainly a variable one as regards its plumage and it
is my impression that most of the paler, yellower birds are males. The
statement by Ashby[44] that the birds at the southern extremity of the
range constitute a good subspecies (*fleurieuensis*) is certainly incorrect:
I have seen quite pale birds near Cape Jervis at the tip of Fleurieu
Peninsula and careful observation shows that a very limited number of
adults approximate to the bright red birds described by Ashby as typical *fleurieuensis*. They are certainly never crimson and the suggestion
that there is an admixture of *elegans* blood from Kangaroo Island is
untenable; a flight of about eight miles across Backstairs Passage at its
narrowest part would be a considerable endurance feat for a Rosella.

The subspecies *subadelaidae* occurring in the southern Flinders Range
is certainly valid; these birds are smaller, their call-note differs from the
typical birds and the males are very pale; this gave rise to the idea that
flaveolus occurred in that area; even an ornithologist of the eminence of
the late Dr A. M. Morgan was misled in this regard.

I have known the Adelaide Rosella all my life, for it is extremely
common in the Mount Lofty Ranges to the east of the city of Adelaide;
in recent years it seems to have spread into the parklands surrounding
the city where it can now be not infrequently seen. In the ranges it keeps
to the higher rainfall areas, only rarely following some of the creeks eastwards towards the River Murray; it was therefore a great surprise when
the species was located a few miles east of the river in July 1968; however, this movement does not seem to have been permanent.

Having now lived in the Mount Lofty Ranges for several years, I have
become increasingly familiar with the species, for it is constantly present
in my garden. I think they are relatively late nesters, since newly fledged
young are seen and heard begging to be fed by their parents from mid-
December; I have not noticed newly fledged birds later in the summer
and have formed the impression that they are not usually double-
brooded.

Aviary Notes

Cayley noted: "The Adelaide Rosella has been bred often, one of the
earliest is recorded by A. J. Campbell in his *Nests and Eggs of Australian
Birds*, 1901, who states: 'Mr White of Reed-beds, South Australia, had
young of this species hatched in his aviary. . . .' "

This is a common cage bird in South Australia but quite rare in other
parts of Australia, not being regarded as particularly attractive in
colouring by most parrot-lovers.

In 1950 I still possessed a hen bird that was in adult plumage when
I obtained her in January 1936; a mate was obtained for her a couple of
months later, and they survived in a mixed collection until the cock was
killed in a fight in 1943; limitations of space and the fact of the species
being so common locally had always predisposed against any attempts
being made to breed from them, although they had always looked a

O

likely pair. In December 1944 an immature male of the northern race was obtained, but again in 1945 they were not segregated. In 1946 the erection of additional breeding aviaries gave this species its first chance to reproduce in my collection. Somewhat to my surprise I found a broken egg in the log on 15th October, and two days later a second egg was laid but this, too, was broken the next day. As the cock was seen emerging from the log he was regarded with suspicion; it is not known if any further eggs were laid that season. In view of this experience I substituted a new young cock of the southern race prior to the 1947 breeding season, and in due course the first egg of a clutch of five appeared on 16th October; four of these were fertile. On 14th November three recently hatched young were found dead in the log, the fate of the fourth egg being unknown; whether the hen did not feed them or whether they were murdered by one or other parent remains a mystery.

Feeling that it was so long since the hen had had a chance to breed that she might be out of practice, I decided to give the same pair another chance in 1948, and a clutch of five, of which the first egg disappeared, was started on 23rd September. The remaining four eggs proved fertile and were incubated steadily, but by 26th October three eggs had disappeared, and the fourth by the next day; investigation revealed two newly hatched dead chicks in the log. Another attempt was made in that a clutch of four was commenced on 24th November, and all proved fertile. Two of these were transferred to another Broadtail that was incubating a clutch of clear eggs and she, incidentally, deserted them before they were due to hatch; the remaining two were incubated by the mother with the usual result, namely death of the chicks shortly after they had hatched on 18th December.

This pair that I had had for several years laid a clutch of six in the middle of September 1949; four of these were fertile, but they were deserted when about due to hatch, and disappeared a couple of days later. A second clutch of four was laid early in November, and three dead young were found late that month. In 1950 the same pair had four eggs by the end of September, but had broken them a few days later, and several more eggs were subsequently laid and broken.

For the 1951 season I obtained a new hen, and she completed a clutch of six eggs, all of which were fertile, by 25th October. Three newly hatched young were observed on 17th November, and four days later there were three young living and one was dead; the two remaining eggs were given to a sitting pair of Western Rosellas, who hatched them, but allowed them to die. The three young Adelaides flourished and the first, a cock, left the nest on 20th December, and the other two, a pair, two days later. This constituted my first success with this species.

In 1952 the hen started to lay early in September, but the eggs were broken almost as soon as they appeared. I thereupon removed the log for a few weeks, and on replacing it, the next egg was laid about the middle of October, and promptly broken; five more followed and were incubated, but only one was fertile, so two Golden-mantled eggs were substituted for the clear ones. The young Adelaide hatched first and the two Golden-mantleds about a week later; the Adelaide died nearly a month after hatching, and the smaller Golden-mantled a week later, the other left the nest prematurely next day, and was obviously being neglected, so was given to a pair of Pale-headed Rosellas who were successful in rearing it.

37 Yellow Rosella

Platycercus flaveolus **Gould**

PLATE VIII

Synonyms

Yellow-rumped Parrakeet, Murray Rosella, Murrumbidgee Lowry, Swamp Lory, Murray Smoker (erroneous).

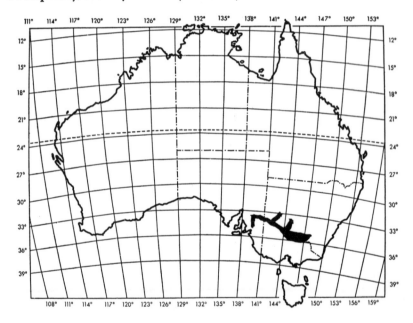

Distribution

The range of this species is the riverine plain of the Murray River and of some of its major tributaries. In South Australia the southern limit is given as Mannum, but it probably does not occur as far south as this point at the present time, the southernmost recent record being on the Marne near Wongulla. From this point it follows the Murray Valley upstream at least as far as Albury.

In New South Wales the species extends up the Darling as far as Pooncarie, along the Murrumbidgee as far as Wagga and eastward from there as far as Tumut. It is widely distributed throughout most of the Riverina and reaches as far as Booligal on the Lachlan.

The distribution along the Victorian tributaries is not well docu-
mented but there are records for Wangaratta and Lower Everton on the
Ovens; J. N. Hobbs states that it must occur at Shepparton on the
Goulburn.

Description

SIZE. About 13 inches (330 mm).

ADULT MALE. General colour above and below pale yellow, with blackish
centres to the feathers of the back and scapulars; base of forehead red,
fore-neck slightly washed with the same colour; cheeks blue; quills black
washed on their outer webs with blue; outer secondaries margined externally with pale blue, inner ones, as well as the inner greater wing-
coverts, with pale yellow; outer wing-coverts pale blue, upper lesser wing-
coverts deep blue, with a black patch on inner lesser and median coverts;
two central tail-feathers blue washed with green at base; the next pair
blue on their outer webs, blackish-brown on their inner webs and tipped
with blue, the remainder blue have their apical half pale blue; bill horn
colour, whitish at the cutting edge and at the base; legs and feet greyish-
black; eyes black.

ADULT FEMALE. Similar to the male, except that the head and bill are
smaller, the general yellow colouring is duller and there is invariably
a considerable amount of red colouring on the throat and upper breast.

IMMATURE. General colour above and below dull yellowish-green, paler
on underparts; the red frontal band, blue cheeks and blue wing-coverts
are present but paler, and dark markings are almost absent. Adult
plumage is acquired by the first complete moult, which takes place
when the bird is twelve to fifteen months old.

Geographical Variations

None recognized. Some individuals exhibit considerably more orange
colouring on the breast than do the typical birds; this variation is more
common in females.

Field Notes

Cayley wrote: "The Yellow Rosella is fairly common in the Murray
River basin, and the districts bordering the Darling, Lachlan, and Murrumbidgee rivers. Rather a shy bird, it is mostly found in pairs or in
small flocks, frequenting the eucalypts bordering river-banks or growing
near swamps and on the adjoining open country. In fact, it is seldom
found far from where the eucalypts flourish, obtaining much of its food
from the seeds and blossoms, and breeding in the hollow limbs. Like the
Eastern Rosella it spends much of its time on the ground in search of
the seeds of grasses and other plants.

"Plentiful in the Murrumbidgee Irrigation area where it is far from
popular with orchardists and farmers as it has developed a fondness for
fruits and grain.

"Clutch: four or five eggs; white, and rounded-oval in form; shell close-grained, smooth, and slightly lustrous. Breeding-season: September to December or January."

My first observation of this bird in the wild state was at Swan Reach in South Australia in April 1949 when several birds were seen feeding on the ground close to the River Murray; this locality is approaching the southern limit of the range of the species. Since that date I have seen the species on many occasions along the course of the River Murray in South Australia; it is relatively common around Renmark but apparently never strays far from the redgums bordering the river and its backwaters. One of my most interesting observations was in June 1956 when I encountered both this species and the Adelaide Rosella where the road from Mannum to Swan Reach crosses the Marne River not far from its junction with the Murray. It appeared that in this area the Adelaide Rosellas had worked down the Marne River from the eastern side of the Mount Lofty Ranges and met the Yellow Rosellas in their normal habitat; both species were in pairs and neither on this nor on any subsequent occasions did there appear to be any mixing of the species. Whether this apparent separation would be maintained were the two groups to be found nesting in the same area, would be of considerable importance to those interested in the taxonomic relationship of these two closely related species.

Aviary Notes

Cayley wrote: "A hardy species in captivity and a free breeder. Some males improve with age, the older they are the brighter the plumage; others remain quite plain in comparison. An interesting pet; easy to keep, and will soon learn to imitate. In captivity its behaviour is similar to the Eastern Rosella. Treatment and diet recommended: as for the Crimson Rosella.

"The only records of breeding in captivity in Australia I have been able to gather are 'hearsay' ones; but many must have been bred and reared successfully, as it is commonly kept in country towns. I have seen many that were taken from the nest and hand-reared; several were fine imitators."

This species has always been rare in captivity in South Australia, and is seldom obtained by the local dealers.

In May 1936 I obtained a fine adult cock bird, and in January 1937 I secured a mate for him in the shape of a tame, obviously hand-reared, hen. This pair were given many opportunities to breed, but although feeding and mating were often observed in the spring, the hen never became really interested in the logs provided for her, and no eggs were ever laid. In 1942 I exchanged the hen for another tame bird, but without any improvement in results either during that year or the following. In 1944 I lent the cock bird to H. J. Packer, of Gilberton, who had a hen of the species that had reared hybrids the previous season when mated with a cock Adelaide; however, his hen did not see fit to lay either that year or the next while mated to my bird. In March 1946 he returned my bird, having had the good fortune to catch another cock bird, obviously an escapee, on his aviaries, and later in that year he succeeded in breeding young from this bird and his old hen, thus securing the bronze medal of the Avicultural Society of South Australia.

Meanwhile, my old pair were reunited, and again did no good in 1946, although looking more promising than in previous years, and after the cock's death in August 1947 I secured a new pair, which made no attempt to breed that year. Mr Packer's pair had meanwhile reared two clutches of young, both in 1946 and 1947, and in March 1948 he was kind enough to let me have them. In the spring they duly went to nest, the first egg of a clutch of six appearing on 16th October. All the eggs were fertile, and young were first observed on 12th November; in all, five chicks hatched and all were reared, the first leaving the nest on 17th December, and the last on Christmas Day. The hen laid again almost at once, the second clutch numbering four. Once again, all the eggs were fertile, and young were seen first on 30th January. One egg failed to hatch, although it contained a fully developed embryo, and of the remaining three, one died when about ten days old. The remaining two, a pair, were reared, leaving the nest on 6th and 8th March 1949.

This pair which reared two clutches in the previous season commenced a clutch of six eggs in the middle of October 1949. These were all fertile and young were seen early in November, and four were later counted; these were all reared and left the nest between 11th and 22nd December.

In 1950 a clutch of six was started early in October, five were fertile, and young were seen by the end of the month; all of these were reared, and left the nest early in December.

In 1951 the clutch of five was started a little later in October, and all were hatched; four were reared in early December, but one must have injured a wing, for it was never able to fly. The following year six fertile eggs were produced towards the end of October; five were hatched and left the nest from mid-December onwards.

38 Green Rosella

Platycercus caledonicus (Gmelin)

PLATES VIII, IX

Synonyms

Yellow-bellied Parrakeet, Tasmanian Rosella, Yellow-breasted Parrakeet, Mountain Parrot.

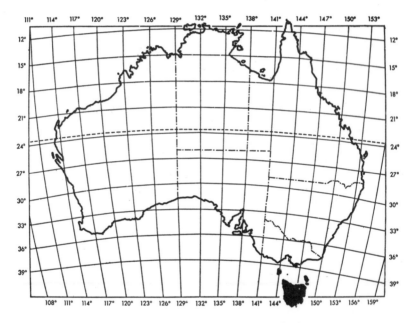

Distribution

There appears to be a generalized distribution of this species over most of Tasmania as well as the larger islands of Bass Strait. According to J. Courtney it is very rare on King Island and occurs mainly in the south-eastern part.

Description

SIZE. About 15 inches (381 mm).

ADULT MALE. General colour above deep green with blackish-brown centres to the feathers; lower back, rump, and upper tail-coverts green margined with yellowish-olive, the margins broader on the latter partially concealing their green bases; scapulars, inner greater wing-coverts, and innermost secondaries like the back but with a yellowish-green tinge on outer webs of two latter regions; quills, except innermost secondaries, dark brown on their inner webs, dark blue on their outer webs; outer and upper lesser wing-coverts dark blue, outer median and greater coverts pale blue, with a patch of black on inner lesser and median wing-coverts; central pair of tail-feathers bronze-green, bluish towards tips of their outer webs, the next pair blackish brown on their inner webs, dark blue on outer ones and narrowly edged with white at tips, their outer webs for three-fourths of their length from base olive-green; remainder dark blue on their outer webs, black on inner ones, and pale blue on their apical half; crown of head and sides of face yellow tinged with olive, feathers below eye tipped with crimson; frontal band on forehead crimson; cheeks deep blue; throat and all under-surface and under tail-coverts yellow, tinged with greenish-olive, some of the feathers on flanks and under tail-coverts margined with orange; bill greyish-white, bluish at base; legs and feet greyish-brown; eyes brown.

ADULT FEMALE. Similar to the male, not greatly duller in coloration but with an appreciably smaller head and bill.

IMMATURE. General colour above and below dull olive-green; the markings are browner and the blue areas duller, the forehead dull red with a narrow line of blackish-brown feathers at the base of the cere. Adult plumage is attained at the first complete moult, which is completed when the bird is about fifteen months old.

Geographical Variations

None recognized.

Field Notes

Cayley wrote: "The Green Rosella is similar in habits and economy to the Eastern Rosella. Like that species and the other members of the genus it is at times destructive in orchards and cultivation paddocks. It nests in hollow limbs and holes in eucalypts.

"Clutch: four or five eggs; white, and rounded-oval in form; shell close-grained, smooth and lustreless. Breeding-season: November and December or January.

"Miss Florence M. Irby, of Casino, New South Wales, sends me the following interesting note: 'Seeing a flock of these splendid birds in full plumage, for the first time, one feels that they should be flitting through some tropical jungle rather than inhabiting the coolest of our States. Only the adult birds attain the rich yellow breast that gives them so exotic an appearance. The younger birds are a beautiful olive—almost a moss green—cheeks and wings blue, and narrow crimson frontal marks; a soberly tinted bird of exceeding loveliness, and one that it is hard to believe later becomes the gorgeous yellow-breasted parrakeet.

" 'During numerous visits to Tasmania I met with this bird more frequently than with any other of the parrot tribe. About Mount Wellington, during the autumn, small flocks in immature plumage were usually to be found, sometimes clinging among the gum-tips, but more frequently wandering about the ground diligently searching for grass-seed or other food. Their green plumage assimilated so closely with their surroundings that, if it were not for the soft confidential chatter they keep up among themselves, it would be easy to pass them unnoticed.

" 'At Interlaken also they were very common, chiefly in immature plumage; flocks of them could always be seen feeding on the ground, or pattering over the tops of the tea-trees that grew in such quantities there, their rich olive coats almost invisible amongst the foliage. About Port Arthur too they were very plentiful, often scrambling about the apple-trees in some of the old orchards. At Eaglehawk Neck they were constantly in evidence; but there they might well have been called by their common name of Yellow-breasted Parrakeet, for the flock which came about the house where we were staying were in all the glory of fullest plumage. They were very tame, settling on the ground and pottering after grass-seed until you got almost up to them; then, with a whirl of wings and musical cries, they would rise to the tops of the Bisdan gums that grew to such a height close by.

" 'At the end of January 1928, I found them one of the commonest birds in the Mount Barrow district, their soft musical cries being one of the first sounds heard in the morning, but only odd birds were in mature plumage. By a creek at Mount Barrow large numbers were feasting on seeds of the Silver Wattle (*Acacia dealbata*). About Ben Lomond they were in great numbers also.

" 'Like the Eastern Rosella, the Green Rosella has a varied diet—principally seeds. It is often to be found revelling among the gum-blossoms, and in old orchards feeding on the scale insect. I have been told that, in bad seasons, it will occasionally eat the young green apples and peel the bark from the more slender branches. Many of its notes are similar to those of the Eastern Rosella. Frank M. Littler in *Birds of Tasmania* describes the call as "Cossack Cossack".' "

Having failed to see this bird in the course of previous visits to Tasmania, it was a great pleasure to me to find it on the slopes of Mount Wellington, near Hobart, in May 1964 and also, in good numbers, between Ross and the east coast of the island. A party of birds, both adult and immature, seen in the afternoon light proved to be unexpectedly striking, the bright yellow breasts of the adult birds standing out more vividly than I had anticipated. On a visit to the Launceston area in October 1969 I saw a flock of about a dozen birds, both adult and immature, feeding in a clearing near Patersonia, presenting an attractive sight. The species was also in considerable numbers on the lower slopes of Mount Barrow.

Aviary Notes

Cayley wrote briefly: "The hardiest of all the Rosellas to keep in captivity. In habits and food requirements it resembles the Eastern Rosella."

In 1949, when I wrote my notes for *Australian Parrots in Captivity*,[45] I stated: "Although frequently seen in dealers' hands prior to World War II, it is now extremely rare in this State [South Australia], and I am practically sure that my pair are the only birds in captivity here at present. In pre-war days it was usually available from Melbourne dealers also."

My first hen was obtained in August 1936 and was then in immature plumage; she had attained adult plumage by February 1937, and was mated with three different cocks, but never showed any particular inclination to go to nest. Just prior to the 1942 breeding season I obtained a new pair, but these were never at all friendly, and early in 1944 the cock lost his heart to a one-legged hen Red-vented Blue Bonnet which had escaped and had remained in the garden. In June 1944 a new hen, said to be aviary-bred, was obtained from Melbourne, and though the Blue Bonnet was caught and disposed of, the cock would not be consoled, and would have nothing to do with the hen either that season or the following; in fact, he remained unmated for the rest of his days. In March 1946 I obtained a new cock, and although he tolerated the hen, he was never very keen on her, and when he fell violently in love with another Broadtail hen in the next aviary, I thought it desirable to make yet another change. The new cock was obtained early in October, and immediately seemed pleased with his mate who responded to his attentions and laid the first egg of a clutch of four on 6th November. All the eggs were fertile, and two young were seen on 30th November, and a third a few days later, the fourth egg having disappeared. The third chick only lived a few days, but the others flourished until 23rd December, a very hot day, when they were found dead in the nest, with full crops. This was particularly disappointing as other Broadtail young of the same age survived the heat. The father of these chicks died in the autumn of 1947, and a new cock obtained subsequently seemed no keener on the hen than all but one of his predecessors had been, and no results were obtained that season.

In 1948, although the pair were not actively hostile towards one another, neither feeding nor mating had been noted, and it was therefore somewhat of a surprise when the hen laid the first of a clutch of five on 15th November. Unfortunately these eggs were all infertile, and were replaced by two fertile Adelaide Rosella eggs which the hen deserted a few days before they were due to hatch.

No results were obtained in either 1949 or 1950, but in 1951 the hen of the previous seasons was given a new mate, and she laid the first of a clutch of six on 3rd November. All proved fertile, and the first had hatched by 1st December, and four young could be counted two days later. One of these died quite early, and two left the nest prematurely on

27th December, an extremely hot day, and were replaced. The first young bird did not leave finally until 8th January, and the other two followed two days later. All were successfully reared; they were a cock and two hens, and this was my initial success with this infrequently bred species.

In 1952 the same pair laid a clutch of seven fertile eggs at exactly the same time of the year, all hatched and five chicks survived, leaving the nest in mid-January.

39 Northern Rosella

Platycercus venustus (Kuhl)

PLATE VIII

Synonyms

Brown's Parrakeet, Smutty Rosella.

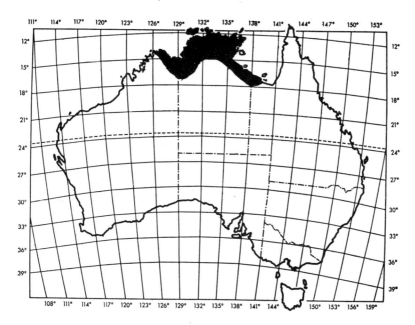

Distribution

This species inhabits a coastal belt of up to two hundred miles in width
from the western end of the Kimberley division of Western Australia
across to the vicinity of the Northern Territory–Queensland border.
near the Western Australian–Northern Territory Border it has been
seen at Spring Creek, on the Stuart Highway it is recorded as far south
as Katherine and eastward, near the Queensland border, in the Nicholson River area. However, C. N. Austin claims to have considerably extended the range by observing the species throughout the Gulf country
from the McArthur River to as far east as the Gilbert River at the base
of Cape York Peninsula.

Description

SIZE. About 12 inches (305 mm).

ADULT MALE. Crown of head, nape, lores, a line of feathers below the eye, and ear-coverts black; cheeks white, bordered with blue, except on their anterior parts; feathers of hind-neck, back, and scapulars black, margined with straw-yellow, broader on scapulars; lower back, rump, and upper tail-coverts straw-yellow, the feathers fringed with black; their basal portion with black centres; upper wing-coverts deep blue, with a black patch on the inner series; quills blackish, innermost secondaries broadly margined externally with straw-yellow; outer webs of remainder deep blue, becoming paler on the apical half of the outermost primaries; four central tail-feathers dark blue, the central pair washed with green, remainder dark blue at base of outer webs and blackish-brown on inner ones, their apical half pale blue with white tips; feathers of fore-neck and chest straw-yellow with blackish-brown at their bases; remainder of under-surface straw-yellow, the feathers distinctly fringed with black; under tail-coverts scarlet; bill horn colour; legs and feet dark slaty-grey; eyes blackish-brown.

ADULT FEMALE. Resembles the male and is usually only very slightly duller in coloration. The size and shape of the head and bill is a help in some examples, but quite a number of birds are hard to sex.

IMMATURE. Nestling plumage is a duller replica of the adult, with all the colours less vivid and less clearly defined and often with some red flecking on the head; sexing can be extremely difficult. Assumption of adult plumage is a gradual and not very noticeable process and appears to take about a year to be completed.

Geographical Variations

Birds from the north-western part of the range, *hilli*, are stated to have more blue and less white on the cheeks and less obvious black margins to the yellow feathers of the underparts; certainly birds seen in the Perth Zoo, presumably derived from the Kimberleys, looked quite different in the foregoing respects from the Northern Territory birds with which I am familiar.

Field Notes

Cayley wrote: "Several bird-trappers I have met say that the 'Smutty', as they generally call the species, is found in scattered pairs or family parties of four or five in number; that it feeds both on the ground and on seeds and fruits of trees; also, that it visits the drinking-places very early in the morning and in the late afternoon. It nests in hollow limbs, and holes in trees, usually in those growing in the vicinity of water.

"Clutch: two or three eggs; white, and rounded-oval in form; shell close-grained, smooth, and lustreless. Breeding-season: August to October (Mathews).

"*Platycercus venustus*, owing to its isolation, has a fixed and distinctive colour development; more suitable, as Iredale suggests, to a colder climate like Tasmania than tropical Australia. The chief variations noticeable are in the cheeks; in some examples these are almost entirely white, in others almost blue except for a narrow white line of feathers near the black below the eyes. Occasionally a few red feathers are noticeable on the forehead, above the eyes and on the upper breast, but these are undoubtedly immature plumage phases. I know of several birds in captivity that are remarkably rich in coloration. Apparently their plumage improves with age as these are all very old birds."

The status of this bird in the wild state remains somewhat of a mystery to me and I am inclined to the opinion that, unlike all other species of Rosella, it is relatively rare.

In July 1964, during a visit to the Northern Territory, three ornithologist friends and I first encountered two of these birds, apparently an adult and an immature in roadside savannah some miles north of Katherine, but we did not meet the species again until early the following month, when in the course of two successive day trips from Pine Creek to the South Alligator River we observed about six pairs in all. We found them surprisingly shy and relatively silent, and unlike others of the genus they were never flushed from the ground.

In July 1967 the R.A.O.U. field outing to the Northern Territory failed to locate the species although a great deal of suitable country was covered. However, the ornithologists' tour in July 1969 was more fortunate as when a stop was made on Goodparla Station to investigate an interesting patch of rain-forest, a pair of these birds flushed from beside the track and allowed all of the party to have a good view of them as they obligingly remained in nearby eucalypts. Later on, a single bird was thought to have crossed in front of the bus on the track to Shoal Bay near Darwin. Although the bird is known to occur in the Kimberleys, inquiries made at Kununurra revealed that local authorities did not know the bird and the party failed to locate it.

Aviary Notes

Cayley wrote: "This lovely rosella (commonly known as Brown's Rosella or Parrakeet, and the Smutty Rosella) is deservedly popular with aviarists, but is by no means common either in Australia or abroad. During recent years several large consignments of living birds from Darwin have reached Sydney, the majority in excellent condition after their long sea voyage. Although not as hardy as other members of the genus, there are exceptions; several aviarists in Australia have bred and reared one, and sometimes two broods in a season. The best results have been achieved with pairs housed separately, although it will breed, and has been bred, in mixed company.

"In general character and requirements it resembles the Western or 'Stanley' Rosella, except that as a rule it is inclined to be sulky. When birds first arrive from tropical Australia they need special attention as they are very susceptible to colds."

Always a rare bird in captivity, the Northern Rosella appeals to most parrot-lovers, even though they may be unattracted by the majority of the larger of the broadtails.

I obtained my first example of this species, a hen, from the late A. Wachsmann, of the Sydney suburb of Beecroft, in January 1936, but this bird survived only a couple of months in my collection. Later in the same year Mr Wachsmann was good enough to let me have a pair of these birds. However, the cock bird never liked his mate and always seemed to be attracted by every other hen broadtail in sight until he died suddenly late in 1937.

In March 1938 I was fortunate enough to obtain a new cock, and the pair seemed to be satisfactorily mated from the start. The first egg of a clutch of five was laid on 8th August and four of the eggs were fertile. The first young bird was hatched on 3rd September and two more emerged within the next couple of days, but one did not survive long; the other two flourished until 16th September, when they were found dead in the nest, and thereafter both parents immediately started a heavy moult.

In 1939 a clutch of four eggs was started on 16th August; of these, three were fertile and young were first observed on 13th September. All these flourished and two left the nest on 14th October, and the third the next day, all being fine specimens. I was extremely uncertain in regard to the sexes of these birds at first, but they eventually turned out to be two hens and a cock. This success gained the bronze medal of the Avicultural Society of South Australia, being the first breeding by a member, although the species had been bred in the Adelaide Zoo prior to this.

In 1940 the first clutch consisted of three fertile eggs laid in mid-June; three young hatched early in July, but only one survived to leave the nest on 12th August. A second clutch was laid later in that month, but all the eggs were clear, and shortly afterwards the old pair were killed by a pair of Twenty-eights when the latter bit a hole in the wire dividing their adjacent flights and entered their cage.

For some years thereafter the species was not represented in my collection, and it was not until 1945 that I obtained the loan of a pair which were said to have laid numerous clutches of eggs which had always been infertile, probably because the cock was almost devoid of toes as a result of fighting. True to form, a clutch of four was laid in May of that year and incubated steadily without result. The following year clutches of three and four were laid in March and August respectively, without any improvement in results.

In January 1947 I succeeded in obtaining a fine new cock bird, but the hen expressed her disapproval of the arrangement by not even laying that year! In September I lent the cock to an acquaintance who had an unmated hen and the old hen was restored to her former mate to the undisguised joy of both! Early in 1948 I obtained a pair of the progeny of my loaned cock bird, but one did not survive long, and I finished the year with the hen of this pair and a recently received aviary-bred cock that settled down well together.

In 1949 the pair that had been mated up the year before started with an infertile clutch in July, and followed with four more eggs in September, all of which were hatched and reared. This was the precursor of three remarkably successful seasons, for in 1950 they reared five young from the first clutch laid early in July, and five more from the end-of-September clutch. The year 1951 saw a very similar result, four being obtained from a clutch laid late in June and four more from a mid-September laying.

For 1952 the results were three from the early clutch and a further four from the later one; thus the total works out at twenty-nine hatched and all reared from seven clutches in four seasons.

Northern Rosellas are early breeders and whilst they do not always have an autumn nest like Hooded Parrakeets usually do, they almost invariably commence nesting operations in mid or late winter. This peculiarity in not adapting themselves to the seasons has been a great trial to overseas aviculturists, but does not appear to be a disadvantage locally.

P

40 Pale-headed Rosella

Platycercus adscitus (Latham)

PLATES VIII, IX

Synonyms

Mealy Rosella, Moreton Bay Rosella, Blue Rosella, Blue-cheeked Rosella (the northern, nominate race).

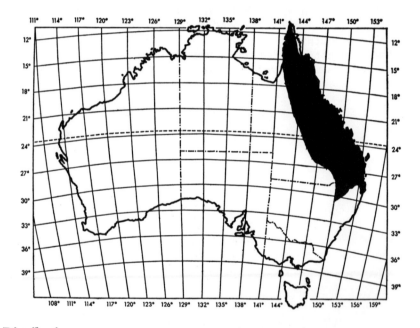

Distribution

This species occurs only in north-eastern New South Wales and over most of eastern Queensland. The well-known race, which is the subspecies *palliceps*, extends as far south in inland New South Wales as a line about 100 miles south of the Queensland border, starting at Inverell and running through Delungra, Bingara, Warialda and Moree. From the Queensland border there is probably an unbroken distribution northward, the westernmost recordings being successively Charleville, Augathella, Blackall, Barcaldine and Richmond; this corresponds roughly with the western slopes of the Great Dividing Range. How much farther north it extends along this line is undetermined. The species also occurs on the far north coast of New South Wales but not south of the Clarence River; from there it extends northward to Rockhampton, Mackay and Townsville and presumably it occurs between the coastal and western limits wherever suitable habitat occurs.

The strikingly different subspecies *P. a. adscitus*, formerly designated *cyanogenys* or *amathusiae*, occurs from the extreme tip of Cape York over the whole peninsula and as far south as Cardwell; Thomson[19] states that it is well distributed over the Peninsula, particularly in the central highlands. This range must then include Keast's[12] alleged isolate of the Cairns-Atherton area, but further reference to his isolate of the Bowen area has not been found.

Description

SIZE. About 13 inches (330 mm).

ADULT MALE. Head pale yellow, deeper towards base of neck; hind-neck and scapulars and upper back black, all feathers broadly margined with rich yellow; lower back, rump and upper tail-coverts pale greenish-blue, some feathers having black centres on the lower back; upper wing-coverts blue, darker on upper lesser series, with a black patch on inner lesser and median series, some feathers being narrowly tipped with blue; quills dark blue, edged externally on apical portion of primaries with ashy-white, outer secondaries margined externally with pale blue, inner ones with greenish-yellow at their tips; central pair of tail-feathers dark blue tinged with green on their basal half, the next pair dark blue on their outer and blackish-brown on their inner webs and tipped with white, the remainder having their basal portion dark blue, pale blue on their apical half, with white tips; cheeks white or washed on their outer portions with blue; all the under-surface pale blue; under tail-coverts scarlet; bill bluish-white; legs and feet dark grey; eyes yellowish-brown.

ADULT FEMALE. Similar to the male, but slightly smaller and less brightly coloured, especially as regards the blue underparts; usually has a smaller head and bill.

IMMATURE. The nestling plumage is a duller edition of the adult in every respect and there are often some red or grey feathers on the head. Full plumage is acquired rather gradually and not very noticeably; it is completed by the first full moult at the age of about fifteen months.

Geographical Variations

The foregoing description is of the southern race, *palliceps*. The nominate race, known as the Blue-cheeked Rosella, differs in having almost entirely blue cheeks and in the colour of the margins of the scapulars, which are cream, suffused with pale blue. In addition. the sides of the chest are yellowish and the rump is greyish in tone. There is considerable intergradation between the two extremes.

Field Notes

Cayley wrote: "The Pale-headed Rosella is fairly common in the north-western portion of New South Wales, where I have observed the species on numerous occasions. It is usually found in pairs or small flocks frequenting the plains in search of food, and resting and breeding in the belts of timber, known locally as 'ridges', which divide these areas. In habits and economy it resembles the Eastern Rosella, a species it often associates with. Like that Rosella it apparently has a partiality for the roadside as many were flushed from where they were feeding on the seeds of the Scotch thistle that grow profusely all through this district.

"It nests in the hollow limbs of dead trees and occasionally in an up-right hollow stump or tree, the nesting-cavity being from two to six feet from the entrance.

"Clutch: three to five eggs; white, and varying in form from elliptical, oval, to rounded-oval; shell close-grained, smooth and lustreless. Breeding-season: in New South Wales and southern Queensland, September to December; in northern Queensland, at any time of the year after rains."

I became very familiar with this species whilst stationed at Redbank on the outskirts of Brisbane in 1942-43; it was commonly seen in and around the camp area, and a pair nested in a hollow spout of a tree growing alongside the operating theatre of my hospital in the spring of 1943.

I saw this bird again on Mount Tamborine in 1949 and found it very plentiful in the vicinity of Inverell in northern New South Wales when visiting A. C. Hunt's property in the May of both 1960 and 1961. The interesting observation in this district was the apparent frequency of some degree of interbreeding between this bird and the golden-mantled race of the Eastern Rosella; a number of the predominantly pale-headed birds showed evidence of Eastern blood to a greater or lesser degree.

In May 1965 my son and I found the species to be common in most areas between Toowoomba and Gayndah in southern Queensland. During the bird-watchers' tour of May and June 1970 the southern race, *palliceps*, was found to be present in most places along the Bruce Highway from Gin Gin northwards as far as Gumlu, between Bowen and Ayr. On the Atherton Tableland the members of the tour were surprised to have only sighted two pairs of the nominate, blue-cheeked race; these were in open forest and we were informed that it is never a rain-forest inhabitant. As we proceeded southward we again encountered the familiar race, *palliceps*, from the vicinity of Charters Towers down the inland road to as far south as Gayndah.

Thomson[19] found these birds, which would be of the blue-cheeked race, numerous on Cape York Peninsula; he stated that it was a bird of savannah woodland and forest country, usually occurring in pairs or in small parties, never in large flocks.

Aviary Notes

Cayley wrote: "An exceptionally hardy inmate of one's aviary; is double-brooded and a free breeder. In habits and requirements resembles the Eastern Rosella. Pairs should be housed separately, as many males have the reputation of being very pugnacious in mixed company. Commonly kept in captivity in Australia where it has been bred and reared successfully for many years."

Cayley's statement above in regard to hardiness is not in accord with my early experiences, for I lost about half a dozen recently trapped birds in a comparatively short space of time.

An acclimatized hen obtained in January 1937 proved a much better proposition and went to nest late in September of that year, laying eight eggs, the first two of which were broken. Though she incubated steadily, all the eggs proved clear, and this tended to confirm the doubt which had always existed in my mind in regard to the sex of her alleged mate. In the following year a definite cock was not obtained until late in September, and no nesting took place. In 1939, however, a clutch of six eggs was laid in August, three of which were fertile. One young bird was seen on 13th September and another the next day, the third fertile egg failing to hatch. Both these birds died when just over a week old. A second clutch, on this occasion consisting of four eggs, was commenced on 17th October; one egg was broken, another was clear, the third failed to hatch, and the fourth hatched on 14th November, and the young bird, a hen, was reared and left the nest on 13th December.

In 1940 this young bird was mated to a very fine cock, obviously an escapee, that had been caught on the aviaries during the previous year. She commenced a clutch of six eggs in late September, when just nine months old, but these were all infertile. The next two years' clutches of eight and nine eggs produced no results, and in 1943 a log was not even provided. In 1944 a clutch of eight was commenced on 11th August, incubation proceeded steadily and young were first seen on 15th September. In all, five hatched, two eggs being clear and the other containing a half-grown embryo. The five were all reared, leaving the nest between 19th and 26th October. As the hen laid an egg on the ground on 1st November, I replaced the log, and a further four eggs were laid therein and incubated until the hen suddenly started to moult and deserted; on examination, all the eggs were found to contain half-developed embryos.

In 1945 the same pair experienced a series of misfortunes. A first clutch of five was commenced in mid-August, but the eggs were spoilt by the nesting material all falling out of the log; a second clutch of five commenced towards the end of September met with a similar fate. When a new log was provided, a third clutch was begun on 31st October. On this occasion six eggs were laid and the first young bird was seen on 29th November; in all, four hatched but one died during the first week. The other three flourished until Christmas time, when they all succumbed during a spell of very hot weather, though they were within a week of leaving the nest.

The following season, 1946, a clutch of eight was begun early in August, and although the first two eggs were broken, five of the remaining six proved fertile and four young had hatched on 9th September, and the fifth a couple of days later. One of these died in the first week but the remaining four were reared and left the nest between 11th and 15th October.

A second clutch, of five, was started on 27th October and all chicks had hatched by 26th November; once again, one chick died early, and the remainder were reared and left the nest about Christmas time. I see from my notes that I thought at first that probably seven of these eight were hens; actually only five proved to be, but this serves to illustrate the difficulty which can be experienced in sexing this species, both in the immature and in the adult stage. In 1947 the hen died egg-bound in September, having started the clutch with a soft-shelled egg and then producing four satisfactory ones.

A new hen was obtained a week later and she went to nest early in October, but her four eggs were all clear. She laid a second clutch, of five, in mid-November, three of which were good. Young could be heard early in December, and two were later seen, but they survived only a few days, the other fertile egg having failed to hatch. In 1948 the old cock died during the winter and a new one was obtained in time for the breeding season. A clutch of four, of which only two were fertile, was laid late in August. Only one of these hatched and it was deserted by its parents when about a fortnight old. A second clutch, of five, was started on 20th October, four proved fertile and young were seen on 18th November; eventually three were counted, but one died when quite young and the other two, both hens, were reared and left the nest just before Christmas. A third clutch was laid, and two young were seen on 30th January; one of these died when very young and the other survived until mid-February.

The same pair which had reared two young the previous year started the 1949 season with an infertile clutch, and only reared one out of three hatched in the second nest. The following year the same hen, with a new mate, did not even lay.

In 1951 I acquired a new pair which had been regular breeders for several years. They laid their first clutch, of six, late in August, hatched the lot, and reared five of them. The second round, of five, was laid in the middle of November, all hatched and the young were all reared by early January. Carrying on in 1952, the same pair reared four out of five hatched from their August clutch, and only one out of the two hatched from the November clutch, in addition to a Golden-mantled Rosella from an egg added to their clutch.

In 1965 I was given a pair of the northern blue-cheeked race of this species. They were young birds, obviously wild caught, and very timid at first, but they gradually settled down and by the time I moved to the hills in the spring of 1966 they had steadied down considerably and moulted into fine adult plumage. They were housed in one of my new aviaries, with a flight 13 feet long, 3 feet wide and 6 feet high, and a shelter at the rear 5 feet long, 3 feet wide and 7 feet in height. The pair soon showed signs of wanting to go to nest. They were supplied with a log 2½ feet long, with an internal diameter of 6 inches and with a side entrance near one end. The log was, at first, hung in the shelter about 5 feet from the ground at an angle of approximately 45 degrees. Between eight and ten eggs were laid and broken whilst the log was at this angle and it was not until it was suspended vertically that a clutch of five eggs was completed and eventually incubated.

The eggs were laid on alternate days and incubation did not commence until the clutch had been completed; the incubation period was approximately twenty days and as is invariable with the broadtails was carried out entirely by the hen. Of the five eggs incubated, only one was hatched, another had a fully developed embryo, another a partly developed one and the remaining two were infertile. During November, approximately four weeks after hatching, the young bird left the nest, being obviously female by the size of the head and bill and being appreciably duller generally than the adults, with less blue on the cheeks. Three days after leaving the nest it was observed bathing, which I considered unusual for so young a fledgling.

The food supplied consisted of the usual seed mixture of sunflower, hulled oats, canary seed and panicum and, in addition, seeding grasses and apple. For the first fortnight after hatching, the male fed the female, who in turn fed the chick; after this time the male as well as the female fed the young bird directly. In about two weeks after leaving the nest, the young bird was quite independent; its acquisition of adult plumage was by a slow, rather imperceptible, moult which was completed by the following spring, when the bird was about nine months old.

Following this success, I expected the old pair to breed regularly but their egg-breaking habits have been persistent.

In 1967 a clutch was successfully incubated and three young hatched, but they were allowed to die when half grown; apart from this, many eggs have been laid and although three or four have been allowed to accumulate at times, they have always disappeared in the end and no incubation has occurred. I have always suspected that the male was the culprit; for a broadtail, he always appeared to take an unseemly interest in the interior of the logs at this stage. Ultimately, I tired of their peccadilloes and gave them away to a friend, whereupon they immediately went to nest and reared two fine youngsters!

41 Eastern Rosella

Platycercus eximius (Shaw)

PLATE VIII

Synonyms

Red Rosella, Common Rosella, Rosehill Parrakeet, Golden-mantled Rosella (the northern race).

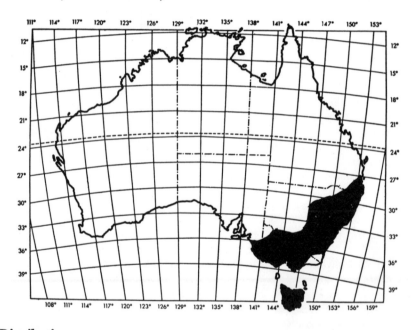

Distribution

If the isolated pocket in the southern Mount Lofty Ranges, which may well be an introduction, is overlooked, the range of this species in South Australia is the whole of the south-eastern portion of the State coming as far north as Culburra and Salt Creek.

To the east, it extends over most of Victoria, although sparsely distributed in the north-western corner and missing from far eastern Gippsland, and thence into southern and south-eastern New South Wales, the limits on the west being roughly Euston, Hay, Narrandera, West Wyalong, Parkes and in the north, Cobbora, Merriwa and Muswellbrook. About the 32nd parallel, according to White,[46] sees the quite sudden transition to the golden-mantled race, *P. e. cecilae* (= *splendidus*) of which Scone is the southern limit and the old inland New South Wales–Queensland railway line the approximate western limit. This subspecies extends northward, being found on the Manning, Bellinger and Clarence rivers, and thence into Queensland where it is recorded from Toowoomba, Warwick and Cunningham's Gap. Its northernmost limit is uncertain, although there are suggestions that it extends as far as Maryborough and Bundaberg: the specimen in the Queensland Museum from Gympie is definitely not *cecilae* and is presumably a cage bird. In June 1970 I saw two birds near Tansey; this may well be the northernmost recording.

In Tasmania the distinct subspecies *diemenensis* is widespread but M. McGarvie states that it does not occur on King Island now, and according to old residents has never done so.

Description

SIZE. About 13 inches (330 mm).

ADULT MALE. Head, sides of neck and upper breast scarlet, nape yellow; feathers of back and scapulars black margined with greenish-yellow; rump and upper tail-coverts yellowish-green; quills dark blue on their outer webs, blackish on their inner ones, outer secondaries margined externally with light blue, those of inner series of greater wing-coverts with yellowish-green; primary coverts dark blue, the lesser, median and outer series of greater wing-coverts violet-blue, with a black patch on inner lesser and median coverts; tail-feathers blue, the four central feathers washed with green, remainder dark blue at their bases, light blue on their apical portions with white tips; cheeks white; lower breast yellow with narrow dusky edges to the feathers; abdomen yellowish-green; under tail-coverts scarlet; bill bluish-horn colour; legs and feet dark grey; eyes dark brown.

ADULT FEMALE. Similar to the adult male but usually somewhat duller; some are, however, nearly as bright as the males and in such cases the presence of a wing-stripe is an invariable guide. The head and bill are only slightly smaller.

IMMATURE. All the colours are duller and the red of the head is much reduced in extent and replaced by green; particularly is this so in the case of young females, so that immatures are usually easier to sex than adults. More red feathers are acquired in the first autumn and winter but full plumage is not assumed until the first complete moult at the age of a little over a year.

Geographical Variations

The northern population, known as the Golden-mantled Rosella, *cecilae* (formerly *splendidus*), differs in having the margins of the scapulars a rich golden-yellow and the rump greenish-blue; females often have a few yellow feathers scattered over the head. The Tasmanian birds, *diemenensis,* exhibit considerably larger white cheek-patches than the mainland birds.

Field Notes

Cayley wrote: "The Eastern Rosella (more commonly known as the Rosella, this name being probably a corruption of Rose Hill, Parramatta, where the species is believed to have been first collected and named the Rosehill Parrot) has figured so largely in trade marks and advertisements that it is perhaps the most popularly known Australian parrot.

"Its scientific name, *eximius,* is befitting a bird with such a lovely plumage; in fact, it is one of the most beautiful parrots in existence. If it were not so common it would be appreciated at its true worth.

"Plentifully distributed throughout the south-eastern portion of the continent and most parts of Tasmania. Frequents alike scrub and open forest lands, showing a decided preference for cleared areas interspersed with belts of timbers and cultivation paddocks. Very commonly seen about the roadside of most country districts. Usually met with in pairs or family parties, and passes much of its time on the ground in search of seeds of grasses and other plants; these, with native fruits and berries, constitute its normal food. Like the Crimson Rosella, it is considered a pest, being very troublesome to orchardists and farmers. When disturbed it will merely fly off to the nearest tree, or fence, where it will remain while one is in the vicinity, returning again to the ground when one passes by. Its flight is short and undulating; on the wing it utters its rather pleasing whistling note.

"Nests in hollow limbs and holes in trees, usually dead ones, and often in hollow stumps and hollow logs. One nest I found in a hollow stump had the nesting-cavity a foot below the surface of the ground; many others were in hollow limbs forty feet from the ground.

"Clutch: four to nine eggs; white, and rounded-oval in form; shell close-grained, smooth, and lustreless. Breeding-season: September to January. Usually two broods are reared each season. Still fairly common in the outer western suburbs of Sydney; occasionally seen in the public parks and gardens right in the heart of the city itself."

As with the Crimson Rosella, my first meeting with this species was during a holiday in the Sherbrooke and Marysville districts of Victoria in 1918. Since then, I have frequently encountered it in the south-east of South Australia and western district of Victoria where it is extremely common, preferring the more open type of country. I have also seen it on the outskirts of Sydney and in southern New South Wales.

The golden-mantled subspecies, *cecilae* (formerly *splendidus*), was seen briefly in the Toowoomba and Warwick districts, Queensland, during 1942-43, but it was not until I visited A. C. Hunt at Inverell, New South Wales, in May 1960 and May 1961 that I became properly acquainted with this distinct variety in the wild state; the difference in the rump colour between this northern race and that of the southern birds is very noticeable in flight. We saw the subspecies again in May 1965 between Inverell and Toowoomba and for a very short distance north of the latter, and in May 1971 found it common near Grafton, New South Wales.

The Tasmanian subspecies, *diemenensis*, I first met with in the Domain on the outskirts of Hobart in May 1964 and again near Hobart and also near Launceston in October 1969; the noticeably larger white cheek patches are very obvious.

The occurrence of a small isolated population in the southern Mount Lofty Ranges of South Australia remains somewhat of a mystery and is probably the result of an introduction. Its occurrence there was not recognized by the older South Australian ornithologists, Symonds Clark[47] in an article on the parrots of South Australia stating categorically that it did not occur there. When the late Neil McGilp reported it at a meeting of the South Australian Ornithological Association he was ridiculed: accordingly, he collected a specimen and exhibited it at the next meeting of the Association.

Aviary Notes

Cayley wrote: "Another excellent aviary bird, being exceptionally hardy and a free breeder. Young birds soon learn to talk and whistle, but only odd ones become at all affectionate; usually they are most spiteful when caged.

"Being such a common species many aviarists in Australia do not attempt to breed them, preferring to keep them in mixed collections, more for display than anything else. Still, it is often bred. During recent years many interesting hybrids have been produced.

"Generally housed in pairs, chiefly owing to the pugnacious tendency of breeding males, more especially towards their own kind.

"A perpendicular hollow log placed in the open flight makes the best nesting-place. One end can be either embedded in the ground, or filled with earth or decayed wood-mould if hung to the sides of the aviary. Two nesting-logs should be provided as this bird is double-brooded; the female often lays her second clutch of eggs before the young of the first brood have left their nesting-place.

"Food suggested: a mixture of canary-seed, millet, hemp, sunflower, and oats, with peanuts and plenty of green food and fruit. Native seeding grasses and thistles should be provided as often as possible."

This is probably the best known of all the Australian parrots. It is very commonly kept as a cage bird in Victoria and New South Wales, and many of the hand-reared birds make good whistlers. It is a showy bird in a mixed collection, but no less pugnacious than any of the rest of the group.

Although the species was practically continuously represented in my collection, it was not until 1946 that I possessed sufficient breeding aviaries to warrant devoting space to these relatively common birds. In that year I had a cock Golden-mantled that I had brought back from Queensland in 1943, and a hen of the common variety obtained from a local bird-shop. The first egg of a clutch of six was laid on 3rd September, but although the hen sat closely, all the eggs proved clear and were removed towards the end of the month.

The hen soon went to nest again, eggs being seen under the sitting bird on 15th October. This time the clutch consisted of five, of which only two were fertile. Two young birds were seen during the first week of November and the first, a hen, left the nest rather prematurely on 2nd December and was replaced; the other, a cock, made its first appearance on 5th December, and the hen reappeared in much better shape, the next day. On leaving the nest, these birds could scarcely be distinguished from typical young Eastern Rosellas, but when they assumed adult plumage, they were more or less intermediate between the two races in colouring.

In 1947 the hen died and another pair of typical Easterns did nothing. The old cock Golden-mantled was mated to a young Golden-mantled hen obtained late in the previous year. This pair were seen feeding on many occasions in September and October, but did not get any further.

In 1948 yet another pair of the common race were tried and the first of five eggs was laid on 3rd October. Young were seen on the last day of the same month and eventually five were counted; the first left the nest on 27th November, and by 4th December all five had left it, but they all exhibited the unusual habit of returning to it for several days thereafter. This clutch consisted of four hens and one cock.

In 1949 the hen that had been successful in the previous year was mated to one of her sons. She laid a clutch of five eggs towards the end of October and incubated steadily, but all proved infertile. In August of the following year the son, having fallen in love with a Golden-mantled hen in a nearby aviary, proceeded to commit matricide, since when the common race has not been kept.

Towards the end of 1947 I had been lucky enough to secure a pair of Golden-mantleds which had laid two clutches of eggs that season while in the possession of H. J. Packer, of Gilberton, South Australia, but had been disturbed on each occasion. In 1948 the hen of this pair laid the first of a clutch of four on 25th September; all proved fertile, and young were first seen on 23rd October, and all were successfully reared, leaving the nest between 23rd and 25th November. Of these, two were obviously hens and another equally obviously a cock, but the fourth, which eventually turned out a hen, was much brighter than her two sisters and was thought to be a cock for a long time. The hen appeared likely to lay again, but was found dead in the log early in December, possibly as a result of egg-binding.

The cock that had bred in 1948 was mated to one of his daughters the following season, and although she laid three eggs in November, she did not incubate. In 1950 she was given an unrelated mate, and she started to lay early in October. Although most of the early eggs were broken, I removed eleven from the nest early in November! Undeterred, she recommenced laying late in the month, and when I removed seven eggs at the end of December I was amazed to find one contained a chick on the point of hatching!

In 1951 the same pair had a clutch of six, laid late in September, of which three were hatched and reared. In 1952 bad habits were again in evidence, for many of the early eggs were broken, ten were removed in November, and two of these were hatched by Adelaides and one young was eventually reared with the help of the Pale-headeds.

42 Western Rosella

Platycercus icterotis (Kuhl)

PLATES VIII, IX

Synonyms

Stanley Rosella, Yellow-cheeked Parrakeet, Earl of Derby's Parrakeet.

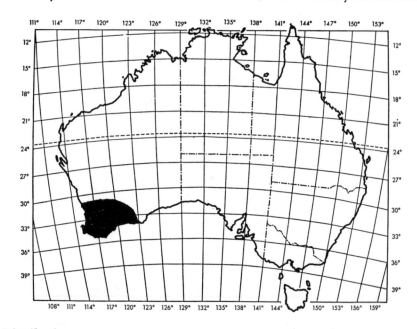

Distribution

Serventy and Whittell[10] give the range of this species as being confined to the south-west corner of Western Australia, north to Moora and east to Wongan Hills, Moorine Rock (near Southern Cross) and the Dundas district. The inland form, *xanthogenys*, appears to be reasonably well defined but there does not seem to be a well-marked boundary between it and the typical race.

Description

SIZE. About 11 inches (279 mm).

ADULT MALE. General colour above green; feathers of upper back and scapulars with blackish centres and margined with yellowish-green on the hind-neck, dull scarlet and broader on back and scapulars; upper wing-coverts blue, with a black patch across lesser and median series; inner greater wing-coverts green with blackish centres; primaries dark blue on their outer and blackish-brown on their inner webs; secondaries green on their outer and blackish on their inner webs; four central tail-feathers green, remainder greenish-blue at base, pale blue on apical half, and white at tips; cheeks yellow; forehead, crown of head, nape, sides of neck, all the under-surface and under tail-coverts scarlet; bill bluish-horn; legs and feet mealy-brown; eyes dark brown.

ADULT FEMALE. Considerably duller than the male, having the scarlet replaced by brick red which has a large amount of greenish-olive mixed with it, especially on the breast and abdomen; the yellow cheek-patch is sometimes incomplete.

IMMATURE. Resembles the adult female but has more green and less red in the plumage and entirely lacks the yellow cheek-patches, unlike all other immature Rosellas which exhibit the white or blue cheek-patches; the mantle feathers are uniformly green without black centres. Young birds are not easy to sex as there is often little difference in the size and shape of the head and bill. During the first autumn and winter some of the green feathers on the head and breast are replaced by red ones and at this stage the young male is more obvious. Full adult plumage is not achieved till the bird is about fourteen months old, when a fairly rapid complete moult takes place.

Geographical Variations

The inland form, xanthogenys, has paler yellow cheeks and the red colouring is of a duller, brickish shade; however, there does not appear to be any sharp line of demarcation between the two races.

Field Notes

Cayley wrote: "The Western Rosella (also called the Yellow-cheeked and Stanley Parrakeet, and Earl of Derby's Parrot) has a habitat restricted to the south-western portion of Western Australia. Its habits and economy are similar to the Eastern Rosella: what is written about that species applies in every respect to the present one, including its destructiveness in orchards and cultivation paddocks.

"Usually found in pairs or small flocks inhabiting open forestlands and partly cleared country. Known to be fearless, and is common about homesteads and gardens.

"Food: the seeds of grasses and other plants, and wild fruits and berries. Nests in hollow limbs and holes in tall gum-trees; often the nesting-place is some distance from the entrance to the hollow.

"Clutch: three to seven eggs; white, and rounded-oval in form; shell close-grained, smooth, and lustreless. Breeding-season: August to November."

I am relatively unfamiliar with this bird, having seen it only in small numbers in the south-west of Western Australia in August 1948 and again in the course of a day excursion to Dwarda in October 1964. I formed the impression that it is the species which fills the gap caused by the absence of the Red-rumped Parrot from Western Australia and that it may well constitute the link between the Rosellas and the genus *Psephotus*; the marked sexual dimorphism alone occurring in this species of Rosella is possibly further evidence of this relationship.

Aviary Notes

Cayley wrote briefly as follows: "The smallest of the genus *Platycercus*; has the reputation of being a hardy and free breeder in captivity. Similar in habits to the Eastern Rosella and should be treated in exactly the same way as that species. Has often been bred in confinement in Australia."

This is one of the most popular of the broadtails on account of its relatively small size and the ease with which it can be bred. In a mixed collection it is perhaps the least quarrelsome of all the Rosellas.

From 1936 onwards I possessed a pair which consisted of a male of the common race and an elderly female of the inland subspecies. This hen was fed by the cock each spring and spent a good deal of time ejecting the rotten wood from the nesting logs provided for her, but as far as I am aware she never laid. A new pair were obtained towards the end of 1942 and the following season a clutch of eggs was laid, and although the cock died shortly afterwards, the hen carried on single-handed and reared three fine youngsters, a cock and two hens.

It was not until September of 1944 that I was able to secure a new mate for this hen; when introduced she appeared anxious to go to nest immediately, and laid the first egg of a clutch of eight on 26th September. All the eggs were fertile and young were first observed on 24th October; eventually it was seen that six had hatched, the other two eggs failing to do so although containing fully developed embryos. All the young were reared, leaving the nest between 28th November and 5th December, and all were good specimens, except the youngest, which was a little on the small side.

Early the following year, 1945, the hen met with an accidental death and the young bird kept as a mate for the father turned out to be a cock. A new hen was not obtained until after the breeding season was over, and in 1946 feeding was noted in September. In October the hen spent a lot of time in the log, but no eggs were ever seen and she was found dead in the nest in mid-November.

For the 1947 season a new pair was obtained, and although the cock apparently pulled his upper mandible off in September in trying to disentangle his foot from the wire door catch, he recovered and was seen feeding his mate early in November, and the first of four eggs was laid on the 20th of that month; all were fertile and duly hatched, but one young bird died within the first week. The first two of the survivors left the nest on 13th January 1948, and the third very prematurely two days later; ultimately this bird developed into a good specimen.

In the 1948 season one of the young cocks of this clutch was mated with his mother, and although he was still in juvenile plumage, two eggs out of the clutch of five commenced on 31st October proved fertile. Two young were seen late in November, and the smaller was found dead in the log on 20th December, the parents having inexplicably ceased feeding. The other young bird left the nest somewhat prematurely that day, but fared no better, and died a few days later. As the parent birds did not start their moult for several weeks afterwards, their sudden desertion was all the more difficult to fathom.

No results were obtained either in 1949 or 1950 from the pair which had laid and hatched young in 1948. A new hen was obtained for 1951, and although she laid a clutch of five early in November, all the eggs were broken. She was given a new mate for 1952 and laid a clutch of six in mid-October; three were fertile, but only one was hatched, and it promptly died. Three more infertile eggs were laid in November, and another two in December, which were not incubated. A second pair of immature birds had laid five eggs early in November 1952, but did not incubate.

PSEPHOTUS Gould
Lesser Broad-tailed Parrots

This genus comprises seven distinct species and separates naturally into the three groups to which Mathews[23] gave generic names but which the 1926 R.A.O.U. Checklist relegated to subgeneric rank. Tavistock[3] called the genus the Lesser Broadtails, and the name has persisted for want of a better one.

The first group, the true *Psephotus*, comprises two well-known species, the Red-rumped and Many-coloured Parrots. The Red-rumped is the predominantly eastern form and is absent from Western Australia where its place is to some extent taken by the Western Rosella. The Many-coloured is mainly an interior and western form, although the range of the two species overlaps considerably and the Red-rumped may be gradually replacing the Many-coloured as the mallee is increasingly cleared.

The second group, the subgenus *Northiella*, contains the two Blue-bonnets, widely separated by the Nullarbor Plain. The western form, the Little Blue-bonnet, has a restricted range whilst the eastern form, the Blue-bonnet, ranges widely from southern Queensland through the interior of New South Wales and Victoria into South Australia and has two very well-defined races, the red-vented in the north and the yellow-vented in the west and south, with a fairly narrow zone of intergradation between.

The third group, the anthill nesters, of the subgenus *Psephotellus*, is probably the most worthy of generic status on account of its greater differentiation. Of the three species, the Paradise Parrakeet, possibly on the verge of extinction, is or was the most southern in its range. The other two, the Golden-shouldered and the Hooded, are obviously closely related but are very distinct; the former inhabits a limited area of Cape York Peninsula, Queensland, and the latter a relatively restricted area of the Northern Territory. It needs to be stressed that the "anthills" in which the members of this subgenus excavate their nesting cavities are in fact termitaria.

In this genus mutual preening, unique amongst the broadtails, occurs in all species with the exception of the anthill nesters, *Psephotellus*.

The display varies in each of the subgenera. In the true *Psephotus* it closely resembles that of the Rosellas and Ringnecks, with shoulder-squaring and tail-wagging. In *Northiella* there is a certain amount of shoulder-squaring and the tail is fanned but wagged to a lesser degree and there is some bobbing of the head with the erection of the forehead feathers in the form of a small crest. In *Psephotellus* the male alights near the female on a perch or on the ground and approaches her with a marked swagger, with shoulders squared and wings depressed and with frontal feathers erected as a tiny crest; there is no tail-spreading or wagging.

In all members of the genus there is the customary courtship feeding which is continued during the three-week incubation period and after the young hatch. Later the male feeds the young directly, both before and after fledging. The chicks are clothed in the usual white down and have yellow bills on leaving the nest. In most species this rapidly changes to horn colour but in *chrysopterygius* it remains cream coloured for several months and in *dissimilis* even longer.

The wing-stripe varies with the different subgenera. In the true *Psephotus, varius* and *haematonotus*, immatures of both sexes exhibit a marked wing-stripe, which is invariably retained by the adult female and lost by the adult male. In *Northiella* the stripe is fairly constant in immatures, with a tendency for it to be less marked in males. Adult males do not exhibit it, but a fairly large proportion of females retain some trace of the stripe, more particularly *narethae*. In *Psephotellus* the stripe is invariably well marked in immatures and in adult females and completely absent in adult males.

All members of the genus are free bathers in the wild state and in captivity.

Being essentially ground feeders, their feet are rarely if ever used to hold objects of food but are used to hold down the stalks of seeding grasses to enable the bird to reach the heads. Head-scratching is performed from behind the wing.

The flight of these birds is generally strong and fairly swift, with less undulation than is present in the Rosellas. The Red-rumped flies more directly than the Many-coloured, which has a more buoyant, fluttering effect; the Blue-bonnets are somewhat erratic and more undulating and have a stiffer appearance, possibly due to the way in which the wings are held between beats. The Antbed Parrots show slight undulations in their swift flight.

43 Red-rumped Parrot

Psephotus haematonotus (Gould)

PLATE X

Synonyms

Red-backed Parrot, Grass Parrot, Grassie.

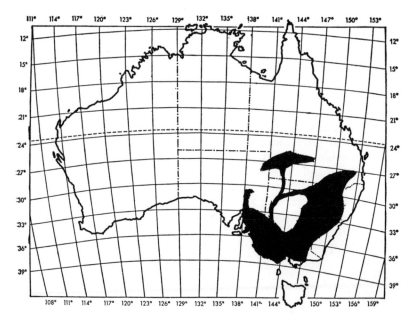

Distribution

In south-western Queensland there are records for this species as far north as Quilpie, Charleville, Augathella and south-west of Windorah, and it also occurs on the Darling Downs as far north as Jandowae and east to Condamine and Meandarra.

In New South Wales the species can be said to occur almost everywhere except in the extreme west and in some parts of the northern coastal strip, to which it appears to be extending.

In Victoria it is present over most, if not all, of the State but is rare in Gippsland.

In South Australia this species occurs over most of the eastern portion

of the State, extending as far as the north-eastern corner where the pale
bluish race *caeruleus* occurs. However, the species does not occur west
of Spencer Gulf and the Flinders Range.

Description

SIZE. About 11 inches (279 mm).

ADULT MALE. Head turquoise green, tinged with blue on forehead and
cheeks; back and scapulars dull bluish-green; rump red; upper tail-
coverts yellowish-green; upper wing-coverts and outer webs of inner
secondaries bluish-green, the outer median series greenish-yellow;
shoulder of wing, primary coverts and outer webs of primaries deep
blue, the latter greyish on their apical portion; outer webs of outer
secondaries blue with whitish margins; inner webs of quills blackish-
brown; central pair of tail-feathers bluish-green shading to black at
tips; remainder greenish at their bases shading to blue with whitish
tips; inner webs dark blue at their bases shading to light blue with
whitish tips; foreneck and upper breast yellowish-green; lower breast and
abdomen yellow washed with green on sides; thighs pale bluish-green;
under tail-coverts dull white; under wing-coverts deep blue; bill bluish-
horn; legs and feet mealy-grey; eyes light brown.

ADULT FEMALE. Much duller in coloration than the male, the head and
upper parts grey washed with pale greenish-olive; rump and upper tail-
coverts green; upper wing-coverts and inner secondaries like the back,
the outer series of the lesser median coverts tinged with blue; cheeks,
foreneck and upper breast olive-grey; the lower breast dull yellow,
centre of the abdomen and under tail-coverts dull white, the latter
washed with blue.

IMMATURE. Easily sexed on leaving the nest, the young females being
only slightly duller than the adult whereas young males are considerably
duller, the red area on the rump being considerably reduced in size and
the bright green of the head and breast being of a much duller shade.
Adult plumage is acquired by a complete moult of body feathers which
usually occurs when the birds are about three months old.

Geographical Variations

The race *caeruleus*, which occurs in the extreme north-east of South
Australia, is almost certainly continuous with the population found in
parts of the channel country of south-western Queensland. In this race
the males are considerably bluer and the females much greyer than in
the nominate race; in addition, the plumage of the young males is much
duller than that of the typical birds.

Field Notes

Cayley wrote: "The Red-backed (better known as the Red-rumped or
Grass Parrakeet) is fairly numerous throughout its wide range, being

more plentiful in the inland areas than nearer the coast. Not uncommon in the cleared lands and open forest country in the vicinity of Parramatta, even closer to Sydney, and would be more so, if it were not for that introduced pest, the starling. These verminous birds have so infested nesting-trees, that parrots and other birds that breed in hollows in trees, have been forced to abandon their usual nesting-sites and seek others farther afield. In nearly every district where this pest occurs, it is noticeable that the numbers of many useful indigenous species are diminishing each year. Unless some drastic action is taken, it seems certain that several species will disappear altogether.

"Common near the roadside of most country districts, and about country homesteads; it is a general favourite: the least harmful as well as one of the most beautiful of all species. Spends much of its time on the ground searching for food which consists entirely of the seeds of grasses and other plants. As it eats and destroys the seeds of many noxious plants it is a very useful bird. Owing to its feeding habits it cannot be classed as troublesome in wheat areas, although most species of parrots are considered to be so, and are destroyed accordingly. It is definitely not a fruit eater.

"Breeds in hollow limbs and holes in live and dead trees. I once saw a pair in the Lower Hunter River district, that reared a brood of young under the bark roof of a barn.

"Clutch: four to six eggs; white, and globular in form; shell close grained and lustreless. Breeding-season: September (in some seasons even as early as the end of July) to November or December."

I have been familiar with this species all my life because it has always been a common bird in the vicinity of Adelaide, occurring in the parklands around the city and not infrequently nesting in crevices in city and suburban buildings. When I kept an extensive collection of parrots at my home in North Adelaide it was not uncommon for pairs of Red-rumps to alight on the aviaries and squabble with some of the occupants.

The species is widely distributed over the eastern half of South Australia and seems to be extending its range with the clearing of mallee country and the development of pasture. It occasionally gathers, outside the breeding season, in flocks of up to a hundred birds.

Aviary Notes

Cayley wrote: "A delightful inmate of an aviary, but quite unsuited to cage life. Hardy and a free breeder, producing two or more broods in a season. Very popular and commonly bred in captivity in Australia. Some interesting hybrids, as well as several xanthic sports are on record. One of the latter, exhibited at the Sydney shows, was, I understand purchased and forwarded to England by Mr W. R. Smith, the president of the Ornithological Society of New South Wales.

"A hollow log hung in the flight makes the most suitable nesting-place, although it nests readily enough in boxes. The female does all the brooding, being fed by her mate who also assists in feeding the young. This species will breed more readily if kept to themselves, as the male has a reputation for spitefulness in mixed company.

"Food suggested: a mixture of canary-seed, millet, hemp, oats and sunflower-seed, with a liberal supply of seeding grasses and other green food."

Being such a common bird in South Australia this species is not greatly sought after as an aviary bird. In a mixed collection it is inclined to be rather aggressive, and the combined assault of a pair will usually result in the rout of a much larger adversary.

I usually had one or more of the species in a large mixed aviary in the early days of my collection but made no serious attempt to breed them until 1944 when a hen that I had obtained late in 1938 and a cock secured about a year later were segregated. The hen laid the first egg of a clutch of five on 17th September and young were first observed on 16th October, having obviously then been hatched for some days. A few days later four could be counted, the fifth egg being clear. The first two young, both hens, left the nest on 10th November, the third, another hen, on the 13th, and the fourth, the only cock, on the 16th.

In 1945 the old hen died and the cock escaped, but one of the young hens was mated to her brother and they went to nest early in November, laying four eggs, all of which proved clear. The following season two eggs were laid late in September and disappeared, then another was laid from the perch, and ultimately seven more in the log. These were incubated but were all clear.

The year 1947 saw a repetition of the previous year in that a clutch, commenced at the end of August, were all clear as were a further clutch of five laid early in October. About this time a wild cock bird became very attentive to the hen, and I eventually caught him and liberated the old cock, who had become extremely fat. The hen seemed very pleased with the change and laid a third clutch early in November but became egg-bound with the fourth egg, and after eventually laying it, did not incubate. In 1948 four eggs were found in the log early in September, but the hen then looked sick and eventually laid a soft-shelled egg and thereafter did not incubate. She spent a good deal of time in the log early in October but did not produce another clutch.

This species was not kept in either 1949 or 1950. A pair obtained in 1951 had an infertile clutch of six early, then started non-stop laying early in October, and had a clutch of four in December, three of which were found to be fertile when deserted. In 1952 a different pair did nothing.

During the winter of 1968 I was given a pair of the inland race, *caeruleus*, which had been bred in captivity the previous year by R. Rowlands; these birds went to nest in October, laying four eggs and rearing two young, a pair, which left the nest about Christmas time. It was immediately apparent that the young male was much duller than the juveniles of the common race, being scarcely any brighter than the female and with a very small dull red rump-patch; the young female was of the same rather greyish shade which is typical of the females of this race.

44 Many-coloured Parrot

Psephotus varius **Clark**

PLATE X

Synonyms

Mulga Parrot, Varied Parrot.

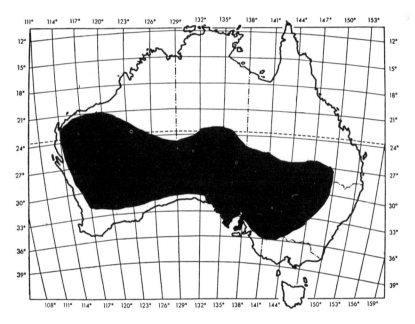

Distribution

The records of this species for Queensland are few and far between; the only ones obtained are those for Eulo, Quilpie, Charleville, Meandarra and **Moonie River.**

In New South Wales it is entirely a bird of the western two-thirds of the State, not reaching the western slopes of the Great Dividing Range: the easternmost records obtained are from Collarenebri in the north and West Wyalong and Griffith in the south.

In Victoria it is confined to the north-western corner of the State with an extension as far south as Ararat and a highly suspect record from **Wangaratta.**

In South Australia the species is extremely widely distributed, avoiding only the high rainfall areas of the Mount Lofty Ranges and the south-east, and extending to the far north-east of the State, in continuity with the New South Wales and Queensland populations and also into the far north-west. This range continues on into Central Australia where the northernmost recordings are from Macdonald Downs and Missionary Plain.

Similarly there is a continuous presumed distribution of this species from the western parts of South Australia on into Western Australia, where again it is widely spread, extending, according to Serventy and Whittell[10], north to the Pilbara district and again avoiding only the higher rainfall area of the south-west—that is, west and south of a line joining Moora, Grass Valley, Quairading, Kweda and Dundas.

Description

SIZE. About 12 inches (305 mm).

ADULT MALE. General colour above green tinged with blue on feathers above eye and on sides of neck; a broad chestnut-red band on nape; lower back and rump light green crossed with two blackish bands; upper tail-coverts green, some of the smaller coverts dull red; scapulars and outer webs of inner secondaries green; outer greater series of wing-coverts blue, remainder of the upper wing-coverts light green with a golden-green patch on the median series; inner webs of primary and secondary quills dark brown, outer webs dark blue, greyish towards tips of primaries; central pair of tail-feathers dark blue tinged with green on their basal portion, remainder green at their base crossed with a black band and shading to blue towards the tips which are white, the basal half of their inner webs brownish; forehead rich golden-yellow; cheeks, foreneck and breast green; abdomen dull scarlet-red, bases of feathers yellow; under tail-coverts yellow occasionally washed with red; bill bluish horn-colour with blackish tips; legs and feet dark mealy-grey; eyes dark brown.

ADULT FEMALE. Differs from the male in the absence of the green on head, back, throat, and breast, and of the yellow on wing and forehead; and in having the head, back, and breast dull greyish-green, a dull red patch instead of golden-yellow on the median series of the upper wing-coverts, and the abdomen and under tail-coverts pale green.

IMMATURE. Easily sexed on leaving the nest, the young female being only slightly duller than the adult, whilst the young male is considerably duller but still much brighter than the female; the red area on the belly is either absent or considerably reduced. In addition the shoulder patch in the young male is generally yellow but occasionally has a brick-red tinge. Adult plumage is obtained by a complete moult of body feathers occurring when the bird is about three months old.

Geographical Variations

None recognized.

Field Notes

Cayley wrote: "Better known as the Many-coloured Parrakeet, this species is widely distributed over Central Australia, its range extending from inland southern Queensland to Victoria and to Western Australia. Fairly plentiful in the north-western portion of New South Wales where it frequents open scrub-lands and timber bordering watercourses. Usually met with in pairs or family parties and occasionally in flocks of about ten or twelve in number. Much of its time is spent on the ground in search of food, which consists of the seeds of grasses and other plants. It often associates with the Red-backed species. As a rule by no means a shy bird. When flushed from the ground, it flies to a nearby tree, returning again to the ground to continue feeding when one moves away. Its note is a slight chattering call or whistle, often repeated, and usually uttered when in flight.

"Favourite nesting-sites are hollow limbs or holes in trees, usually eucalypts, bordering watercourses. The height from the ground of these nesting-hollows varies from eight to as high as eighty feet; the eggs are laid on the bare wood or mould, at from one to two feet from the entrance.

"Clutch: four to six eggs; white, and globular in form; shell close-grained, some being dull and lustreless, others having a slight gloss. Breeding-season: September to November or December."

My first meeting with this species in the field was in the belt of mallee country, now largely cleared except for a relatively small reserve, which lies to the north of Lake Alexandrina. It has never been particularly common in this area, which is its southern limit in South Australia, but as one proceeds northwards, along the flat country between the Mount Lofty Ranges to the west and the River Murray to the east it becomes progressively more common, and in the country along the Upper Murray, between Morgan and Renmark, is very plentiful indeed. The species is also numerous in the Murray mallee and in the north-western corner of Victoria.

This parrot has a very extensive range to the north and west into Central and Western Australia. In the Centre it is widely but somewhat sparsely distributed in the vicinity of Alice Springs where I have seen it on each occasion that I have visited the area, and it is plentiful in the country west of Port Augusta on upper Eyre Peninsula. I have seen it only once in Western Australia, in October 1964 in the vicinity of Cunderdin.

Cayley's statement that this species often associates with the Red-rumped is almost certainly incorrect; although both may in places be found in the same locality, in my experience they never mingle.

Aviary Notes

Cayley wrote: "A delightful inmate of an aviary, but quite unsuited to cage life. In habits and behaviour resembles the Red-backed species but is less hardy in confinement. Being of a nervous disposition when first caught, care should be taken to protect it from any sudden fright, as it may kill itself by flying against the wire of its enclosure.

"Considered a free breeder by experienced aviarists, in spite of a bad reputation for delicacy given it by some others. Has been often bred in captivity both in Australia and abroad. The female alone incubates, and sits very closely when she has small young or the eggs are on the point of hatching; the male feeds her, and assists in feeding the young.

"Food suggested: a mixture of canary-seed, millet and oats, with a liberal supply of seeding grasses and other green food."

A bird with a reputation for extreme delicacy when first trapped; in fact, many aviculturists declare that they have abandoned the attempt to acclimatize newly caught birds. I cannot help feeling that this supposed delicacy is due to the birds being kept under dirty conditions and badly fed by the trappers.

My initial experiences with this species were in keeping with those of many others in that none of nine trapped birds survived more than a few weeks. In February 1936 I obtained a pair of acclimatized birds which were alleged to have hatched young during the previous season but to have failed to rear them. This pair went to nest in August 1936, the first egg of a clutch of five being laid on the 28th of that month. The hen sat very closely, and young were first observed on 20th September and eventually all five eggs were found to have hatched, but four of the young had died by the beginning of October. The fifth, a hen, survived and left the nest on 20th October. This appears to have been the first record of the species having been bred in captivity in South Australia, although the bronze medal of the Avicultural Society of South Australia had been awarded in 1930 to F. C. Kitchen, a resident of Broken Hill.

The hen of this pair died suddenly in August 1937, and it was not until February of the following year that I was able to procure a satisfactory substitute. This new hen laid two clutches of eggs that season but did not incubate either of them; however, in 1939 she commenced a clutch of six late in July, of which five were fertile. These duly hatched and all the young, being two cocks and three hens, were reared, leaving the nest towards the end of September. A second clutch laid towards the end of October consisted of five eggs, four of which were fertile and from which four young, two of each sex, were reared, leaving the nest in mid-December.

From that time onward this pair of birds had a remarkable record, rearing eight young from two nests in 1940, 1941, and 1942 and four from a single nest in 1943. In 1944 they were again double-brooded, rearing three in the first nest and four in the second and exactly repeating these results in 1945, whilst 1946 saw two reared in the first clutch and four in the second. In 1947 their first clutch was removed and Little Blue Bonnet eggs substituted, and they duly hatched and reared three fine young ones and then proceeded to rear four young Many-colours from the second clutch. By 1948 the cock was beginning to show signs of old age and, although Little Blue Bonnet eggs were again substituted for their first clutch, only two hatched and only one survived to leave the nest. They did not go to nest again, and the cock died in early November and the hen later in the same month. They had, I think, a remarkable record in rearing sixty-five young birds in ten seasons.

This species was not kept in 1949 or in 1950. In 1951 a wild-caught hen mated to an aviary-bred cock did nothing, and a different pair obtained in 1952 were no improvement.

45 Blue Bonnet

Psephotus (Northiella) haematogaster (Gould)

PLATE XI

Synonyms

Crimson-bellied Parrot, Bulloak Parrot.

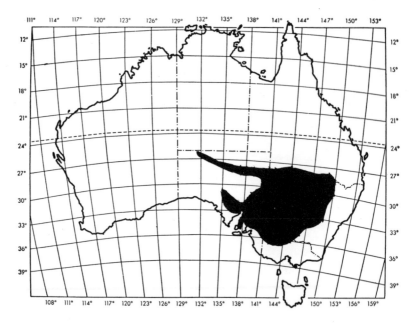

Distribution

In South Australia the yellow-vented race of this species extends as far west as Kingoonya on the transcontinental railway and Kimba on Eyre Peninsula. From these limits it extends over most of the north-eastern parts of the State, avoiding the Flinders Range and reaching as far north as Innamincka and south as far as Two Wells, Wellington East, Narrung and Meningie. It is widely spread through the Murray Mallee and on into Victoria where it occurs in the north-western corner of the State, the Wimmera and as far to the east as Bendigo and Rochester.

Similarly there is a direct spread eastwards into western New South Wales to the Riverina in the south and up through central New South

Wales into south-western Queensland as far north as Nappamerrie, Bulloo, Quilpie, Eulo and Cunnamulla. To the north-east of this range, with a zone of intermediate forms in the vicinity of Barellan and Rankin's Springs in the south and between Cobar and Hermidale farther north, there occurs the distinct red-vented subspecies which is recorded from St George, Meandarra and Condamine in southern Queensland down through Moree, Garah, Warialda, Cobbora, Nyngan, Wellington and West Wyalong to Grenfell.

Description

SIZE. About 12 inches (305 mm).

ADULT MALE. General colour above, including the greater portion of the head, greyish-brown; upper tail-coverts light brown washed with olive-yellow; lesser upper wing-coverts and those on the extreme edge of the wing rich blue; outer median and greater wing-coverts blue; inner series of both olive, becoming paler on outer webs of inner secondaries which are margined with olive; primary coverts, primaries and remainder of secondaries deep blue on their outer webs, blackish-brown on their inner webs, with greyish tips to outer webs of primaries; central pair of tail-feathers dull olive-green shading to dull blue at their tips; remainder dark blue at base shading to light blue with whitish tips; forepart of head and forepart of face blue, lighter on chin; foreneck and chest pale brown, upper breast and sides of abdomen yellow; centre of lower breast and centre of abdomen red; vent and under tail-coverts yellow; bill light horn-colour, bluish at base; legs and feet dark fleshy-grey; eyes brown.

ADULT FEMALE. Similar to the male but smaller and with less red on centre of lower breast and abdomen, the feathers of which are slightly margined with yellow; bill smaller.

IMMATURE. Closely resembles the adult but all colours are slightly duller and the red abdominal patch is much restricted in size. Adult plumage is attained by a moult of body feathers which occurs when the bird is about three or four months old; prior to this the sex can usually be determined by the size of the bill.

Geographical Variations

The foregoing description applies to the nominate, yellow-vented race, although the illustration is of the larger, north-eastern, red-vented form, *haematorrhous*, in which the vent and under tail-coverts are red, the wing coverts are maroon, not olive, and the shoulder is pale green, not blue. I have not seen the birds from the Lake Eyre basin, *pallescens*, in life; skins merely suggest a pale, washed-out form of the yellow-vented birds, perhaps analogous to the pale form, *occidentalis*, of *Barnardius zonarius*.

Field Notes

Cayley wrote: "The Blue Bonnet is fairly common throughout the inland portions of New South Wales where it is generally found in pairs or small flocks, inhabiting timber bordering watercourses and open country dotted with scrub. In habits and economy it resembles the Red-backed and Mulga Parrakeets and is often found in association with either or both. As a rule it keeps silent when feeding, and as the colour of its upper parts so closely resembles its surroundings, it is not unusual for one to approach quite near a flock before being aware of the fact. When flushed, it rises quickly from the ground and flies to the nearest tree, whistling its call-notes while on the wing, and becoming silent again on alighting on the branch where it will remain perched upright watching one's approach.

"For breeding purposes the Blue Bonnet resorts to a hollow limb or hole in a tree, usually a eucalypt or casuarina, and more often than otherwise in a dead tree.

"Clutch: three to seven eggs; white, and varying from rounded-oval to an ellipse in form; shell close-grained and usually lustreless. Breeding-season: August to December."

I first met with the species in the wild state in the course of a weekend spent at Peterborough in northern South Australia in October 1947 and was surprised by the attractiveness in the field of this superficially drab bird. Its jaunty behaviour and characteristic alarm calls lead to its easy recognition as it flushes and flies to a nearby perch. Since that first meeting I have seen the species on a great many occasions in various parts of South Australia and have come to realize that it is much commoner and more widely spread than has been generally recognized.

One of the most surprising meetings was to find the species at Wellington East in October 1951 and to discover subsequently that there is a reasonably large population in that vicinity, extending to Narrung and across the River Murray to the eastern end of Chauncey's Line and the vicinity of Langhorne Creek.

Another surprise was to find in September 1956 that the species was reasonably common not far north of Adelaide in the vicinity of Two Wells and Lower Light; it seems strange that the older generation of local ornithologists had never recorded its presence in either of these areas.

In the course of numerous visits to the upper Murray districts between Renmark and Morgan the species has invariably been seen in goodly numbers and it certainly extends in a southerly direction for some distance from Morgan along both sides of the river.

Further observations have shown that the species is common in the northern areas of the State, notably in the vicinity of Iron Knob and on Carriewerloo Station and on upper Yorke Peninsula.

In May 1960, during a trip with A. C. Hunt from Inverell to the neighbourhood of Moree in north-eastern New South Wales, I was delighted to see examples of the red-vented race and to note its extreme brilliance in the field as compared with the familiar yellow-vented bird which I knew so well in the south. In fact, I was immediately impressed by the thought that records of the Paradise Parrot in this region might well be due to mistaken identification of this highly coloured race.

Cayley's remarks that this species resembles the Red-rumped and Many-coloured species in habits and economy and is often found in association with either or both is of doubtful accuracy. Certainly it is often found in the same locality as the Many-coloured but I cannot recall ever having found it in Red-rumped areas. I have always been impressed by the frequency with which this bird occurs in places where the so-called false sandalwood (*Myoporum platycarpum*) grows. Another observation of interest is its apparent preference for very cramped nesting hollows, often with an uncomfortably small entrance hole.

Aviary Notes

Cayley wrote: "A lively and attractive inmate of an aviary, but quite unsuited to cage life. Has the reputation of being excessively pugnacious in a mixed collection; better breeding results are obtained from pairs housed separately. Said to be rather a shy breeder in captivity, but has been bred successfully both in Australia and abroad.

"A hollow log hung in the flight makes the most suitable nesting-place; care should be taken not to disturb the sitting female unnecessarily when brooding, otherwise she will most likely desert her eggs. Should be given the same food as the Red-backed Parrakeet, with the addition of apple."

Before World War I large numbers of the yellow-vented birds used to appear in the local bird-shops; they were extremely shy when first caught and had the reputation of being rather delicate. In addition, they have always been rather unpopular as aviary birds on account of their notorious pugnacity, pairs being able to take on, defeat, and even kill other broadtails much larger than themselves. The red-vented race is quite unknown in local bird-shops, any specimens that I have possessed having always been obtained from Sydney or Brisbane. Blue Bonnets have always been regarded as extremely shy breeders, both in Australia and abroad, and my experiences with them have been rather unusual.

Dealing first with the red-vented race, I obtained my first pair of these birds from the late A. Wachsmann, of the Sydney suburb of Beecroft, in 1937, but these two birds were never well disposed to each other. Early in 1939 I was fortunate enough to obtain another hen from a Melbourne fancier; this bird had laid whilst in his possession the previous year and it immediately became very friendly with the original cock bird, and the first egg of a clutch of six was laid on 17th August of that year. All the eggs were fertile and eventually hatched, young being first seen in the nest on 13th September. However, three young birds died during the first week and another when about half-grown; the remaining two were reared and left the nest on 19th and 21st October. They were a pair, and it was interesting to note that both had well-marked chestnut wing-patches and that the male had yellow subcaudals,

R

whilst those of the female were red. At the first moult, which took place in December, the subcaudals of the male changed to bright red. This being the first recorded breeding of the species in South Australia gained the bronze medal of the Avicultural Society of that State and also the silver medal of the Society for the most outstanding breeding achievement of the season. Unfortunately the breeding pair escaped during the winter of 1940 and were not recovered.

In March 1943, while stationed near Brisbane, I was able to acquire another pair of birds of this race and brought them back with me when I came home on leave. They made no attempt at nesting that year, but in 1944 the first egg was laid on 28th August, and promptly broken. Five more fertile eggs followed and the first young bird was seen on 23rd September; two days later, three living and one dead young were seen in the log, the fifth egg having failed to hatch although it contained an almost fully developed embryo. Three young were duly reared, leaving the nest between 26th and 30th October, and being one cock and two hens. The following season, 1945, a clutch of three was laid at the end of August. One of these was infertile but the other two hatched and were reared, proving to be two cocks. In 1946 a clutch of six was laid early in August. Of these, two hatched and died when quite young, a third was dead in the shell, a fourth had a very small embryo, and the remaining two were clear. The following year a clutch of five eggs was laid in mid-August but all proved infertile and in 1948 the old hen died in October without having laid.

The old male did nothing with either of the mates provided in 1949 and 1950. A pair of young birds bred in my collection during the war were brought back, but they did nothing in either 1950 or in 1951, and both died in May 1952.

With regard to the yellow-vented race, I had almost given up hope of ever breeding them as they had been represented continuously in my collection over a period of ten years or more without ever showing the slightest inclination to go to nest. For the 1947 season I had an old hen known to have been in captivity for many years, mated to an exceptionally vigorous cock alleged to have bred young when mated to a Red-vented hen in Victoria in previous years. As the breeding season approached he drove the hen about a lot, and when a log was provided he forced her to spend a considerable portion of each day therein, much against her will. However, an egg was laid on 24th August and was soon broken, but it was followed by five more, all of which proved fertile and eventually hatched, the first young being seen on 17th September and the fifth not until a week later. All were reared and left the nest between 21st and 28th October, being two cocks and three hens. This success also gained the bronze medal of the Avicultural Society of South Australia, for this variety had not been previously bred in South Australia. Unfortunately, the hen of the above-mentioned pair died before the next breeding season and was not replaced until too late to expect any results in that year.

The old breeding cock was given a tame hand-reared hen as a mate in 1949, and she laid a clutch of six towards the end of August. Five were fertile and three were hatched and reared, leaving the nest at the end of October. In 1950 the same pair hatched three and reared two at the same time of the year, and in 1951 four were hatched and reared, again at exactly the same time. In 1952 the old cock failed to induce a new mate to lay, even though she spent some time in the log in November.

46 Little Blue Bonnet

Psephotus (Northiella) narethae (H. L. White)

PLATE XI

Synonyms

Naretha Parrot, Oak Parrot.

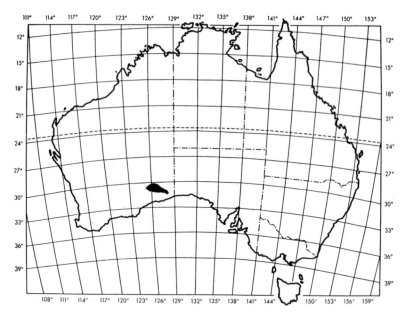

Distribution

Serventy and Whittell[10] wrote of this species in 1967: ". . . a very restricted distribution in Western Australia being confined to the myall country that fringes the north-western edge of the Nullarbor Plain. It has been proved to occur from a point 20 miles west of Naretha to the myall belt 80 miles north of Loongana, a zone some 180 miles in length and probably not more than 20 miles in width. It may extend even further east but it does not occur north in the mallee and mulga country of the Great Victoria Desert."

More recently the species has been stated to extend much farther west towards Kalgoorlie and also south to about halfway between Cocklebiddy and Rawlinna, and from Mundrabilla to Eucla. Ford and

Sedgwick[48] have suggested a possible intergradation with *P. haemato-gaster* on the eastern side of the Nullarbor Plain but specimens from Kingoonya (the westernmost recording) are absolutely typical of the yellow-vented race. It was with great interest that I learnt that a specimen of typical *narethae* had been collected in 1971 in South Australia some distance north of Fowler's Bay but south of the Nullarbor Plain.

Description

SIZE. About 11 inches (279 mm).

ADULT MALE. General colour above, including the greater portion of head, foreneck and chest pale brown becoming more greyish-olive in tone on the back; rump and upper tail-coverts a rich olive-yellow; nape, hind-neck, throat and upper breast mottled with a light buff; forehead and lores verditer green, cheeks a rich purplish-blue with an edging of light cream; abdomen yellow with orange suffusion, flanks washed with greyish-olive; under tail-coverts vermilion; lesser wing-coverts cerulean blue, outer median wing-coverts scarlet vermilion; inner median and greater wing-coverts olive-yellow; inner secondaries olive-yellow; inner webs blackish-brown; outer secondaries and primary coverts a rich blue; primaries, except the first which is blackish-brown, a rich blue extending from their base halfway down their outer webs; the other half of the outer webs a pale mauve; inner webs black; central pair of tail-feathers dull olive-green, apical half of three outer webs and tips dull blue, the remainder dull blue at base, white on their apical portion; all but the lateral tail-feathers with a pale bluish wash on their outer webs extending nearly to their tips; bill whitish horn colour, bluish at base; legs and feet dark fleshy grey; iris dark brown.

ADULT FEMALE. Easily distinguished, for in addition to a smaller head and bill, the turquoise on the forehead is duller, the abdomen is yellow without any orange tinge and the small patch on the wing is brick red.

IMMATURE. Resembles the adult female but duller in all respects; attains adult plumage within a few months of leaving the nest; prior to this can usually be sexed by the size of the head and bill.

Geographical Variations

None recognized.

Field Notes

Apart from recording the fact that he had the pleasure of figuring this species for the first time, Cayley had nothing to say about it.

White's account[49] of the discovery of this bird in 1921 is interesting. He had engaged F. L. Whitlock, the well-known collector, to make a study of the avifauna of the western margin of the Nullarbor Plain and suggested to him that he should base himself at Zanthus, some 130 miles east of Kalgoorlie, but it soon transpired that this point was not far enough to the east. However, whilst there, Whitlock was intrigued to find that a railway employee had in captivity a parrot said to have been taken at Naretha, 75 miles farther east, near the edge of the great plain, the bird agreeing with no published description.

It so happened that White was travelling to Perth at this time and Whitlock met his train at Zanthus and told him the story. White told him to move to Naretha without delay and to report events to him on his return journey a week later. When he did so, Whitlock handed him three skins, saying he thought the bird was new. Conversation with Captain S. A. White in Adelaide and comparison with material in the National Museum, Melbourne, settled the matter conclusively. Later, Whitlock collected clutches of eggs of this species and demonstrated that it bred early in the spring, eggs being laid in August.

Since then further interesting observations on this little-known bird have been made by Calaby[50] and by Ford and Sedgwick.[48]

Although I watched the appropriate area closely while travelling to Western Australia by train in 1966, I did not see any of these parrots and, in consequence, I have not yet seen this bird in the field; however, I hope to remedy this deficiency one day.

Aviary Notes

The Little Blue Bonnet was not known in captivity at the time that Cayley wrote his text.

This bird was quite unknown to aviculture until an Adelaide dealer obtained two small consignments early in 1936. I secured a pair from the first lot and lost the hen after about eighteen months. A substitute was secured and survived about two years, and a third hen obtained early in 1942 escaped, together with the original cock bird, during 1943. None of these hens ever showed any real desire to go to nest, although the log was visited occasionally by the second of the trio.

A new pair obtained in 1944 went to nest in mid-September, breaking the first of a clutch of six eggs but thereafter incubating steadily; unfortunately, the eggs were all infertile.

Before the 1945 breeding season a new cock was obtained and a clutch of five eggs was commenced on 6th October, three of which were fertile and duly hatched. Two of the young birds died very early but the survivor, a cock, was reared and left the nest on 11th October. This success gained the bronze medal of the Avicultural Society of South Australia, the only other known breedings being that in the Adelaide Zoo in 1941, recorded in the *Avicultural Magazine*,[51] and an almost simultaneous success by a Mr Catt, of Carlingford, near Sydney.

In 1946 the same pair commenced a clutch of five eggs on 9th August but investigation in mid-September showed two dead young, two eggs with fully developed young dead in the shell, and a clear egg. In 1947 the first egg of a clutch of five was laid on 15th August and promptly broken; of the remaining four, three proved fertile and in view of past performances were transferred to my reliable old pair of Many-colours and were duly hatched and reared by them, proving to be two cocks and a hen. The Narethas were given the Many-colours' three fertile eggs, which they hatched and they eventually succeeded in rearing two of them; the elder was one of the finest young cock Many-colours I have ever bred but the younger was a miserable little runt.

In 1948 the changes were rung again, but out of four fertile Naretha eggs given to the Many-colours only two were hatched and one reared while the Narethas successfully reared two good young Many-colours from three fertile eggs!

The old breeding hen, with a new mate, had five clear eggs early in September 1949. In 1950 the same pair had six eggs late in September; only one was fertile, but it was hatched and the young bird reared. In 1951 three were fertile out of four eggs laid early in September, and two hatched and both young were reared. In 1952 a new hen was obtained, but she did not lay, although the cock seemed more vigorous than in previous seasons.

47 Paradise Parrot

Psephotus (Psephotellus) pulcherrimus (Gould)

PLATE XI

Synonyms

Beautiful Parrakeet, Red or Scarlet-shouldered Parrakeet, Soldier Grass Parrot, Anthill Parrot, Ground Rosella.

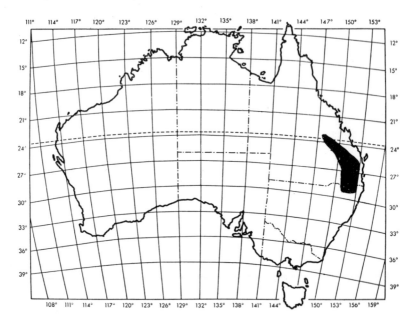

Distribution

Perusal of available records of this species suggests a former distribution from the Nogoa River in central Queensland southward along a strip roughly one hundred miles wide to the Queensland-New South Wales border and thence into north-eastern New South Wales as far south as the vicinity of Inverell to the west and Casino to the east.

Description

SIZE. About 12 inches (305 mm).

ADULT MALE. Forehead crimson; crown of head and nape black; scapulars and back brown; rump and upper tail-coverts turquoise-blue; mesial lesser and median upper wing-coverts crimson; remainder of upper wing-coverts, bastard wing, primary and greater coverts blackish-brown; innermost secondaries brown like the back, remainder of secondaries blackish-brown; primaries brown, basal portion of their outer webs bluish-black shading to grey at their apical half; central tail-feathers bronze-green at basal portion becoming darker towards tips; remainder greenish-blue at base shading to blue, with white tips and crossed in the centre with a black band; feathers around eyes yellowish-white stained with red; sides of face, hinder crown, and neck turquoise-blue; foreneck and breast turquoise-green shading to turquoise-blue on lower breast and blue on sides of breast; abdomen, thighs and under tail-coverts scarlet; bill bluish-horn with paler tips; legs and feet mealy-brown; eyes brown.

ADULT FEMALE. Forehead yellowish-white stained with red; crown of head and nape blackish-brown; lower hind-neck, back and scapulars brown; rump and upper tail-coverts pale turquoise-blue shading to green towards end of latter; mesial lesser and median upper wing-coverts red; remainder of upper wing-coverts, bastard wing, primary and greater coverts blackish-brown, the latter tinged on their outer edges towards their apical portion with pale purplish-grey; secondaries dark brown with paler margins; primary quills dark brown, the outer webs tinged with pale purplish-grey, the inner ones light-brown with paler margins; primary quills dark brown, the outer webs tinged with pale purplish-grey, the inner ones light-brown; central tail-feathers bronze-green becoming blackish at tips and tinged more or less with blue on their outer webs; remainder of tail-feathers blue at their basal portion shading to white at their tips and crossed in the centre with a black band; feathers round eyes and sides of hinder crown yellowish-white with red tips; sides of face and throat pale yellow; fore-neck and breast yellowish with minute orange and dusky barrings; abdomen, flanks, and under tail-coverts pale blue, with some light red and white feathers about the centre of the abdomen.

IMMATURE. Resembles the adult female, but duller in coloration generally; the young males may be distinguished by their darker heads and broader and brighter wing-patches. The time of assumption of adult plumage is not known but it is probable that it would take at least twelve months.

Geographical Variations

None recognized.

Field Notes

The beauty and the rarity of the Paradise Parrot, seen alive by very few people still living, warrant an account of its historical record in some detail. The species was discovered by John Gilbert in 1844 on the Darling Downs and named by Gould "the most beautiful" (*pulcherrimus*). As recorded by Chisholm,[52] Gilbert found the bird occurring as far north in Queensland as the Comet River; it was not until some six months later, a few days before his death, that he again reported the species in the vicinity of the Mitchell River on the Gulf of Carpentaria. This latter observation has always been suspect because of the occurrence of the closely related Golden-shouldered Parrot in the same area, but there are persistent rumours, emanating from this region, of a "red-shouldered" parrot which nests in termite mounds.

For several decades after Gilbert's discovery virtually nothing was written about this species although, as Chisholm points out, Diggles in his unfinished work, published about 1868, was the first to draw attention to its habit of nesting in termitaria.

In the 1880s, or possibly a little earlier, numbers of living specimens were exported and the bird became well known in English and continental aviaries; A. Reichenow, in his excellent work published between 1878 and 1883, figured a male.

H. G. Barnard of Coomooboolaroo, near Duaringa, Queensland, reported that the bird was never plentiful in that district, but that in 1882 it was common on Fairfield, less than one hundred miles to the south.

In 1884 Greene[53] published his *Parrots in Captivity* in which he gives accounts of his own and Canon Dutton's experiences of the species in England.

In 1887 Lumholtz[54] wrote *Among Cannibals*, describing therein the finding by the Barnard boys of nests on Fairfield Station during the month of September; later he describes his collection of a pair near the Nogoa River.

At about this time, too, Wiener[55] writing in *Foreign Cage Birds* gave an extensive account of his experiences with the species; and Gedney[56] (in a different work of the same title) goes as far as giving the incubation period and describing the nestling plumage, although he does not specifically claim to have bred the birds himself. There seems, then, little doubt that some breeding successes were obtained by Continental aviculturists as recorded by Prestwich.[57]

For some unexplained reason, from about the late 1880s there do not appear to have been any further accounts of the species overseas, so that Seth-Smith,[58] in his *Parrakeets*, published in 1903, says "no specimens have been imported for many years; ten or fifteen years ago it was comparatively common amongst English aviculturists". It is worthy of note that the *Avicultural Magazine*, first published in 1894, contains no authentic record of Paradise Parrots in captivity from that time onwards, although immature Golden-shouldered Parrots imported in 1897 were first considered to be Paradise.

Why did this export cease, and the species become so suddenly and irrevocably lost to aviculture? To me there seem to be four plausible explanations: (i) The source of supply to the export trade may have vanished with the death or movement to another area of the trapper, although Fred Smith, a Queensland aviculturist of long experience, told me in 1939 that up to the turn of the century, Paradise Parrots could nearly always be obtained in Brisbane bird-shops for the sum of five shillings a pair; (ii) Chisholm's thoughts that the "choice of nesting sites has rendered the Paradise Parrot susceptible to attacks by reptiles, foxes (one might include feral cats) and that most dangerous product of creation, man himself; I incline to think, however, that the chief cause in the decline has been the destruction of the birds' feeding grounds by stock"; (iii) the white man's introduction of his grazing animals into the Paradise Parrot's range may not only have brought about the reduction of important seeding grasses; so also would the competition from the prickly pear (*Opuntia*) which spread through the same districts, in places so thickly as to be impenetrable; (iv) a combination of any of these environmental alterations, exacerbated, as they would have been, by a run of years of severe drought in the nineties, could well have had a disastrous effect on the Paradise Parrot population. There is no real evidence that the Paradise Parrot was a nomadic species, able to move to more favourable areas in times of stress; indeed, a combination of stresses may have been brought to bear late last century on a naturally declining species, unable to adapt to change.

In 1910 Seth-Smith writing in the *Avicultural Magazine*, following on a visit to Australia, said:[59] "Mr Beard, the animal dealer, of Brisbane, told me that he knew of a pair of the Beautiful Parrakeet (*Ps. pulcherrimus*) in captivity, which he hoped to be able to secure. This species appears to be very local, and he knew of a place where a pair regularly bred each year. It is locally known as the Elegant Parrakeet." The last report on the species by an overseas aviculturist came from the Marquess of Tavistock in a note in the *Avicultural Magazine* in 1924:[60] "Within the last few years . . . an odd Paradise Parrakeet or so, have been sent to America." His authority for this statement was neither revealed nor confirmed, and when I questioned him about it nearly thirty years later, he could not recall the source.

In Australia in 1915 Campbell wrote to the *Emu* seeking information regarding this and other rare parrots.[61] Barnard's reply, published in the same issue, was that he had not seen a bird since the 1902 drought, and that it was now reported to be very scarce on Fairfield, where in 1882 it was numerous. In 1917 Mathews[23] published volume 6 of his monumental *Birds of Australia*; in this he says the species "appears to have become extinct".

We now come to what I think of as the Chisholm era in the history of this elusive bird. Cayley wrote as follows: "The Paradise (also known as Beautiful, Scarlet-shouldered, Ant-hill, and Ground) Parrakeet is perhaps the most beautiful of all parrots. Sad to relate, it is also one of the rarest Australian species. It was reported 'missing' for many years; then, an isolated pair or two turned up again in a locality which at one time had formed a small part of one of the strongholds of the species. Its rediscovery is due to the untiring efforts of A. H. Chisholm who during 1918 decided, from hints gathered in conversation with old settlers, that a further search for the 'lost' parrot would at least be worth while.

Accordingly he started an inquiry (bearing the query-caption 'Is it Lost?') through the medium of the leading daily newspapers of Brisbane and the Darling Downs, Queensland, having been the haunt of the species.

"After many 'false alarms' his patience was at last rewarded. On 11 December 1921 he received a letter from a C. H. H. Jerrard stating that the writer had seen a pair of parrots which he was almost sure were the 'lost' species. Further investigation confirmed his observation; the breeding-place was located in a termites' mound, and adults were photographed at the entrance to the nesting-cavity. Mr Jerrard's observations and photographs of this species—the rarest of all with the exception of the Night Parrakeet—form as complete a record as any we possess of the other more common species, and add much to our previous very scanty knowledge of this beautiful parrakeet."

Chisholm's interesting articles on his rediscovery make fascinating reading, and attention is directed to two of his contributions to the *Emu*,[62] also to his *Mateship with Birds*[63] and *Birds and Green Places*.[64]

In 1926 Miss Florence Irby wrote to Cayley as follows: "Between five and six o'clock in the morning of 21 November 1926 I heard parrot notes new to me; at the same time my sister called that from her window she could see some birds, strange to her, resting on a pepper-tree. Going out with field-glasses, five Paradise Parrakeets were found sitting close together on the highest branch. Owing to the severity of the drought, most of the leaves had fallen from the tree and every bird could be seen distinctly. Evidently they had been travelling (probably by night) for they seemed tired and took no notice of me.

"There were three females and two males, and from the colouring I concluded they were an old pair with three of that season's young.

"On that hot dry morning with a dense haze of smoke hanging over everything the five birds with their beautiful colouring made an unforgettable picture. One male in particular was especially beautiful; he was sitting above the others and looked as if he had a tight little cap on. They stayed for about ten minutes, sometimes preening their feathers and calling as if lost. Then two flew down to the ground searching for food and the remaining three pottered about the trees, sometimes hanging head downwards as they nibbled at some half-dead leaves. Then, as at a given signal, all flew; for half an hour or more we could hear them calling in the distance. The weather had been very hot and dry, and all through the previous week much of the back country from twenty-five to fifty miles away was on fire. So we decided that these beautiful strangers had been driven from their usual haunts and were searching for a new locality to settle in.

"Writing a few months later about bird-life in Queensland some thirty years before, my uncle, Mr C. A. Irby of Cremorne, said: 'I know the Ground Parrakeet very well, it used to be seen in fairly large flocks about Roma; also on the head of the Dawson River, in the latter district, I've found their nests in the river-bank very much the same as a kingfisher. We used to call them "Soldier Parrots" up there.' "

In the same year, Chisholm, who had previously suggested taking some young birds from the nest under observation, advocated attempting the breeding of the species in captivity and a motion was passed by the Royal Australasian Ornithologists' Union urging State governments to encourage the breeding of rare species in approved private aviaries with a view to ultimate re-establishment by liberation in suitable sanctuaries. In retrospect it seems a great pity that this resolution was not acted upon for the closely related Hooded and Golden-shouldered Parrots have proved to be free breeders in captivity.

Cayley further records, quoting Miss Irby: " 'About the same time [that is, 1926-7] Mr B. M. Robertson of Woodlands, Casino district, told me he knew these beautiful birds well when living near Inverell, their stronghold being Kulki Station in that district. He said they used to tunnel into the banks of the Severn River and Fraser's Creek (branches of the Macintyre). They usually laid three eggs and occasionally four or five. They were still plentiful in that district when he left it in 1910.

" 'Writing to me from the same locality on 20 April 1927, Mrs Gordon Woods of Narrallen, Inverell, said: "The Ground Parrakeet is very scarce about here now, but there are a few; they nest in the banks of the creek. My husband says he had heard of them nesting in trees but has not seen them."

Cayley himself goes on:

"A correspondent who does not wish his name disclosed, found a nesting-place in a hollow stump containing two young ones on his property in November of last year (1936). He had seen these parrakeets on several occasions, but this was the first time he had found them breeding. As his property is a large one he is hopeful the species will multiply. For obvious reasons he has requested me not to mention the name of the locality.

"The entrance to the nesting-chamber was on the side of the stump about a foot from the ground, and the cavity about fifteen inches below the surface of the ground. He also mentions that there are many termites' mounds and several creeks with permanent water on the property— altogether an ideal breeding-ground for the species."

From this time onwards, very little authentic information has come to light. In January 1936 Jerrard wrote to Chisholm saying that he had not seen the birds for eight years, his last record being in November 1927.

In an obituary notice of A. Wachsmann published in the *Avicultural Magazine*[65] I quoted from his letters to me as follows: "A friend and I recently undertook a search of a district near the Queensland–New South Wales border, where the birds have been seen at intervals along the river banks, which are very steep and in which the birds nest. We had a couple of aboriginal drovers with us, and they assured us they knew the birds but we were unable to locate any in a stay of five days. An old resident of the district mentioned that he could recollect them well, and had searched their nests in anthills; he was of the impression that they nested more frequently in river banks which are only accessible by ropes. They bred in September." On another occasion, speaking of a friend, Mr Wachsmann wrote: "Three years ago he discovered a pair in central Queensland; they had nested in an anthill; one of the station hands caught the cock bird when it entered the burrow and placed it among other parrots in an aviary. When my friend arrived he was handed the dead bird; it was hard luck after locating them and watching them for months. He seems very sanguine of getting on to them again."

A. C. Hunt, of Charters Towers, Queensland, lived most of his life in the Inverell district. He is a nephew of the Mrs Gordon Woods quoted above in Cayley's extracts from Miss Irby's letter. Despite a life-long interest in birds, and in parrots in particular, he has never seen what he has thought to be this species, although he has had a number of reports of their continued presence in and around the district. In May 1965 he and his son accompanied me and my elder son on an all too brief trip to the Burnett district in the footsteps of Chisholm. We were able to locate two elderly Jerrard brothers and learnt from one of them that Cyril, the ornithologist, had been drowned in December 1943; they themselves knew little about birds and could not recall Cyril's having seen the species for long after Chisholm's visit. Ernest Jerrard was, however, able to locate the spot where his brother had photographed his pair at their nesting mound, and we spent some time walking through this wooded, undulating area, well dotted with termitaria, but to no avail.

Ernest also told us that the Cayley painting of a pair of Paradise Parrots, which Chisholm had sent to Cyril, was still hanging in the old homestead, and we were able to see this through a window; it was disappointing in that the birds were depicted in the plump shape of Red-rumped Parrots, although the colouring was accurate.

Our only other promising contact in the district put us onto a hillbilly type family living in a ramshackle house, surrounded by small bird cages. However, one member of the family knew the little "Ground Rosella" of the district for they had kept one in a cage, until it escaped, some fourteen or so years previously. It had been caught by an uncle who was currently blind and an inmate of the local hospital; we visited "uncle" that evening and found him pathetically anxious to give us all details he could recall of the little "Ground Rosellas" he used to know in some numbers. He remembered them in pairs nesting in stumps, and in small parties in bloodwood country, feeding on the ground and only flying low when disturbed. We visited areas suggested by him on the following day without result.

The latest episode in my story of this *rara avis* relates to a colour slide shown to me a few years ago of an obvious male Paradise Parrot; although taken without a telephoto lens, it is quite unmistakable. The owner of the slide steadfastly refuses, probably wisely, to disclose the source of the photograph but it would appear to be convincing evidence that the species is not extinct.

Cayley's final note reads as follows: "Frequents sparsely timbered grasslands, where it is usually in pairs or small flocks, presumably family parties, and is believed to be local in habits. Generally observed feeding on the ground, and when disturbed flies to a nearby tree. Food of the species consists of the seeds of grasses and other plants.

"The nesting-place is a hollowed-out chamber in a termites' mound on the ground, entered through a narrow tunnel. Also said to breed in hollows in trees, and to tunnel into the banks of rivers after the fashion of kingfishers.

"Clutch: three to five eggs; white, and rounded-oval in form; shell close-grained, smooth and slightly lustrous. Breeding-season: usually August to December, but as late as March or April."

Aviary Notes

Cayley wrote: "It is very many years since this beautiful parrakeet has been kept in captivity either in Australia or overseas.

"A. H. Chisholm, in his *Emu* article, writes: 'In regard to the behaviour of the species in captivity, the following interesting instance is given by Mr J. O'Neill Brenan, an experienced Brisbane naturalist. "Prior to the year 1880 a few were regularly caught by a bird-catcher and dealer then living in Brisbane; and in January of that year his catch included three or four young 'Beautifuls'. They were not nestlings, but had not been long upon the wing, that fact being apparent from the colour of their beaks, which were light yellow or cream coloured. I bought one, a young cock; he learned to whistle the usual 'Pretty Joey', and at times made attempts to imitate the song of a Canary. He had, however, been trapped a little too late to make a good artificial whistler, and invariably broke into his native bright little call. Although quite friendly, always greeting me merrily when I approached his cage, he would never submit to the slightest handling, and would often attack the hand of a person attending to his food and water tins. He was a very hardy bird, did well on canary-seed, was fond of bird's-eye chili and milk thistles, and enjoyed perfect health from the day I bought him until nearly thirteen years afterwards, when a wind storm blew his cage down. The fall injured him internally, and he died the next day." ' "

The experiences of the Reverend F. G. Dutton in regard to this species are worthy of repetition. He writes in Greene's *Parrots in Captivity*:[53] "*P. pulcherrimus*, the Paradise Paroquet, as dealers call it, is not only the most beautiful *Psephotus*, as its name says, but surely the most beautiful Paroquet that exists. The vivid emerald green and brilliant carmine of the cock, beautifully contrasted with the grey of the rest of the plumage, make him 'a joy for ever'. But 'handsome is as handsome does', and I regret I cannot give any of those I have kept a good character as a cage bird. They are very shy, and the cock is much given to driving about the hen. They do not appear to have been bred in captivity, but I do not think it impossible that they should do so. A pair I had were most anxious to burrow into the wall of a room in which they were. Had they done so, they would have got into a loft and escaped, so they were caged and sent to the Zoological Gardens. I regretted afterwards that a box covered with tin was not fastened on the other side of the wall into which they wanted to burrow; I think they might then have bred." As Tavistock[3] remarked, "To-day any aviculturist who was lucky enough to own a pair in breeding condition would gladly sacrifice every wall in his house if a nest of young were likely to be reared!"

48 Golden-shouldered Parrot

Psephotus (Psephotellus) chrysopterygius (Gould)

PLATE XI

Synonyms

Golden-winged Parrot, Antbed Parrot.

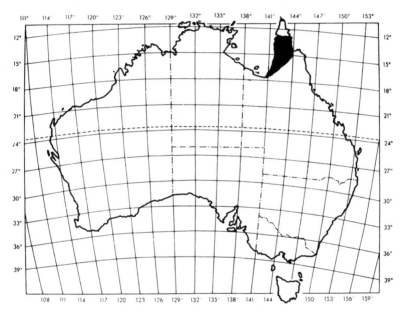

Distribution

Available records suggest that the 1926 R.A.O.U. Checklist was reasonably accurate in stating the range of this species as North Queensland from Normanton to the Watson River; there may well be seasonal movements within Cape York Peninsula. It seems unlikely that it occurs north of 12 degrees or, on the eastern side, south of about 15 degrees.

Description

SIZE. About 10 inches (254 mm).

ADULT MALE. Forehead, lores, and feathers below eyes pale yellow, slightly tinged with green; crown of head and nape black; back, scapulars and lesser upper wing-coverts greyish-brown; rump and upper tail-coverts turquoise-blue; mesial lesser and median upper wing-coverts golden-yellow; bastard wing blackish-brown tinged with blue on outer webs; outer greater wing-coverts, primary coverts and primaries black with bluish outer margins, paler towards tips of latter; inner greater coverts and innermost secondaries greyish-brown with lighter margins; central tail-feathers dull bronze-green shading to black at tips, remainder blue on basal portion shading to white at tips; sides of hinder crown, sides of neck, cheeks, and throat turquoise-green shading to turquoise-blue; foreneck, breast and sides of body turquoise-blue; abdomen and under tail-coverts scarlet, the feathers having white bases and white margins; bill pale bluish-grey; legs and feet fleshy-grey; eyes brown.

ADULT FEMALE. Forehead pale buffish-yellow; crown of head dull bronze-green; hind-neck, back, scapulars and wings dull yellowish-olive; rump and upper tail-coverts pale turquoise-blue; central tail-feathers dull bronze-green shading to bluish-black at tips, the remainder bluish-green at basal portion shading to white at tips; bastard wing, outer greater wing-coverts, primary coverts and primaries greyish-brown with bluish margins on outer webs; sides of hinder-crown and inner cheeks greyish-green with dusky tips to the feathers; outer cheeks, sides of neck, throat and upper breast dull grass-green, shading to pale turquoise-blue on lower breast and sides of body; abdomen, flanks and under tail-coverts greyish-green, with some pale red feathers on centre of lower abdomen.

IMMATURE. Resembles the female; the young male can be distinguished by the blue cheek-patches which are absent in females of all ages, and by the darker colour of the crown of the head; in addition, the young male usually shows some pinkish-red feathers on the abdomen. Adult male plumage is obtained by a slow moult which is not usually completed until the bird is a little over twelve months old.

Geographical Variations

None recognized.

Field Notes

Cayley had not seen this species in the field but he quoted Thomson's notes[19] as follows: "Known locally as the 'Ant-bed Parrot' on account of its habit of nesting in ant-beds. It is an exquisite little parrot, and one of the most beautiful of the group. The Golden-shouldered Parrot is local, but by no means rare in suitable country on Cape York Peninsula, at about the 14th parallel of latitude. In 1928, during a journey of about one thousand miles on the Peninsula with a team of pack horses, we noted only one pair of these birds, and one old nest, on the Edward River. In the following year, a number of birds were seen, and specimens of the birds and their eggs were secured.

"The Golden-shouldered Parrot inhabits open forest country in the vicinity of extensive flats, where large ant-beds are numerous. To the south and west of Port Stewart, it is by no means uncommon, but its range does not appear to extend north of the Watson River, where it was noted by McLennan in 1922. During June 1929, I examined between twenty and thirty nests, some of which were in use that year. Frequently two broods are reared in a season. The first clutch of eggs is usually laid in May, and the young hatched towards the end of May, or early in the following month, the second brood being reared in July or August. The nesting-site is an ant-bed or termitarium, either 'spire-shaped', i.e. circular in cross-section, and rising to a sharp point, or 'meridian', a larger type with angular sides generally facing north and south. Into this the birds drill a tunnel, terminating in the nesting-chamber, on the floor of which the eggs are laid. . . . As with most parrots, no nesting material whatever is added. Six forms the clutch. In all the nests that had contained young birds, lepidopterous pupae, in cocoons aggregated in masses resembling honeycomb, were noted; these were the pupae of the scavenging caterpillars (*Neossiosynoeca scatophaga*) which live commensally with the young of the Golden-shouldered Parrakeet, devouring their faeces. The existence of these remarkable larvae was first recorded by McLennan in 1922."

E. R. McKechnie, of Cudlee Creek, South Australia, sent me the following interesting notes: "In the course of a visit to central Cape York Peninsula in May 1963 much information was obtained in regard to this species. It appears that these birds start to nest in March or April, quite soon after the end of the wet season. Apart from the suitability of food at that time, it is thought that the work involved in excavating the nesting chamber may be much easier when the ant beds are still damp after the heavy rains.

"It was noted that the birds prefer to nest in anthills actually standing in shallow water; of course, this state of affairs only persists for a few months after the end of the wet, in suitable flats. In every case where nests were found on land that had already dried out, the contents had been destroyed either by black ants which had installed themselves around the base of the nest or by a small monitor lizard which was occupying the nest cavity.

"It was observed that spire shaped anthills were invariably preferred to the magnetic type, probably because they were easier to excavate. The height of the nesting chamber varied from eighteen inches to twelve feet above ground level, usually about three feet; this seemed to depend on the height of the mound chosen, it being necessary to choose a height which would allow the excavation of a cavity about eight inches in depth; the entrance hole being quite short and the cavity extending almost the full diameter of the mound. Over a stay of about four weeks, about fifty nests were discovered, some containing eggs and others young in all stages of growth; in addition, some adult pairs were seen with clutches of newly fledged young. The average clutch appeared to be four.

"The birds seemed to hold quite large territories as seldom were nests found closer together than 150 yards although there was always an abundance of suitable antbeds. In every nest containing young birds, the presence of caterpillars was observed, confirming Thomson's observations in this regard.

"Local information suggested that the birds leave the area soon after the young have fledged and do not return until the next nesting season."

Mrs W. Eastman, who with her husband spent a considerable time in northern Australia, wrote to me as follows: "There are *Psephotellus* as far north as 12° on Cape York Peninsula. As with the Hoodeds, the Golden-shouldered are inland near nesting mounds before, during and for a very short time after nesting. Then they seem to move out in family groups towards the coast for the dry season."

Aviary Notes

Cayley wrote: "With the exception of the four living examples presented to the trustees of Taronga Park, I have no record of this species ever having been kept in captivity in Australia. These particular birds (which I had many opportunities of observing and sketching) were extremely tame, often alighting on my arms or shoulders. In habits they resembled the Hooded Parrakeet and, I understand, were fed with the mixture of seeds usually given to that species.

"On several occasions I noticed the birds investigating holes in the ground underneath the concrete foundation of the shelter shed built within the large wire-netting flight of their aviary. In this aviary was a mixed collection of birds. The parrakeets occupied a hollow log hung there, but made no attempts to breed. Unfortunately during a recent severe storm the last remaining bird, a female, died."

My personal experiences of this rare and lovely species are all comparatively recent and mainly relate to my original pair of birds, possibly brother and sister, which the late Sir Edward Hallstrom generously presented to me in August 1959; at that time the cock bird was about half-coloured and he attained full plumage in November of that year when presumably about a year old.

The first year's experience was disappointing in that four eggs were laid in mid-September and three young seen on 12th October but these were all dead about a week later.

In 1961 a clutch of five was laid at the end of August and early in September; three young had hatched on 23rd September and the remaining two the following day. These birds all flourished and left the nest between 25th and 27th October; my inexperience at that time caused me to speculate greatly as to their sexes but they ultimately proved to be all cocks and had become fully coloured by November of the following year.

In 1962 the clutch consisted of four eggs, of which three were fertile, but for some unexplained reason only one hatched. This bird was reared and proved to be another cock.

In 1963 the clutch consisted of six eggs, five of which had hatched by 13th September. Of this brood, four survived and left the nest between 17th and 19th October; it was immediately obvious that they were three hens and one cock, being easily recognizable on leaving the nest, unlike their nearest relative, the Hooded.

For the next two seasons the fertility was disappointing in that only two eggs hatched each time from clutches of four and six; both birds hatched in each of these clutches proved to be one of each sex and in each case both birds were reared.

In the late winter of 1966 I moved my birds to my new home in the Mount Lofty Ranges and I did not encourage them to go to nest quite as early; however, the result was disturbing for although three hatched from four fertile eggs in a clutch of six, none survived. This caused me to wonder whether the colder climate was likely to prove unsuitable for this tropical species. However, in 1967 a further pair were successfully reared, leaving the nest early in December, and in 1968 I decided to permit the birds to nest in the milder autumn weather; the result was not encouraging for only a single cock bird was reared. In the late spring, however, four were hatched and although one bird inexplicably died a few days before it should have fledged, the other three (one cock and two hens) were satisfactorily reared.

For the year 1969 I tried another autumn nest, but all the eggs were clear; however, three hatched from a spring clutch of six and were reared, proving to be two cocks and one hen.

49 Hooded Parrot

Psephotus (Psephotellus) dissimilis Collett

PLATE XI

Synonyms

Black-hooded Parrot, Golden-shouldered Parrot (erroneously).

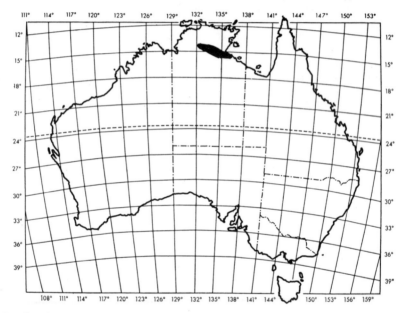

Distribution

The few records available suggest that this species has a very limited range in the Northern Territory; nearly all records are from the vicinity of Pine Creek and Katherine but there are specimens taken at Borroloola on the McArthur River, suggesting that there may be a more or less continuous distribution between the two areas. The R.A.O.U. field outing in July 1967 observed the species at the Elsey turnoff, the southernmost record; however, M. McGarvie states that he saw a pair at Warlock Ponds, a few miles farther south.

Description

SIZE. About 11 inches (279 mm).

ADULT MALE. Forehead, lores, crown of head and fore-part of cheeks black; back, scapulars and innermost secondaries dark greyish-brown; upper wing-coverts rich yellow; bastard wing, primary coverts, primary and secondary quills blackish-brown; the primaries have paler tips and are edged with green on the outer webs; rump and upper tail-coverts turquoise-blue; central tail-feathers bronze-green becoming blackish at tips, outer feathers bluish-green shading to white at tips and crossed at basal portion with a black band, with dark brown fringes on inner webs; hinder face, sides of neck, throat, breast, abdomen, sides of body, and under wing-coverts turquoise-blue; under tail-coverts salmon-red, feathers margined with white; bill greyish-white; legs and feet mealy-brown; eyes dark brown.

ADULT FEMALE. General colour above and below yellowish olive-green with a pale bluish tinge on cheeks, lower breast, abdomen and rump; central tail-feathers bronze-green becoming blackish at tips; the remainder greenish-blue broadly tipped with white; under tail-coverts pale salmon-red.

IMMATURE. Resembles the adult female; young males can sometimes be sexed by their possession of slightly brighter blue cheeks than those of their nest mates. Adult male plumage is acquired by a slow moult which is not usually completed until the bird is about eighteen months old; the period seems to vary according to whether the bird was hatched in the autumn or in the spring.

Geographical Variations
None recognized.

Field Notes
Cayley, who had not seen this species in the field, wrote: "This beautiful parrakeet is more often called the Golden-shouldered, a mistake quite easily understood owing to the confusion that existed for many years with it and the previous species. This is the lovelier, and by far the better known. Small consignments of live birds regularly reach Sydney from Darwin, and it is to be found in most public and private collections.

"Generally in pairs or small flocks, inhabiting the open forestlands and spinifex country, where it is usually observed feeding on the ground on the seeds of grasses and other plants. When disturbed, it flies to a nearby tree. Its flight is swift and slightly undulating.

"This species is another 'Ant-hill Parrot' and breeds in termites' mounds, usually in the large, magnetic, spire-shaped termitaria. The birds excavate a tunnel, the end of which they enlarge into a nesting-chamber. It would be of great scientific value to know whether the same lepidopterous scavenger (or another species of its genus) found in the breeding-places of *P. chrysopterygius* also lives commensally with this species.

"Clutch: two to six eggs; white, and rounded-oval in form; shell close-grained, smooth, and slightly glossy. Breeding-season: not recorded; but probably May to January.

"In *Australian Cage Birds* of 9 January 1937, R. Perez, a well-known bird-trapper writes: 'The Golden-shoulder is a very early arrival at the waterhole, generally to be seen in pairs or small numbers. They always perch a fair distance from the waterhole, say, 300 or 400 yards away, in the highest trees, and will not come down to drink until a fair number of other birds are at the waterhole drinking. When they arrive in the trees, they alight on the highest branches and seem to work their way down to the lower branches; then, if they see the waterhole has been interfered with, they become very suspicious and will wait in the trees for an hour or more to satisfy themselves there is no one about before they will come down to drink. On some occasions they will not come down at all, but fly off for miles in search of another waterhole. Of course, this does not always happen. Sometimes, when they come down for a drink, they seem to just touch the ground with their feet and, without drinking, fly back to the trees, wait a few minutes, then return to the ground—and fly back again without drinking. This performance might happen four or five times before finally drinking. . . .

" 'These birds only appear at the waterhole once each day, and feed early in the morning and late afternoon; but, should they decide to feed during the day, they always do so in the shade of some trees. They feed on grass-seeds and also insects.

" 'Their nests are built in white-ant beds. The beds are from four to twelve feet high and from eighteen inches to ten feet in diameter. Ant beds are very numerous. The birds will burrow into the ant beds to a depth of about a foot and about three-quarter way from the bottom of the bed. The entrance is just large enough for the bird to enter, but the nest itself is about six inches in diameter. They lay their eggs on the dirt of the ant bed. The eggs number from one to five, but you will find the majority of nests contain two eggs.' "

In the course of a visit to the Northern Territory in July and August 1964 my companions and I were disappointed not to see this bird. Again on the R.A.O.U. field outing in July 1967 we failed to find the species until the eleventh hour when, late in the afternoon, we were returning from the Elsey Station area and the bus pulled up at the railway crossing before reaching the Stuart Highway. As it did so, three slim parrots flew up and perched on the telephone wires, allowing the party to spill out of the bus and have a good look at what proved to be a female and two subadult males; a little later another female, possibly the same bird, was seen.

Most members of the July-August 1969 ornithological tour were rewarded by the sight of at least one of the two adult pairs of this species located in the vicinity of the Edith River.

Mrs W. Eastman sent me the following interesting notes regarding this species: "The Hooded Parrots are inland near nesting mounds before and for a very short time after nesting; then they seem to move out in family groups towards the coast for the dry season. With the exception of the use of the termite mounds I found these parrots to be very much like the Red-rumped in its habits; it follows the roads and tracks and feeds on the tender grass and seeds exposed there. Shortly after sunrise every morning the same group of parrots goes to the nearest water in their area and have a bath in a very shallow spot—several of them at a time—while the rest of the family watch from a preening tree; they use the same bathing spot and the same perch each day. The area was south-west of Florina on the Katherine River.

"My feeling is that the relative scarcity of this bird is due to food. The cane grass becomes very dry and tall, hard with no seed head during the dry season and so much of the area is constantly burned and then no vegetation grows at all until the wet season and this parrot does not seem to like really damp areas.

"When we went north to Darwin, we saw about thirty on telegraph wires near Pine Creek; this was at about the end of the nesting season. Two weeks later there were no birds to be found in nesting mounds or in the vicinity of Pine Creek, though we searched the area for a couple of days.

"We talked to an old trapper in Darwin and he told us he used to trap them some twenty-five miles south-east of Katherine; they used to come in small groups to a lagoon. An old miner told us he knew them east of Ferguson River in small parties."

Aviary Notes

Cayley wrote briefly: "A lovely inmate of an aviary, but quite unsuited to cage life. The species is a general favourite with Australian aviarists, and has been successfully bred and reared in captivity on numerous occasions both here and abroad."

A hardy and most attractive aviary bird and one which has proved a relatively free breeder in captivity, this species is, however, quite unsuited to a mixed collection on account of its pugnacity.

I obtained my first pair of these birds in October 1935, the male being almost fully coloured when procured. They first went to nest late in March 1936, laying three eggs, all of which hatched and were reared, the young leaving the nest between 20th and 24th May and all three being cocks. At the end of July the hen commenced a second clutch, which on this occasion consisted of five fertile eggs, all of which hatched but only three of the young were reared. These three left the nest at the end of September, the youngest having deformed feet which necessitated its being destroyed.

The old pair of birds started to moult early in October, and in the following year, 1937, the first clutch consisted of four eggs laid towards the end of March. Three of these were fertile and the chicks were duly hatched and reared, leaving the nest in the middle of May. A second clutch of four was laid about a month later and were inexplicably deserted early in July; they were all fertile and were on the point of hatching. Of a third clutch of four laid in August, only two were fertile but these young were duly reared and left the nest early in October. The hen, who was not young when obtained, died in November while in the moult.

For the 1938 season the original cock bird was mated to an unrelated hen and for a period of eight years thereafter they had a remarkably consistent record of success. They started slowly with two young reared in September 1938, followed by three young each in April and August 1939. For the next four years the tallies were six, five, six, and four young successfully reared; on some occasions three clutches were laid in a season but two was the usual and in 1943 the only clutch was not laid until the late winter. In 1944 the first clutch was laid late in July but the eggs were deserted when the hen sustained an injured foot, only two of the five being fertile. A second clutch, consisting of four, laid early in September, resulted in a single bird leaving the nest on 1st November.

In 1945 the first clutch did not appear until mid-August; only three out of five were fertile but these were successfully hatched and reared. A second clutch of six was laid late in October, but the hen deserted when the ring on her leg caused a constriction which ultimately resulted in the loss of her foot. She laid two clutches of five eggs each late in 1946, but all were infertile and I did not try to breed from her again.

For the 1947 and 1948 seasons I had one of the 1945 cocks mated to an unrelated hen, but they showed very little inclination to go to nest in either year although they had produced eggs in 1946.

No results were obtained during the next four years, although three different pairs were tried.

NEOPHEMA Salvadori
Grass Parrots

This genus comprises the birds widely known as the Grass Parrots and contains, like the genus *Psephotus*, seven very distinct species which are readily separable into three groups, on each of which Mathews[23] conferred generic rank but which the 1926 R.A.O.U. Checklist considered merely subgenera.

The true *Neophema* contains two closely related forms, the Turquoise in the east and the Scarlet-chested in the west. Early reports of one intruding into the territory of the other have been shown to be fallacious—they probably resulted from the similarity between the females of the two species.

The subgenus *Neonanodes* comprises four closely related species which can be divided into two pairs of which one species is predominantly eastern and the other western. The first pair, the Blue-winged of the east and of Tasmania and the Elegant of the west, overlap to a considerable extent in South Australia and to a lesser degree also in western Victoria and western New South Wales and both range widely into the interior. The second pair, the Orange-bellied of the east and of Tasmania and the Rock of South and Western Australia overlap to a very limited extent in South Australia and both are almost entirely coastal in their distribution.

The last species, the Bourke, almost certainly warrants a genus of its own—namely, *Neopsephotus*—for although superficially similar, it is totally different in basic coloration and is a bird confined to the dry interior of the continent.

None of the members of this genus ever indulge in mutual preening. The display is very similar in all species, and consists of the male alighting near the female, drawing himself up to appear tall and simultaneously fanning the tail and spreading his wings slightly to display the blue margins, the characteristic call-note of each species being given at the same time.

The courtship feeding, feeding of the incubating hen and of the chicks, period of incubation and time of fledging are identical with those of the other members of the broadtailed group. The chicks have the characteristic white down and leave the nest with bright yellow beaks which rapidly assume the dark colour of the adults.

The wing-stripe is extremely variable in this genus. In the Bourke (*Neopsephotus*) it is almost always absent or slight in immature males and well marked in immature females and the same applies to adults. In the subgenus *Neonanodes* the wing-stripe is very inconsistent in immatures; if it is present to any extent the bird is almost certainly a female. In adults, it is almost invariably absent in males and only retained, often to a very slight extent, in mature females. In the true *Neophema* the wing-stripe is nearly always present and well marked in immatures of both sexes of the Turquoise, *pulchella,* but is invariably lost in adult males and nearly always retained to some extent in adult females. In the Scarlet-chested, *splendida,* the wing-stripe is extremely variable in immatures; if exhibited, the bird is a certain female. In adult males it is invariably absent and is quite inconstant in adult females, usually being either well marked or completely absent.

All members of the genus bathe in pools or water containers with the notable exception of the Bourke, which enjoys a shower of rain or wet grass.

Being entirely ground feeders and predominantly seed eaters, the members of the genus do not use the feet for holding food; they will, however, hold the stalk of a seeding grass down with the foot in order to get at the head.

Head-scratching is performed behind the wing.

The flight of the "green" Neophemas is strong, swift and somewhat erratic; they often rise to considerable heights when flushed. *Neophema pulchella* and *N. splendida* are said to have a more fluttering effect over short distances. Immelmann[66] has suggested that the silhouette is not unlike that of some of the small Sandpipers. The flight of the Bourke Parrot is different, being swift and much more direct and is accompanied by a quite characteristic whistling or whirring noise, rather reminiscent of the Crested Pigeon (*Ocyphaps lophotes*).

50 Bourke Parrot

Neophema (Neopsephotus) bourkii (Gould)

PLATE XII

Synonyms

Pink-bellied Parrakeet, Blue-vented Parrakeet, Sundown Parrot, Night Parrot (erroneously).

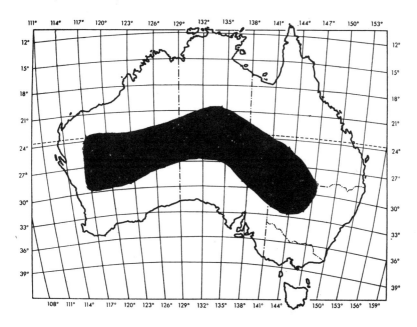

Distribution

The only records of this species for Queensland are of a flock at Dirranbandi and those of Forshaw[5] for Windorah, Adavale and Cunnamulla in the south-west of the State.

Recent New South Wales records are from the Barrier Range in the Broken Hill district, and from the vicinity of Ivanhoe; McGill[67] believes that the species is not uncommon in the north-west of the State. However, Forshaw[5] has extended the range greatly to the eastward by a personal sighting at the Bogan River west of Peak Hill and a report of an observation near Narrandera.

In Western Australia, Ford[68] has shown that the species is widespread and common throughout the pastoral district of the mid-west—that is, between the mulga-spinifex line in the north and the mulga-eucalypt line in the south, and extending as far west as the upper reaches of the Ashburton, Gascoyne and Murchison rivers and south to Morawa. The range possibly extends in continuity into South Australia, where it occurs between Lake Eyre and the northern border of the State and westward to the Everard and Musgrave ranges and into Central Australia, where it has been recorded from Finke, Ernabella, Palm Valley and the vicinity of Alice Springs. Members of the R.A.O.U. field outing of July 1967 observed it as far north as the Devil's Marbles on the Stuart Highway.

Description

SIZE. About 9 inches (229 mm).

ADULT MALE. General colour above greyish-brown, darker on centre of rump and upper tail-coverts; head and hind-neck tinged with salmon-red; primaries, secondaries and primary coverts brown washed with blue on their outer webs; edge of wing and lesser upper wing-coverts blue; remainder of wing-coverts brown margined with yellowish-white; outer webs of inner secondaries yellowish-white; central tail-feathers blackish-brown tinged with blue on their outer webs; remainder tipped with white, except the outermost feather on each side which is wholly white except at the base; lores, space round eyes and forepart of cheeks white; forehead and frontal band blue; hinder cheeks, sides of neck, throat, chest and breast pale salmon-red with narrow brownish margins to the feathers; abdomen salmon-red; flanks, under tail-coverts, sides of rump and outer series of upper tail-coverts turquoise-blue; bill dark horn; legs and feet brown; eyes brown.

ADULT FEMALE. Resembles the male but duller and slightly smaller; cheeks and throat ashy-white, the feathers margined with brown and the breast feathers have narrower margins of pink, resulting in a somewhat scaly appearance; the blue frontal band is almost invariably absent; the head and bill are also smaller.

IMMATURE. Resembles the female but exhibits less pink on the abdomen; the sexes can usually be determined by the larger, flatter heads of males and the very restricted area of pink on the females. Adult plumage is acquired at the first moult of body feathers, which usually occurs about three or four months after the young bird has left the nest.

Geographical Variations

None recognized.

Field Notes

Cayley wrote: "The charming little Bourke Parrakeet (also called the Pink-bellied or Blue-vented Parrot or Parrakeet) is indeed now very rare in those inland areas of New South Wales and the adjoining parts of South Australia where it was once so plentiful. During the past few years, however, it has been found in great numbers in Central Australia near Alice Springs, where the birds are being trapped, with and without permits, indiscriminately. If the present wholesale trafficking continues, it will not be long before this lovely parrakeet will be completely wiped out of existence."

Once again, Cayley's pessimism has fortunately proved incorrect and his remarks make interesting reading some twenty-five or so years later when compared with the authoritative article published by Ford[68] in the *Emu*: as mentioned above, Ford shows that the species is plentiful throughout its entire range in the pastoral district of mid-western Australia. A summary of his paper is as follows:

1 In mid-Western Australia the Bourke Parrot is going through a phase of comparative abundance.

2 The phase can be correlated with a widespread diminution in the sheep population since 1936. Additional data are necessary to establish whether this correlation is real or coincidental.

3 It is suggested that the species exhibits a peculiar type of nomadism which is probably similar in some respects to that of the Flock Pigeon (*Histriophaps histrionica*).

4 This nomadism may account for the paucity of records from Central Australia and the abundance of records from the west.

5 The availability of surface water undoubtedly governs its distribution to some extent.

6 The mulga vegetation is the parrot's chief habitat.

Cayley quoted Macgillivray in regard to nesting habits as follows: "They nest in a hollow in a scrub tree, at from three to ten feet from the ground, and rarely in a box-tree at the edge of scrub. The eggs, from four to five in number, are deposited on the decayed woody material at the bottom of the hollow. The eggs are laid on successive days and incubation starts with the first egg laid, the female alone attending to the task. The male feeds the female during courtship and whilst she is incubating, by regurgitation. She usually sits very closely, leaving the nest but once a day and only for a short period."

In August 1964 one of my companions and I attempted to reach a dam about ten miles north of Alice Springs where this species was reputed to water at first light; however we did not reach the spot until it was comparatively light, and although numerous other parrots were coming in to drink there was no sign of any Bourkes; we were almost certainly too late. However, members of the R.A.O.U. field outing of July 1967 were more fortunate, for small numbers were seen drinking at a dam about sixteen miles north of Alice Springs, others were observed crossing in front of the bus between Barrow Creek and Wauchope, and a few birds were seen as far north as the Devil's Marbles. In August

1968 we found the birds drinking again at the same dam as the previous year, and we also encountered a small party on the Hermannsburg road; they were said to be very numerous in the region of Alice Springs that season, which was a very good one. According to S. A. Parker, by July to August 1969 the birds appeared to have moved away from the district, and that year's ornithological tour failed to locate the species.

In view of the habitat preference of this species it seems unfortunate that the name Mulga Parrot was not applied to this bird instead of to the Many-coloured Parrot.

Aviary Notes

Cayley wrote: "Quite a common aviary bird in Australia, and is bred extensively. It prefers a hollow log, but will also nest in boxes, and usually will rear two or more broods in a season. Food suggested: a mixture of canary-seed, millet, and oats.

"Dr. Macgillivray states: 'These birds are easily bred in captivity, but each pair should be kept by themselves, and the fledged young should be separated as soon as the female shows signs of nesting again, as the male is apt to persecute the young birds and cause them serious injury. One pair that I have in an aviary reared five broods in the one season, extending from August until the middle of March.

" 'When first hatched the young are covered with smoky-grey down. In fourteen days' time the primaries and rectrices are showing well, the feathers sprouting on all other tracts. Ten days later they are fully feathered and peeping out of the nesting-hole. Three days after this the earlier ones leave the hollow, one perhaps returning towards dark. Two or three days later all the clutch will be out. They are fed by the parent birds for a week or ten days after leaving the nest, and then have to fend for themselves.' "

Although I kept Bourkes for a good many years, they have not proved quite as reliable breeders in my hands as they have with many other aviculturists, as the following account of my experiences will show. My first pair were obtained late in 1935, and the following season they had two nests, rearing five young in October and two more, as well as two Splendids, in January. In 1937 three young were hatched from a clutch of five laid late in September, but two of these died when half-grown, and the sole survivor left the nest late in November. The hen then proceeded to lay ten eggs without making any attempt to incubate them, and when these were removed a further five eggs were laid and incubated. Only one of this clutch proved fertile, and the young bird was reared, leaving the nest in mid-February. However, 1938 was another good season, five young being reared in October and a further four in December.

Before the 1939 breeding season the old hen was mated to one of her two-year-old sons. She laid a clutch of seven in mid-September, all of which proved fertile and hatched, and although one chick died quite soon the remaining six were reared, leaving the nest in October and early in November. The hen thereupon resorted to her bad habits of 1937, and laid eleven eggs without incubating. After these were removed she laid a further nine, and although five of these were fertile only two chicks hatched, and these died in mid-January 1940, when about two weeks old. For the next four seasons (1940-43), during my absence on service, the same pair of birds invariably had two nests each year, but never succeeded in rearing more than three young in any one nest, and frequently only managed two.

In 1944 an early clutch of seven eggs was laid in August, but only one of these was fertile, and the young bird died soon after hatching. Of a second clutch of seven again only one was hatched, and this bird survived but a fortnight. At this stage, owing to urgent need for accommodation, the Bourkes were put in an aviary with a pair of Superbs, whose large log they promptly appropriated. They laid five eggs and hatched four young, two of which died when nearly fledged; the two survivors left the nest in mid-January.

After a good start in 1945, four young being reared from the first clutch of five eggs laid late in August, the hen had one of her old lapses and laid no less than fourteen eggs! A third clutch of four was laid in mid-December, but only one was fertile; however, the young bird was duly reared. In 1946 four were hatched from the first clutch of six, but all four died quite soon. Of the second clutch of six, five were fertile, and four hatched and were reared almost to the point of leaving the nest. At this stage the parents unaccountably ceased feeding, and although three young birds left the nest only one managed to survive and the fourth was found dead in the nest. Out of a third clutch of eight only three were fertile, and these young birds were deserted when a week old.

The years 1947 and 1948 were blank as far as the breeding of this species was concerned, although one bird was reared by foster-parents (Turquoisines) in the latter year. For the 1949 breeding season one pair of birds hatched all of the first clutch of five eggs, and reared four of them in mid-November. A second clutch of five were all hatched, but the young birds were deserted early in January. A second hen had two clutches of five infertile eggs and then, when given a new mate, laid and hatched all of a further clutch of five and succeeded in rearing three of the young late in December.

In 1950 the first pair was the old cock with a new mate. They hatched and reared four young in the first clutch, but only reared three out of five hatched in the second try. A second pair reared only three out of six hatched in their first attempt, then laid eleven eggs without incubating, and finally reared only two young birds of six hatched at the third try. In 1951 the first pair only brought off two out of five hatched the first time, but reared all four young that hatched in the second attempt. The second pair laid ten eggs, of which I left them seven, all of which they hatched and five of which they reared. The hen

T

then laid a further ten eggs, of which I left her six, all of which hatched, but only three young survived.

In 1952 the results were not as good. The first pair started by hatching five and letting them all die, and followed with two hatched and reared. The other pair also let die all five that they hatched in the first nest, but reared four from eight young hatched at the second attempt.

51 Orange-bellied Parrot

Neophema (Neonanodes) chrysogaster (Latham)

PLATE XII

Synonym

Orange-breasted Parrot.

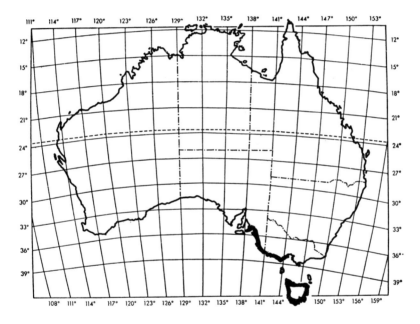

Distribution

This species occurs in South Australia from the Outer Harbour area (with one record from the opposite side of Gulf St Vincent) south and east along the coast, and in coastal Victoria from the South Australian border to the western shores of Port Phillip Bay.

In Tasmania it has been widely but sporadically reported, mostly along the northern and western coasts, and for King Island M. McGarvie reports that the birds appear each year, arriving late in March and all departing by the end of July.

The records from New South Wales appear to relate to an isolated population in the vicinity of Sydney about the turn of the century; A. R.

McGill thinks it unlikely that the species will ever be recorded again in New South Wales.

Description

SIZE. About 8½ inches (216 mm).

ADULT MALE. General colour above, including upper part of head, sides of neck, most of the inner upper lesser and median wing-coverts and the inner secondaries grass-green; outer lesser upper wing-coverts, bastard wing, primary coverts, outer greater coverts and outer aspect of primary and secondary quills ultramarine-blue becoming paler on outer margins of primaries towards tips, the remaining portion of quills blackish-brown; central tail-feathers green, bluish towards tips; remainder greenish-blue on outer webs, blackish-brown on inner webs and broadly tipped with yellow, which increases in extent towards the outermost feather on each side; across the forehead a blue band margined with a narrower line of pale greenish-blue; lores yellowish-green; throat, chest and flanks grass-green, passing into yellowish-green on the abdomen, which has a rich orange patch in the centre; under tail-coverts yellow; under wing-coverts and edge of wing deep blue; bill bluish-horn; legs and feet mealy-grey; eyes hazel.

ADULT FEMALE. Similar to the male but of an appreciably duller shade of green; the frontal band is considerably less obvious and appears to be single. There is a large orange abdominal patch, which is only slightly duller than that of the male.

IMMATURE. Duller than the adult female, but still of a considerably brighter shade of green than their near allies; frontal band only faintly indicated, and orange belly-patch smaller than in the adult. Adult plumage does not appear to be acquired until late spring, probably eight to nine months after leaving the nest; prior to this they are extremely difficult to sex.

Geographical Variations

None recognized.

Field Notes

Cayley had never seen this species in the wild state, nor for that matter in captivity, until just before he wrote as follows: "The Orange-breasted Parrakeet (more commonly called Orange-bellied Grass-parrot) is extremely rare, both on the mainland and in Tasmania. From the evidence available it appears to be more nomadic than migratory in its habits, as its occurrences both in Tasmania and on the mainland, during the past ten years, are in the nature of irregular visitations.

"In New South Wales the species has not been recorded for over forty years. In fact, the only authentic records I can find comprise five specimens: three procured by J. A. Thorpe and two by George Masters. Thorpe obtained a male and female at Middle Head, Sydney Harbour, where he found them breeding in a low hollow stump, also a specimen at Long Bay; Masters' specimens were also procured from the latter locality.

"When in Adelaide in November of last year (1936) I had the pleasure of visiting the aviaries of Dr W. Hamilton, where were several pairs. These had not been long in his possession; they were caught somewhere on the south-east coast of South Australia. This was the first time I had seen the species alive; it is, I am told, the first time the species has been kept in captivity in Australia. It is much more robust in build than either the Blue-winged or Elegant, and could not possibly be mistaken for either.

"Before seeing this parrakeet alive, I, like many others, believed it to be a race of *N. elegans*, as many old males of that species have an orange patch on their abdomens. But it is easily recognized by the rich green of its plumage which is quite unlike the golden-olive of the Elegant, or the olive of the Blue-wing.

"Very little is known of its habits and economy except that it is usually in pairs or small flocks, frequenting grass-lands, swampy areas of the coastal areas, and partly timbered lands. Like other members of the genus, it is generally seen feeding among the grass and herbage. When disturbed, the birds usually rise simultaneously, uttering feeble call-notes, but soon settle again, either on the ground or in a nearby tree. Its food consists of the seeds of grasses and herbaceous plants.

"It nests in a hollow limb or hole in a tree; sometimes in a hollow stump or log lying on the ground.

"Clutch: four or five eggs; white, and almost globular in form; shell close-grained, smooth, and lustreless. Breeding-season: November to January."

The late F. E. Parsons, of Adelaide, wrote to Cayley on 22nd March 1937 as follows: "*N. chrysogaster* is undoubtedly the rarest of the genus. Mr Ashby has often told us of his experiences many years ago when first he came to South Australia, and this species was in fair numbers in the vicinity of what is now the Outer Harbour; then they disappeared and it was many years before they were again found in South Australia. The reappearance of this bird was only noted about ten years ago, when three companions and myself were doing some collecting in the south-east of this State. About thirty birds were found feeding on a small clearing almost in the township of Robe. Four were collected; one pair of which went to the South Australian Museum. It was during the end of October that these birds were found. For the three following years about the same number of birds were seen on this same little clearing at the end of October in each year; although a good watch was kept for others along the coast, none could be found. I visited the spot again the fourth year after first finding them, and found a bird-trapper with nets set, and I know he succeeded in netting quite a few. Unfortunately I fear they were all cleaned out, for since then no birds have been seen. The reason why these birds visited this small clearing has since occurred to me. This cleared patch grew quite a lot of 'Dandelions' which are seeding during October. The crops of the birds collected were full of small seeds that I now know to be 'Dandelion' seeds.

"I have searched along this coast for other places with this weed growing, but have failed to find any."

The most authoritative article on this species is undoubtedly that by Jarman[69] in the *Australian Bird Watcher*. My personal experience of this species in the field is almost entirely limited to visits, in company with Jarman, to the Little River area in Victoria. In May 1949 I had a fleeting glimpse of a single bird in this locality; thereafter it was not until May 1956 that I had a most satisfactory view of a party of nineteen birds which were feeding quietly, relatively close to me, in the same locality; the most striking diagnostic feature in the field is the brilliance of the dark green upper parts when seen in a good light; under such conditions there should be no possibility of confusion with the closely allied species.

Since that date my only encounter with the species was in December 1961 when, in the company of R. W. McKechnie, a brief glimpse was obtained of three birds which were undoubtedly *chrysogaster* at the I.C.I. saltfields north of Adelaide. However, in October 1970 Jarman again took me to the Little River area and we were rewarded with a sighting of a flock of about forty of these rare birds, which were feeding in open paddocks with small swampy patches interspersed, a little farther inland than where I had seen them previously.

There is so little, if any, information that can be regarded as authentic concerning the nesting habits of this species that one is tempted to speculate as to whether it may not be a terrestrial nester, possibly on off-shore islands, like its close relative the Rock Parrot.

Aviary Notes

Cayley wrote: "With the exception of a record that the species had been represented in the Zoological Society's collection many years ago, and the birds at present in the possession of Dr W. Hamilton, of Adelaide, South Australia, it is practically unknown to aviarists. Dr Hamilton's birds are kept in a large flight aviary and hollow logs are hung in the open for nesting-places."

This species is undoubtedly the rarest of the genus, and is quite un-known to the majority of aviculturists. Very occasionally an odd bird has been trapped with Elegants but, as far as I am aware, only once has a consignment reached the Adelaide bird market. That was in the middle of 1940, when a few dozen birds were obtained from the south-east of South Australia. Most of these were immature birds, and two of them were obtained on my behalf, but unfortunately both proved to be cocks, and they survived only until 1943. In November of the following year I obtained two more cocks, the survivors of three birds which had been in the possession of S. Harvey before the war. One of these I still had in 1951, but the other died late in 1945. In May 1946 I obtained the loan of a hen, the sole survivor of a small batch of the 1940 trapping which had been sent to a Victorian aviculturist. About Christmas time that year the hen was seen to be taking an interest in a log, and one day in mid-January she was noticed to be looking a little off colour, and inspection of the nest revealed a single egg; next day the hen was found dead, and it was obvious that the effort of egg-laying after so long in captivity had been too much for her. The egg was placed under a sitting Blue-winged in a friend's aviary, but it was not fertile. The following season the cock mated with a hen Rock, and she laid three eggs late in December. Only one of these was fertile, and it hatched in mid-January, but the young bird survived only a few days. I should particularly like to have reared this hybrid, as I have always felt that the Rock was the closest relative of the Orange-bellied. It was not until January 1949 that I was able to obtain another hen of this species, and about Christmas time she began to take an interest in a log, and continued to do so for over a month without laying, as far as is known. Unfortunately the old cock, who had by then been in captivity for over ten years, was never observed to feed her and seemed quite uninterested when she was obviously in breeding condition.

In 1950 the hen became interested in the log early in December, and laid her first egg on the 30th of that month. The clutch consisted of four, which she incubated steadily, but unfortunately all were clear. Early in 1951 the late Sir Edward Hallstrom was kind enough to let me have a new cock to replace the old one, known to have been in captivity since 1938! This year the hen was seen in the nest, and feeding was observed late in December. On 4th January the cock was dead, and three days later the hen laid an egg. However, she did not incubate, but produced another egg early in February. Early in 1952 I was lucky enough to obtain yet another cock, the best specimen that I had ever possessed, but unfortunately the hen died in September. The only pair that I knew of in captivity at that time was at the Adelaide Zoo, and although the hen laid and incubated most years the eggs were always clear.

Turning to more recent experiences, in 1966 I secured two males of this rare species and about a year later was lucky enough to obtain two females. No signs of breeding activity were noted either in that year or in the two following years, and after the death of one of the males I parted with the odd female.

In December 1970 the remaining pair raised great hopes by evincing considerable interest in one of the hollow logs provided, but quite suddenly their interest terminated abruptly, for no apparent reason. Early in December 1971 the hen began to spend much time in the same log, to the accompaniment of encouraging calls from the cock, and the first egg, of a clutch of four laid on alternate days, was seen on 22nd December.

Although no courtship feeding had been observed the cock was extremely attentive as regards feeding his mate whenever she left the nest during the period of incubation; an inspection on one of these emergences revealed that only one of the eggs was fertile. On 15th January faint noises were heard indicating that the egg had hatched, but it was not until 25th January, when the hen came off the nest and had a bath, that the presence of a young bird was finally established beyond doubt. A period of very hot weather then ensued, during which time I was away from home, and when I returned on 5th February the young bird was dead in the nest; if, as has been suggested, the species breeds in southwestern Tasmania, it is probable that the summer temperature rarely, if ever, approaches 100°F. in the area. The foregoing constitutes what is believed to be the only occasion on which a fertile egg has been incubated and hatched by the parent species in captivity, and raises hopes for the ultimate breeding of this difficult species.

52 Rock Parrot

Neophema (Neonanodes) petrophila (Gould)

PLATE XII

Synonym

Rock Elegant.

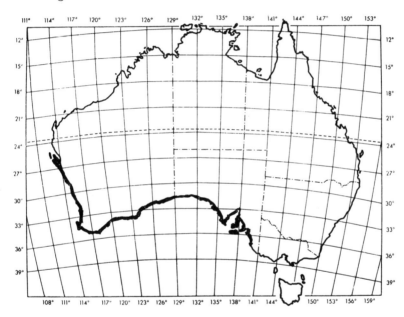

Distribution

Along the South Australian coastline this species extends in a south-
easterly direction as far as Baudin Rocks near Robe and includes
Kangaroo Island in its range. Westward, the distribution appears to be
unbroken right through to Western Australia wherever the coastline or
islands afford a suitable habitat. In Western Australia, Serventy and
Whittell[10] express the distribution clearly by saying that the species
"frequents coastal islands and mainland dunes and rocks (both granite
and limestone) from the Great Australian Bight to Shark's Bay".

Description

SIZE. About 8½ inches (216 mm).

ADULT MALE. General colour above, including upper wing-coverts and inner secondaries, dull brownish-olive; extreme outer wing-coverts blue, the greater series with dull olive-green tips; inner webs of quills brownish-black, primary coverts and outer webs of primaries dark blue; central tail-feathers dull greenish-blue, brownish on inner webs, the remainder yellow on apical portion, the yellow increasing in extent towards outer-most feather on each side which is almost uniform yellow except at the base; band on forehead deep rich blue, bordered before and behind with greenish-blue which extends in a narrow line over the eyes; lores and forepart of face pale greenish-blue; throat, upper breast and flanks olive-green shading to yellow-olive on lower parts of breast, and pure yellow on abdomen and under tail-coverts; bill bluish-horn; legs and feet mealy-brown; eyes dark brown.

ADULT FEMALE. Not appreciably duller than the male and this species is consequently a particularly difficult one to sex, the only reliable guide being a somewhat narrower frontal band on most females. Adults of both sexes occasionally exhibit a large, dull orange abdominal patch.

IMMATURE. Only slightly duller than the adult, but the frontal band is lacking and the face is greyish-olive, not blue as in the adult. Adult plumage is attained rapidly by a moult which occurs about three months after leaving the nest.

Geographical Variations

None recognized.

Field Notes

Cayley wrote: "The Rock Parrakeet is still fairly plentiful, and although more sombrely-coloured than the other members of the genus, is, because of its peculiar habits, one of the most interesting of Australian species. Usually observed in pairs or small flocks, chiefly frequenting the islands near the coast, and swampy situations of the coastal areas. Its flight is swift and erratic; at times it mounts to a great height in the air. The food of the species consists chiefly of the seeds of grasses and herbaceous plants; a favourite is the seed of a species of *Mesembryanthemum* common on most islands off the south-western coast.

"It nests in holes in cliffs, in a cavity under a rock, or on the ground among rocks and low scrub.

"Clutch: four or five eggs; white, and rounded-oval in form; shell close-grained and almost lustreless. Breeding-season: August to October."

The late F. E. Parsons of Adelaide wrote to Cayley as follows: "*N. petrophila* is perhaps next to *elegans* in numbers. It is only infrequently met with on the mainland, and then never away from the coast, but is quite plentiful on some of the small rocky islands in Spencer and St Vincent Gulfs and off the west coast. They nest under flat boulders on these islands."

H. B. Scholz, then of Yaninee, South Australia, and now of the Adelaide suburb of Underdale, sent Cayley the following notes: "As regards *N. petrophila* I usually go to a small island in Venus Bay to observe these dull-coloured but very interesting birds. On this particular island, which is also a breeding-place for seabirds, these parrakeets nest every year. Contrary to expectations they rarely nest in cliffs, but mainly among loose rocks covered with 'ice plant'. They feed on the seeds of grasses, milk thistles, and the ice plant, and one can approach them very closely for observation purposes.

"Two to five white eggs are laid for a clutch during September and there is rarely a second clutch. I have found only two second clutches. The eggs are often deposited on the bare rock, but when the birds can scratch a little earth or guano to lay the eggs on, they do so. Apparently these parrakeets like access to water, as they have been observed several miles inland drinking at a freshwater spring. This species is extremely difficult to sex, as I have seen females often brighter-coloured than males. I have a female, which has laid several clutches of eggs, with a distinct orange patch on its lower abdomen, and it is much brighter coloured than its mate. This species is slightly larger than the other *Neophema* parrakeets, and their eggs are, on an average, also larger. These birds are not rare; one can see fairly large flocks of them at times."

My first meeting with this species was in January 1948 when I found the birds to be common in the vicinity of Port Lincoln, South Australia, and to be nesting on the small islands called The Brothers in the harbour there.

Until recently, when the land was reclaimed, the species could almost always be seen in swampy land between the Outer Harbour and the mouth of the Port River less than fifteen miles from Adelaide. Strangely enough it is only very occasionally recorded from the I.C.I. saltfields, which are only a short distance from the Outer Harbour and where the Elegant Parrot is so frequently to be seen.

On Kangaroo Island it is not uncommon along much of the south coast where I saw it both in April 1965 and January 1967. In the field it can easily be distinguished from the other closely allied species by its habitat, its drab, brownish-olive coloration and the blue lores as opposed to the yellow of its congeners.

Rock Parrots are seldom found far from their coastline habitat.

Aviary Notes

Cayley wrote: "In a letter dated 14 May 1937, W. K. Penney, 'Mount Cooper', Anzac Highway, Plympton, South Australia, writes me as follows: 'Having secured three pairs of Rock Parrakeets. (*Neophema petrophila*), in July 1934, I housed them in an aviary 10 ft 6 in. by 5 ft wide, the shelter being 4 ft 6 in. by 5 ft by 9 ft high, fibrous plaster lined, and containing six hollow logs.

" 'Until the end of January 1935 my only success was two broken eggs on the earthen floor. I had noticed by this time the upper mandible and claws had grown to about twice their normal length so after having "pruned" them I placed several large rocks in the pen. The way the birds made use of them warranted the space they occupied and has prevented a recurrence of that trouble.

" 'June 1935. My stock now reduced to two pairs. I decided to build a rock warren in the flight and finished up with a mound about 4 ft long by 18 in. wide and as high as wide, with eight apertures running in laterally about one foot. To my complete satisfaction the birds accepted this immediately and spent a lot of time inspecting the various openings. Any time I visited the aviary, the slamming of the door would bring the four birds to the surface.

" 'By the end of August movements were reversed by the birds disappearing into their selected warren when anybody approached the aviary. Just one month later I discovered two white globular eggs in one nest and broken egg-shell in the other.

" 'Twenty-eight days later (end of October) only broken egg-shell to be found; the eggs appeared to have been fertile but no trace of any young. On closer inspection I found the whole rockery to be riddled with mice. Although the birds spent a great deal of their time in and about the rocks no further attempt was made at breeding.

" 'During the winter of 1936 I built them a new rock home on a solid mouseproof foundation, making the whole thing nine inches higher than previously and all apertures on the top, which made close inspection easier by leaving a loose stone over the nesting position. By August I had lost one hen so I promptly removed the odd cock bird. The remaining pair selected an aperture about the centre on the eastern side and, although they could be seen almost any time in or about the nest, no eggs were observed until the end of September. From then on both birds occupied the nest almost permanently.

" 'During the first ten or twelve days of incubation the opening of the pen door was sufficient to bring the cock bird to the surface, but as time went on nothing seemed to disturb him and neither bird was seen for some eight or ten days. Being somewhat concerned I removed a stone above the nest only to find both birds sitting quite unconcerned at the intrusion. On and after 28 September both birds were seen out feeding frequently but on the approach of a person they would disappear into their nest. Being afraid to risk too close an inspection I awaited results, and eight weeks later a fully grown and feathered young one left the nest. Apart from the horn-coloured beak and a browner tinge all over the body, it was very hard to distinguish from an adult bird.

" 'Food given: eight varieties of seed dry; various sprouting seeds sown in their pen; assorted greens including young *Mesembryanthemum.*' "

This species has never been very plentiful in captivity, partly because it is seldom trapped, and also because it is the least colourful member of the group, and has the reputation of being relatively short-lived and difficult to breed. Always a plump bird, it tends to become extremely fat and sluggish in captivity, and many birds seem to die suddenly when apparently in good health. It was first bred in South Australia by G. Pearce, of Port Augusta, in 1936, a feat which gained the bronze medal of the Avicultural Society of South Australia and also the silver medal for the outstanding breeding success of the season. On this occasion the birds nested amongst stones or rocks, but most subsequent successes have been achieved in the ordinary type of log nests.

My personal experiences with this species have been disappointing, as the following account relates. I obtained my first pair late in 1935, and for the next five seasons they gave no indication of wanting to go to nest, although the cock was occasionally observed feeding the hen during the spring. Then in 1941 they surprisingly went to nest in a log laying a clutch of three eggs early in October. Two eggs hatched, and the young birds were reared, leaving the nest early in December.

Before the 1942 breeding season both parents and one of the young birds died, and though a mate was obtained for the surviving young hen, no inclination to breed was apparent either that season or the following one. However, in both 1944 and 1945 considerable interest was evinced without eggs actually being laid. Before the 1946 season I had acquired a further hen, and she occupied the same aviary as the mated pair. She came into breeding condition late in October, and frequently implored the cock to feed her, without result; she then laid four eggs in mid-November, which, as expected, were infertile. Just about this time I was lucky enough to secure a new cock, and he immediately mated with the odd hen, and she laid a further clutch of three eggs early in December 1946, all of which were fertile. Two young were hatched and reared, leaving the nest at the end of January and proving to be both cocks.

In 1947 the cock of this breeding pair died early in October, and the only other Rock that I could obtain proved to be another hen. However, the old hen mated with an odd cock Blue-wing, laid two eggs late in December, one of which was fertile and a chick was hatched and reared to leave the nest early in February. The second hen mated up with an odd cock Orange-bellied, laid three eggs late in December, only one of which was fertile, and although it hatched in mid-January the youngster unfortunately lived only a few days. This last-mentioned hen was mated to a new cock in 1948, and she laid three eggs early in November, but only hatched one of the two fertile ones, and the chick only survived a fortnight. Similarly, in 1949 two eggs were fertile out of the clutch of four laid early in November, both chicks hatched, but one died in a few days and the other survived nearly a month but failed to leave the nest.

In 1950 the old hen had a new mate, and she laid three eggs in October, hatched two of them, but allowed the chicks to die when a fortnight old. The same pair had two clear eggs in 1951, and a new pair in 1952 did not lay, although the hen was in the log a great deal.

53 Blue-winged Parrot

Neophema (Neonanodes) chrysostoma (Kuhl)

PLATE XII

Synonym

Blue-banded Parrot.

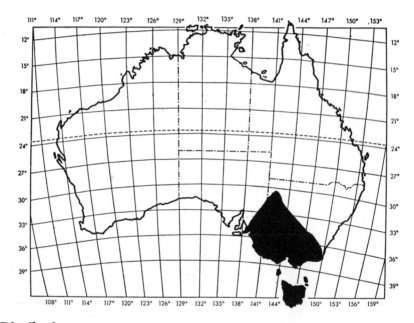

Distribution

The distribution of this species for New South Wales would appear to be the western and south-western portion as far north as Broken Hill and Tibooburra and east to Griffith and Deniliquin, with isolated observations at Pilliga and Narran Lake, and in the Australian Capital Territory.

In Victoria there are records from almost the whole of the State, but the species is probably commonest in the south-west.

In South Australia it is plentiful in the south-eastern portion of the State, extending as far north as the vicinity of Adelaide, and the Mount Mary Plains. Records farther north than this in South Australia must be regarded as suspect and probably referring to *N. elegans*.

On King Island and in Tasmania this parrot is plentiful and widely distributed. It is not clear whether "coastal sandhills and interior" of the 1926 R.A.O.U. Checklist is intended to refer to Tasmania only.

Description

SIZE. About 8½ inches (216 mm).

ADULT MALE. General colour above olive-green, the head slightly washed with yellow; inner secondaries like the back; upper wing-coverts bright ultramarine-blue; bastard wing, primary coverts and quills blackish-brown, outer edges of some outer primaries pale blue; central pair of tail-feathers blue, washed with green on their basal half, the next pair blue margined on their inner webs and broadly tipped with yellow, the yellow increasing in extent towards the outermost feather on each side; a band across the forehead and extending above anterior portion of each eye dark ultramarine-blue; lores and a circle round eyes yellow; cheeks, sides of neck, throat, and breast pale green; abdomen, flanks, thighs, under tail-coverts, and lower aspect of tail yellow; often a large, rather irregular area of an orange shade in centre of abdomen; under wing-coverts deep ultramarine-blue; lower aspect of quills dark brown; bill bluish-horn; legs and feet mealy-grey; eyes brown.

ADULT FEMALE. A slightly duller shade of olive, and the yellow areas on the face and abdomen are not as bright as they are in the male. In addition, the blue area on the wing is not as vivid, being slightly suffused with green, and the frontal band is narrower and less obvious and lacks the faint pale blue line which can usually be seen in the male.

IMMATURE. Duller in all respects than the adult female, the blue on the wing being rather slaty in shade, and the frontal band is absent or rudimentary. Adult plumage is not acquired until early spring, about eight or nine months after leaving the nest; until then it is difficult to sex them with any certainty.

Geographical Variations

None recognized.

Field Notes

Cayley does not appear to have encountered this bird in the wild state. However, he stated that the latest reports from Tasmania were encouraging: "The species appears to be fairly plentiful there, in certain seasons making its appearance in several districts at irregular intervals.

"Similar in habits and economy to N. chrysogaster, it is usually observed in pairs or small flocks, frequenting alike grass-lands and sparsely timbered country. It breeds in holes in trees, stumps, and logs.

"Clutch: five to seven eggs; white, and rounded-oval in form; shell close-grained and lustreless. Breeding-season: usually commences at the latter end of September or early in October, and continues until the middle of January."

Miss Florence M. Irby of Casino, New South Wales, sent Cayley the following notes: "Small wonder early writers were charmed with this bird; it would be hard to find a more exquisitely dainty little creature than this small delicately coloured parrakeet, its plumage so softly shaded that it is almost veiled in effect.

"Quietly feeding in the long grass they are so inconspicuous that one might pass within a few feet without noticing them. Indeed, their notes while feeding are so low-toned that unless very much on the alert one might take no heed.

"In Tasmania, during the early autumn of 1926, I saw a flock of six feeding in the grass at the edge of some densely timbered land on Tasman's Peninsula. The soft twittering notes as they fed first attracted my attention. They were sitting in the long grass gathering seed with graceful finch-like movements, keeping up the softest chattering the while. Their delicate colouring blending with the soft greens and browns of the long seeding grasses in the small clearing made a strikingly beautiful picture. These were the first Blue-winged Parrakeets I had seen in a natural state.

"At the end of January 1928, I again met with this beautiful species in Tasmania, when a flock of nine were noted feeding in the grass at Epping Forest; something startled them, and with sharp notes of alarm the flock rose as one bird and almost in a moment were lost to sight. About three miles farther along the road a solitary specimen was sitting on a wire fence; it made no attempt to fly and seemed quite unconcerned as it balanced itself on the wire watching us, with its beautiful blue and yellow tail-feathers widely spread.

"Observers of this bird, from earliest times have remarked upon its wonderful powers of flight; this seems to be a special feature of all the *Neophema*, and it seems doubtful if any of the species could be identified while on the wing, more especially as they frequently fly at a very great height."

The late F. E. Parsons of Adelaide wrote to Cayley as follows: "*N. chrysostoma* is not at all plentiful in this State. When found they are usually in company with the common species *N. elegans*; but in my experience do not extend north of Adelaide nor to any distance east of the coast. Yet in contradiction of this statement the largest flock of this species I have encountered was on the margin of the mallee scrub on the east of Mount Lofty Ranges. They were in company with *N. elegans*, and the mixed flocks must have contained a couple of hundred individuals. This is the only occasion that I have met *N. chrysostoma* so far from the coast."

My first meeting with this species in the field was in January 1950 when my elder son and I found them to be extremely plentiful in the vicinity of Portland in south-western Victoria; they were in pairs and in small flocks, many of which consisted of immature birds. On subsequent visits to the south-east of South Australia and western district of Victoria in

October 1951, March 1957 and October 1968, birds were seen but they were not nearly as plentiful as on the first occasion.

The species appears in the vicinity of Adelaide on occasions and my observations have all been between the months of August and October; thus in September 1951 three birds were seen on the site of what is now the Adelaide Airport and in October 1957, August 1958 and September 1962 small numbers were seen at the I.C.I. saltfields north of Adelaide. My only other observations have been of a small flock in the Otway Ranges, Victoria, in October 1959, and a few birds at Mallacoota, eastern Victoria, in December 1968. Strangely enough I have not met with the species in Tasmania where it is reputedly common.

Aviary Notes

Cayley wrote: "Lives remarkably well in captivity on a simple diet of canary-seed, millet, and green food, especially seeding grasses. Quite unsuited to cage life. The best results are obtained with pairs kept to themselves in flight aviaries.

"S. Harvey, of Adelaide, South Australia, who successfully bred and reared this species, sends me the following notes: 'Being anxious to breed the Blue-wing Grass Parrot, I set aside two breeding aviaries, 6 feet by 3 feet over all, and placed one pair in each. The best pair had a pair of Gouldian Finches with them, the other pair were alone. The latter commenced nesting, and on 15th September (1936) had one egg, on the 18th there were three eggs, and on the 20th, four eggs; this completed the clutch. On 7th December (twenty-two days after the first egg was laid) all the eggs had hatched. On 11th January, five weeks to the day from date of hatching, the first young one left the nest, and two more the following day; the fourth young one died when one week old.

" 'They resemble the parents, only of course the colouring is more sombre. There are two males and one female; the males have the blue band on the forehead and yellow feathers round the eyes; one is a much better coloured bird than the other. The female has a very faint blue band on the forehead. The male's head is decidedly broader than that of the female.

" 'They nested in a log eighteen inches long and five inches in diameter, hung in the open flight.' "

This bird has not proved a free breeder in the hands of local aviculturists, and I have been singularly unsuccessful with the species, as the following account will show. In 1937 the hen of the pair in my possession at that time laid four eggs towards the end of November and proceeded to incubate, but was found dead in the nesting log some three weeks later. The following season a new hen, mated to the same cock, had a clutch of infertile eggs, and in 1939 the same pair went to nest early in December, a clutch of six being laid. Five of these eggs proved fertile and hatched in due course, but two young birds died within the first

U

few days, and a further two when half-grown; the sole survivor, a male, left the nest late in January, and although possessed of what Budgerigar breeders call an undershot beak, was otherwise a good specimen. The old cock died shortly after this, and for the next four seasons the old hen, although provided with a new mate, did not even lay. In 1944, however, she relented, and laid four eggs in December, but these soon disappeared.

A second pair obtained prior to this season laid three eggs in the middle of November, and later added two misshapen ones to the clutch, all of which proved clear, and a second attempt in January by this pair resulted in three more peculiarly shaped eggs. The following season this latter pair failed even to lay, although the hen spent a lot of time in the nest. The two following seasons were also blanks, and in 1948 I determined to try and break the hoodoo with four pairs of young birds which moulted into adult plumage just prior to the breeding season. Of these, the first pair laid three eggs about the middle of November, all of which proved fertile, and two of which had hatched by 2nd December; two days later both young birds were dead, and the third egg was found to contain a fully developed chick. The second pair laid a clutch of four eggs at the same time as the first pair, and four young were seen early in December, but unfortunately the log fell off its supporting nail a few days later, with the resultant death of all the young birds. A third pair had three infertile eggs, and the fourth pair did not lay.

The 1949 season was no more successful, two pairs being tried. One pair laid five eggs early in November, all of which were fertile, and had hatched by the end of the same month; however, two of these chicks died quite soon, and all had succumbed by the middle of December. The second pair, the hen of which was a young bird of the previous season, started to lay late in October, and continued to do so intermittently until early in December, sixteen eggs being laid in all! Several of these were obviously fertile, but at no time was incubation sufficiently continuous for the embryos to develop very far.

In 1950 the hen of the pair that had hatched young in the previous season broke a wing and did not lay. The other hen ran true to form, and again laid a number of eggs without incubating. In 1951 the profuse egg-layer was mated to the by then bereaved husband of the broken-winged hen; her first clutch of seven eggs was laid in October, which is unusually early for this species, but all proved clear. Five out of a second lot of seven were fertile, only three hatched, and all the young died quite soon. The other cock of the previous year was given a new mate, and she had four hatched from five fertile eggs, but succeeded in rearing only two of the chicks in mid-January. In 1952 this pair hatched all four fertile eggs laid early in November, and had reared three young by mid-December.

54 Elegant Parrot

Neophema (Neonanodes) elegans (Gould)

PLATE XII

Synonym

Grass Parrot (erroneously).

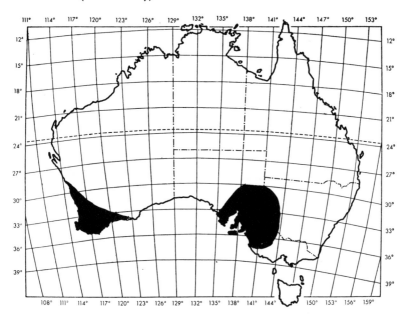

Distribution

As suggested by McGill,[67] the occurrence of this species in New South Wales is uncertain, and if it occurs it is probably only in the western and south-western portions of the State.

In Victoria the records are again few and far between, and the reliable ones are mainly from the western district.

In South Australia the species is widespread but is uncommon in the south-east. It occurs in the lower north, in the Flinders Range and farther north towards Marree and Lake Callabonna; records for Kangaroo Island have recently been verified.

For Western Australia, Serventy and Whittell[10] state: "Until recent years this parrot was known only in the south-west corner, north to

Moora and east to Merredin and near Esperance. Formerly it was not found in the jarrah forest belt or the Swan coastal plain but since 1937 the species has been undergoing a cycle of expansion, radially in the south-west and north to the pastoral country." More recently there have been isolated recordings from as far north as the Gascoyne and Fortescue rivers.

Description

SIZE. About 8½ inches (216 mm).

ADULT MALE. General colour above, including scapulars, inner upper wing-coverts and innermost secondaries golden-olive; outer portion of upper and median wing-coverts and outer secondaries rich light blue darker towards outer edge of wings; bastard wing, primary coverts and primaries black, dark blue on their outer webs; central tail-feathers greenish-blue at their basal portion becoming blue towards their tips, the remainder blue at base of outer webs, dark brown at base of inner webs, the remainder yellow increasing in extent towards the outermost feather on each side; a band across the forehead deep blue edged with light blue on the hinder margin and extending in a narrow line over eyes; lores, forepart of cheeks, throat yellow; upper breast and abdomen yellow with a small orange patch on centre of abdomen in many adult birds; under tail-coverts yellow; axillaries and under wing-coverts dark blue; bill bluish-horn; legs and feet mealy-grey; eyes hazel.

ADULT FEMALE. A considerably duller shade of olive, lacking the golden hue; the frontal band is narrower, and the small orange abdominal spot is absent; the under tail-coverts tend to be yellowish-green.

IMMATURE. Somewhat duller than the adult female in body coloration, but the frontal band is either absent or very faint. They cannot be sexed with any certainty until the first moult of body feathers, which occurs when they are only about three months old and is rapidly completed.

Geographical Variations

None recognized.

Field Notes

Cayley may not have seen this species in the field, but he wrote: "The Elegant Parrakeet (often called Grass Parrot and Elegant Grass Parrakeet) is definitely nomadic, as its movements are regulated by food supply and not, as generally understood, a regular seasonal migration. It is usually in pairs or small flocks and, as a rule, very shy; it frequents grasslands (often out on the plains away from trees), barren sandy belts bordering the coast, and sparsely timbered areas. When flushed, it flies in a peculiar zigzag manner, sometimes alighting on the ground within a short distance, but more frequently ascending to a great altitude and disappearing from sight. Generally observed feeding on the ground on the seeds of grasses and other plants, being very fond of the seeds of the introduced thistle. Its pretty warbling call-note is uttered while on the wing.

"The Elegant Parrakeet breeds in hollow limbs and holes in trees, the eggs being deposited on the decayed wood at the bottom of the cavity, often two feet away from the entrance.

"Clutch: four or five eggs; white, and almost globular in form; shell close-grained and lustreless. Breeding-season: August to October."

The late F. E. Parsons of Adelaide wrote to Cayley as follows: "*N. elegans* is a common bird in our State, and is met with both on the margin of our coast and inland, even through the mallee country, and extending well into the north of the State. I have never come across them nesting, but one always finds a good percentage of birds in a flock are immature. The sweet yet feeble twittering call, only given when the bird is on the wing, is the same with all the species."

Of all members of the genus, this species is the one with which I am best acquainted. I first saw it in small numbers in the Victor Harbour district, South Australia, in my schooldays, and it is still quite common in the area and breeds in the Hindmarsh Tiers and probably throughout the area.

It is frequently seen at the I.C.I. saltfields north of Adelaide, and my records for that area cover all months of the year except July, August and September; presumably the birds leave the area then to breed. It is worthy of note that my only records of the Blue-winged Parrot for this area almost exactly coincide with the months when the Elegant is not present; it is, of course, known that the Blue-winged is a later nester.

The species is not uncommon in the northern parts of South Australia. My sons and I found it breeding in the Flinders Ranges in October 1955. In August 1964 three of my friends and I observed it in large numbers from the train between Marree and Port Augusta. It is not infrequently seen at Chauncey's Line, between the Murray Bridge road and Lake Alexandrina and in the Coorong, but I have not seen it in the south-east or in Victoria where it has been recorded.

The records for Kangaroo Island have until recently been regarded with some suspicion, but I am quite certain that I saw two pairs at the eastern boundary of Flinders Chase in April 1968.

In Western Australia I saw a pair near Williams in August 1948, and in October 1964 it was plentiful near Cunderdin and a nest with young was found. It is said to be increasing in numbers in that State in recent times.

Aviary Notes

All that Cayley had to say was: "A delightful aviary bird, but is quite unsuited to cage life. Very popular with aviarists in Australia. Its habits and requirements in captivity are similar to those of the Blue-winged species."

As a schoolboy during the first world war I possessed two successive pairs of this species at a time when they were extremely rare in captivity; in fact, I know of no others having been kept about that time. Neither pair showed any inclination to go to nest, although they survived for considerable periods in a mixed collection.

In more recent years large numbers of Elegants have been trapped in South Australia, and the species has become very common in captivity and has bred to the extent that it may be regarded as domesticated. The bronze medal of the Avicultural Society of South Australia for the first breeding was awarded to S. Harvey in 1930.

My own breeding experiences of this species have all been achieved with two individuals of each sex. An adult pair obtained in 1935 seemed likely to nest in a mixed collection, until murdered by a pair of Blue Bonnets. In 1936 a new pair was obtained, but they did not go to nest that season; in 1937 a clutch of four eggs was laid in September and October, but they proved clear. The next season a clutch of four was laid in mid-September, and three young hatched and were reared, all of them leaving the nest about the middle of November, plucked to a varying degree, presumably by their mother.

In the 1939 breeding season it soon became obvious that a young hen that had been left in the aviary had mated with her father and, in view of the plucking episode of the previous season, she was not discouraged. She laid a clutch of eggs in August, but these soon disappeared, and early in September she laid a further clutch of five, four of which hatched by the end of the month but the chicks lived for only a few days. The old hen was thereupon restored to her former mate, and she laid a clutch of four in mid-October, three of which were fertile and were hatched and reared to leave the nest in a shockingly plucked condition in December; however, like their predecessors and many successors, the three chicks soon recovered from their ordeal and became presentable-looking specimens.

During the next three seasons a few young Elegants were reared, but the pair were mostly used to hatch and rear Turquoisines, which they invariably plucked. In 1943 the old hen was replaced by one of her daughters bred the previous season; this bird failed to lay that year, but in the following year commenced a very successful breeding career. Her first clutch, laid late in August, consisted of five infertile eggs, but the second clutch, produced early in October, consisted of four eggs, all of which were hatched and reared, the first three chicks leaving the nest early in December, and the fourth not for a further fortnight! A third clutch, commenced about the time the first three young left the nest, proved all to be clear.

In 1945 three young were reared from the first clutch of four laid late in August; the second clutch, laid late in October, was replaced by some Hooded eggs, which had been deserted, without result, and the third clutch of four was infertile. In 1946 the old male, who had been in my possession for ten years, died in August just as the hen commenced to lay, and her eggs were all clear. A new cock was obtained almost immediately, and five were reared from the second clutch, which was laid early in October; a third clutch laid in December were clear. This pair has carried on quite successfully since then, rearing three out of four and five out of five in 1947; three out of three and two out of three in 1948; and four out of four and two out of three during the 1949 season.

The old breeding pair raised three out of three chicks and one out of four hatched in 1950. In 1951 the first clutch was clear; only one egg was fertile in the second, and the chick was reared; four Bourke eggs were substituted for an infertile third clutch, and two chicks of four hatched were reared. For 1952 a new cock was obtained, and though the first clutch was again clear, two young were reared from three hatched in a second try.

55 Turquoise Parrot

Neophema pulchella (Shaw)

PLATE XII

Synonyms

Chestnut-shouldered Parrakeet, Turquoisine, Red-shouldered Parrakeet (erroneously), Beautiful Grass Parrot (erroneously).

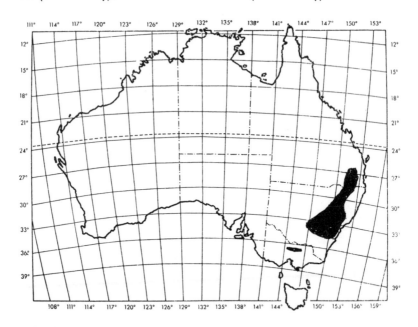

Distribution

The only recent records of this species from southern Queensland are from Stanthorpe, Gayndah and Chinchilla.

As far as New South Wales is concerned there is no doubt that the north-eastern corner of the State is the stronghold of this bird, Inverell, Narrabri, Coonabarabran and Bingara being areas of comparatively frequent occurrence. Other records are from the outer western suburbs of Sydney, where the species appears to be increasing, and from the Upper Hunter and Illawarra districts and, surprisingly, the Griffith district.

The only recent Victorian records are from Bendigo and East Gippsland and the surprising discovery of a small breeding population in
1967 in the vicinity of the Warby Range, near Benalla.

The South Australian record has long since been rejected as the faulty
identification of a female of *N. splendida.*

The statement in the 1926 R.A.O.U. Checklist that this species is
extremely rare is undoubtedly inaccurate. Perhaps the present-day distribution would be best expressed as south-eastern Queensland, eastern
(especially north-eastern) New South Wales and central Victoria.

Description

SIZE. About 8 inches (203 mm).

ADULT MALE. General colour above green, including nape, hind-neck,
back, scapulars, innermost secondaries and upper tail-coverts; upper
wing-coverts turquoise-blue, the inner series chestnut-red; bastard wing,
primary coverts, primary and secondary quills dark blue on their outer
webs, outer edges of primaries greenish-blue, and inner webs of all dark
brown; central tail-feathers green, the remainder green on basal portions
of outer webs, dark brown on inner webs, and tipped with yellow, the
yellow increasing in extent towards the outermost feathers on each side
which is almost entirely yellow; occiput, ear-coverts and sides of neck
yellowish-green; lores, line of feathers over eyes, and cheeks turquoise-
green; a broad band across the forehead deep blue; throat and all the
under-surface and under tail-coverts rich golden yellow washed on sides
of chest with green; under aspect of tail-feathers yellow; axillaries pale
greenish-blue; under wing-coverts dark blue; bill horn-colour; legs and
feet mealy-grey; eyes brown.

ADULT FEMALE. Differs from the adult male in its duller coloration
generally and in the absence of the chestnut-red patch on the wing;
there is less blue on the face, and the under-surface is greener.

IMMATURE. Resembles the female; the young male may be distinguished
by its brighter colouring with more blue on the face and the indication
of the chestnut-red wing-patch. Adult plumage is acquired by a moult of
body feathers which is completed at about the age of four months.

Geographical Variations

None recognized.

Field Notes

Cayley wrote: "The Turquoise (or Red-shouldered Parrakeet) once had a
range extending from southern Queensland to South Australia, with
perhaps New South Wales its stronghold. It is a very rare species, indeed,
although not so very long ago it was quite common in the neighbourhood
of Sydney. When a youth I often observed this parrakeet in the outer
western suburbs of Sydney, and especially in the Camden district and
about the foothills of the Blue Mountains. Occasionally an isolated pair

or two now turn up in their old haunts in these localities. But the bird-trappers soon get to know their whereabouts, and, in spite of the law, they are caught and sold at fancy prices.

"During recent years, however, the Turquoise Parrakeet has been observed in fair numbers in the north-western portion of New South Wales, numbers being caught and sold surreptitiously in Sydney and other cities. Several of these bird-trappers were prosecuted. It is to be hoped the illegal trafficking has now ended and that this beautiful parrakeet will again establish itself.

"It breeds in a hollow limb or hole in a tree, or in a log or fallen tree, usually a eucalypt, sometimes a casuarina, the eggs being deposited on the decaying wood or dust found in these cavities.

"Clutch: four or five eggs; white, and varying from almost globular to rounded-oval and elliptic in form; shell close-grained, smooth and lustreless. Breeding-season is usually August to December."

My personal experiences of this bird in the field are very limited. In August 1955 my elder son and I were taken to an area on the outskirts of Sydney where we obtained an excellent view of a female and a brief glimpse of what we thought was a male; this was in an area where the species has frequently been observed.

In May 1960, when I was visiting him briefly, A. C. Hunt was able to find a female of this species in some open timber on the Glen Innes road not far from the town of Inverell; it was an extremely windy day and the bird in question was very tame and only flushed with difficulty and flew short distances; no other examples were seen.

In May 1971 most members of the bird-watchers' tour to north-eastern New South Wales and south-eastern Queensland were fortunate enough to see a few examples of this species in the Warrumbungle National Park near Coonabarabran. It was noticeable that the birds were relatively tame compared with other members of the genus and that they occurred in well-timbered hilly country, quite unlike the usual habitat of the Elegant and Blue-winged species.

An article on this species has been written by H. E. A. Jarman[70] for the *Australian Bird Watcher* along the lines of those that he has already published dealing with the Orange-bellied and Scarlet-chested Parrots; it should unquestionably be the most authoritative review of the species yet presented.

Aviary Notes

Cayley wrote: "A beautiful and delightful inmate of an aviary, being one of the gentlest of parrakeets, as well as exceptionally hardy, requiring only the simplest treatment. Breeds freely, being even more prolific in captivity than in a wild state, when it is usual for only one brood to be reared in a season. There are records of as many as three broods being reared in one year in confinement.

"Numbers are being kept and reared in captivity both in Australia and abroad; some stocks include birds of four generations.

"Dr Garnet Halloran, of Sydney, New South Wales, a successful breeder, sends me the following notes: 'Observation of this parrakeet in Sydney, New South Wales, shows it to be hardy and prolific in captivity.

" 'It was confined in an aviary seven feet high by four feet wide with an open flight twelve feet long, the floor being of natural soil on which grew buffalo grass, privet and oleander shrubs. A partially enclosed house with concrete floor added another three feet to the length of the flight. In this was found protection from the elements and therein were placed nest-boxes, tea-tree, and feed-troughs. Running water was provided in summer. The diet consisted of seeding grasses given twice weekly, lettuce and apple frequently, hulled oats once weekly and in the seed-trough was a mixture of millet and plain canary-seed in the proportion of three to one.

" 'Logs were hung both within the semi-dark seed-house and outside in the open flight. A decided preference was shown for the outside log. Only once were eggs laid in the large nest-box within the seed-house and then because the outside log had been temporarily removed.

" 'The log selected was twenty inches long with diameter of eight inches. It is very desirable that a natural spout about six inches long should lead into the log and more important still that the log should be suspended horizontally, with the spout pointing upwards. The ends of the log are closed with movable panels. The log should be protected from rain by a sheet of fibro-cement. A rain-soaked log drives the young out and, should the spout of the log not be pointing upwards, the brood constitutes itself a "suicide club" by crawling out and falling to the wet ground. In captivity, the family reared consists usually of two, but on one occasion four were reared. Only one pair of parrots should inhabit an aviary. Identical results accrued in an adjoining aviary with the same methods.

" 'In my experience, in Sydney, New South Wales, the broods usually left the log in December, January and February. From two pairs of birds in two seasons a total of ten young were reared, but in addition, two or three broods were lost in the early stages before the above technique was evolved. Among the young, neither sex predominated and it was noticed occasionally that a suspicion of red was present on the wing of the male as early as the first day of leaving the nest.' "

After having been a well-known aviary bird in the nineteenth century, this species disappeared from the ken of aviculturists both in Australia and abroad, and during the early years of the present century many ornithologists in Australia believed the species to be extinct. However, a few reached the hands of experienced Sydney aviculturists in the early 1920s, and since that time the species has steadily increased its numbers in captivity in most parts of Australia, and can now be considered to be satisfactorily established in a state of domestication.

My early experiences with the species were most unsatisfactory, two pairs of trapped birds acquired in 1935 failing to survive for more than a few months. Then, in August 1936, I secured a nice pair of well-acclimatized birds, only to lose the hen egg-bound a few weeks later. A substitute was obtained, but the cock never became reconciled to the change, and it was not until late in October 1937 that I was able to exchange her for another hen. The cock at once approved of the new-comer, and she laid a clutch of seven eggs late in November and early in December, but did not incubate them, a trait in her character which was destined to prove a great trial in future years. In 1938 she commenced to lay early in September, and produced thirteen eggs without becoming broody; four of these were placed under a pair of Cockatiels, and were hatched and reared, but the foster parents would not feed the chicks after they left the nest, and they all succumbed. A second clutch of nine was laid in November, but again was not incubated.

In 1939 she again started laying in mid-September, and broke many of the first batch of fourteen eggs, but behaved better in regard to the second lot of eleven commenced in November; once again, however, no incubation ensued. For the next four years she was rightly regarded as a hopeless proposition; nevertheless, seven young birds were reared by transferring eggs to a pair of Elegants whenever opportunity offered.

Prior to the 1944 season a new hen was obtained, and she laid a clutch of five fertile eggs late in September. All of these hatched and four young were reared, leaving the nest about the middle of November. A second clutch of four was laid later in the same month, and all chicks were hatched and reared by mid-January. Another good season for this pair was 1945, four eggs being laid late in August and four young being hatched and reared. A second clutch was laid late in October, and although one of the four chicks died early the other three were reared, in addition to a young Splendid which had been transferred to the nest.

The 1946 season started poorly in that the hen became egg-bound with her fifth egg in mid-August, and on recovery proceeded to break the clutch. However, she laid five more eggs early in September; of these three were fertile, but only one chick hatched; it was successfully reared. A third clutch of six eggs late in October resulted in five good young being reared, and two more were obtained from the fourth clutch laid in mid-December, only three of the six being good.

The 1947 season was poor: the first clutch of six, laid in August, were all clear, and a second batch of five in mid-September resulted in the three fertile eggs hatching in early October and, although one chick died early, the other two and a Splendid which had been placed in the nest were reared early in November. Although five out of the third clutch of six, produced early in November, were fertile, the only two chicks to hatch died within a few days.

In 1948 the first two clutches, of four and two respectively, were clear, and at this stage the old hen was mated with one of her previous year's progeny, and she laid a third clutch late in October—two out of five being fertile. The clear eggs were removed and replaced by a partly incubated Bourke egg and, in due course, two Turquoisines and a Bourke were reared. At the same time the old cock was mated with a newly acquired hen, and she laid a clutch of six fertile eggs in mid-October, and though the old fellow (who had been over twelve years in my possession) died soon after they hatched, she carried on single-handed and succeeded in rearing four very good youngsters.

For the 1949 season the old hen again started with two infertile clutches before eventually producing three fertile eggs out of five laid early in November; from these, three young were reared. The second hen had a very stormy time with a new mate, who knocked her about very badly at times; of the first clutch of five eggs, three were broken, and only one chick hatched and was reared early in December. She laid two more eggs in mid-December, and reared two young birds. A third pair laid a clutch of five in mid-October, and hatched four of the chicks, lost one early on and one later, but reared the other two.

In 1950 one pair did not lay; the other pair did not sit on the first clutch and reared the only one hatched in the second. The following year this latter pair again did not sit on the first clutch, the second were all clear, and the third again were not incubated. A new hen provided for the cock of the other pair had an infertile first clutch, and reared only one chick of the three hatched in the second. In 1952 a single pair laid eleven eggs late in the season, but did not sit.

56 Scarlet-chested Parrot

Neophema splendida (Gould)

PLATE XII

Synonyms

Splendid Parrot, Orange-throated Parrot.

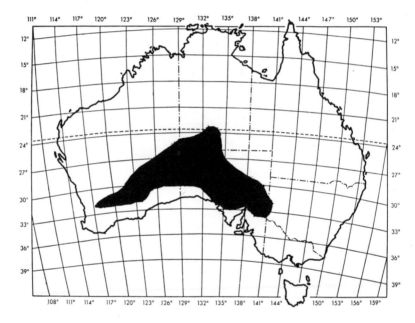

Distribution

Serventy and Whittell[10] cite fairly numerous recent scattered records of this species in Western Australia, the westernmost being between Pingelly and Corrigin and the northernmost at Laverton.

There are records from the Northern Territory, from Hamilton Downs, Undoolya, Angas Downs and the border due south of Ayers Rock, and more recently from the Petermann Ranges.

In South Australia this parrot is not infrequently recorded on the west coast and in the Gawler Ranges, and in recent years large parties have been seen in the country north of the River Murray, between Morgan and the New South Wales border.

North-west Victoria is given as an early record, and a pair nested at Manya in 1941 and there seems to be nothing recent to justify the extension eastward in New South Wales to the Darling River. Early records from Gilgandra and Lismore almost certainly refer to *N. pulchella*.

The 1926 R.A.O.U. Checklist statement "very rare" is almost certainly due to the sparse settlement of, and observation in, the areas in which the species occurs. A modern assessment of distribution might well be given as inland Western Australia south of latitude 29 degrees and inland South Australia as far east as the New South Wales border.

Description

SIZE. About 8 inches (203 mm).

ADULT MALE. General colour above grass-green, including back, rump, upper tail-coverts, scapulars, inner greater wing-coverts and innermost secondaries; lesser, median and outer greater upper wing-coverts pale blue, slightly deeper in colour on shoulder; inner webs of quills blackish, their outer webs dark blue, apical portion of outer primaries narrowly edged with light green; outer webs of outer secondaries washed with green; central tail-feathers green tinged with blue near their base, the next pair on either side green on their outer webs, blackish on the inner webs, the remainder similar but tipped with yellow, these yellow tips increasing in size towards the outermost feather on each side which is almost entirely yellow, except at base; crown of head and sides of face bright cobalt-blue becoming deeper in colour on cheeks and throat; chest and upper breast scarlet; sides of lower neck, chest and breast green; remainder of under-surface and under tail-coverts rich yellow; under wing-coverts dark blue, paler on outer margins; bill blackish-horn; legs and feet flesh-coloured; eyes brown.

ADULT FEMALE. Differs from the adult male in its duller coloration and less extent of blue on the face, and in the centre of the chest and upper breast not being scarlet but uniform green like the sides. The female of this species is very similar to that of *N. pulchella* but differs in having blue lores and the blue wing-patch lighter.

IMMATURE. Similar to the female but slightly duller or more olive-green in coloration; young males may be distinguished by their brighter colouring and slightly broader heads. In about two or three months a few red feathers begin to make their appearance on the chest of the young males, and in about six months they have achieved a fair imitation of the adult plumage, with considerable restriction in the size of the red area. This does not develop to its fullest extent until the next moult, usually when the bird is between fifteen and eighteen months old. Young females assume practically full adult plumage at the first moult, which is generally completed when they are five or six months old. Very occasionally indeed, young males leave the nest showing a few red feathers on the chest.

Geographical Variations

None recognized.

Field Notes

H. B. Scholz, then of Yaninee, South Australia, and now of the Adelaide suburb of Underdale, supplied Cayley with the following interesting notes: "Early in 1931, I rescued a female Scarlet-chested Parrakeet from a hawk on my farm at Yaninee. It was placed in an aviary with some canaries with which it seemed to live in contentment, although at that time I was unable to identify it. Some considerable time later I read of Scarlet-chested Parrakeets having been brought to Adelaide, and on reading a description of them realized that the bird I had taken under such peculiar circumstances was one of these very rare birds. Probably my bird was the first of its kind in captivity for many years.

"I decided to make a thorough search of this district for more of them, but was unsuccessful the first year. In 1932, however, with a friend of mine, I located four nests and obtained several young ones and one old pair. Since then I have searched over several hundred square miles of country with very little success.

"For two years I did not even see one in its wild state; but last nesting-season (1936) I observed five, and although I searched every likely-looking hollow over a large area, I failed to find their nesting-places. These glorious little parrakeets inhabit the most desolate looking country. Spinifex-covered sandhills with stunted mallee gullies, with an occasional patch of larger mallee seems to be their home. This country in which they are found is waterless and I was puzzled to know how they obtained their drink, until one hot day I saw a pair of them among some low shrubs. Watching them through field-glasses I saw one of them move its beak along the leaves. I thereupon examined this bush and found that it had a very sappy round leaf about $\frac{1}{4}$-inch long, and on pressing it between my fingers, a small drop of quite palatable juice was obtained from a leaf. This, then, solved the problem of how these birds obtained their drink.

"Finding a very good rock-hole containing water in a granite outcrop, in a locality where I had observed a pair of Scarlets, gave me an idea that I could probably trap them there during hot weather. I have patiently watched this rock-hole, and although thousands of other birds came there to drink, not one Scarlet-chested has been observed to come near it. In captivity they are no different to other Neophemas. But I feel quite certain that in a wild state they can exist without a supply of water and obtain their drink in the manner described. Another feature in regard to these birds is that one rarely sees more than a pair at a time—and never a flock. I did on one occasion see seven, but they were a brood of five young with their parents.

"The nesting-habits are similar to the other Neophemas excepting that as a rule they select a fairly low ragged-edged hollow, and do not chew around the edges of the entrance like other parrots, there being no external signs to show if a hollow contains a nesting-place.

"The average clutch in a wild state would be about three. I have found a nesting-place containing only one young one and no infertile eggs, so presume there was only one egg laid. The highest number of eggs or young I have found in a wild state has been five. In captivity the nesting-period is long. This season the first eggs laid by one of my hens was on 4 August, and another hen has just finished sitting on three eggs (16 January 1937). They are comparatively easy to rear in captivity; although this season results have been very poor.

"In flight they are extremely swift. It is a glorious sight to see the scarlet, blue, and yellow flash through the green foliage; the yellow underparts show plainly when the bird turns in flight. They are essentially a 'small seed' eating bird and live on the seeds of grasses, particularly spear-grass, spinifex, and the seeds of various shrubs. They are wonderful aviary birds, agreeing well with other birds and never chewing the woodwork of the aviaries. Above all, their glorious colouring and lack of unpleasant screeching make them the ideal aviary bird.

"Having made a special study of these birds in their wild state, and also in captivity, I have come to the conclusion that there are still a few isolated pairs in the northern portion of Eyre Peninsula; but that they will probably become extinct in the course of a few years, owing mainly to the fact that their natural breeding localities have been ravaged by scrub fires and much of their territory has been cleared of nesting-trees. This gives their worst enemy, the hawk, its chance, as I know from experience, having had definite proof on two occasions of these birds destroying them."

Cayley's only personal note reads as follows: "While in Adelaide recently I met several people who know the 'Centre' (as Central Australia is called). From them I learned that this parrakeet is never found in great numbers; usually in isolated pairs or family parties, local in habits, and scattered over a very large area of spinifex country. Their other observations agree with those given by Mr Scholz. All are emphatic that the species is in urgent need of effective protection against illegal trafficking."

Clutch, according to recent information, is three to five and the breeding season is August to December and January.

This is a species which I have not yet been fortunate enough to encounter in the field. In the last ten years relatively large numbers have appeared in areas north of the River Murray in the vicinity of Barmera and have been seen there by a number of ornithologists; however the birds have not been obliging on the occasions that I have sought them. There have been other sightings in the Flinders Ranges and on Eyre Peninsula in recent years.

v

Jarman's article in the *Australian Bird Watcher*[71] is the most comprehensive review of the history of this species.

Aviary Notes

Cayley wrote: "As Mr Scholz says, this is an ideal aviary bird. When in Adelaide last year I had the pleasure of visiting many beautiful aviaries where I saw numbers of these parrakeets living happily under the most favourable conditions. I would like to specially mention the magnificent aviaries of Simon Harvey, who was the first to breed these lovely parrakeets in captivity in Australia. My first visit was in company with a large party of members attending the 1936 Annual Congress of the Royal Australasian Ornithologists' Union. After inspecting his really wonderful collection of Foreign and Australian birds, we had, for us, the novel experience of having morning-tea served to us in one of the four spacious open-flight aviaries where flowers and shrubs grew profusely and birds were nesting all round us. Mr Harvey has been most successful in breeding many of the rarer species of parrakeets. The collection of Australian parrakeets in the Zoological Gardens, Adelaide, is one of the finest in existence. There, again, I had the pleasure of seeing the Scarlet-chested Parrakeet living happily and breeding freely in properly constructed breeding-aviaries. One pair I was shown has successfully reared no less than nineteen young ones during the last three breeding-seasons.

"In captivity its habits and requirements are similar to the Turquoise Parrakeet."

The reintroduction of this species to aviculture in 1931, and its subsequent breeding in captivity by S. Harvey, of Adelaide, forms the subject of an interesting article in the *Avicultural Magazine*;[72] for this success Harvey was awarded the bronze medal of the Avicultural Society of South Australia in 1932, and he also gained the silver medal of the Society for the outstanding breeding achievement of the season. Since that date the species has been bred extremely freely in Australia generally, and in South Australia in particular, and is completely domesticated; it is all the more tragic, therefore, that the species did not become firmly established in England before the introduction of the apparently insurmountable difficulties in importation.

My first examples of this species were obtained late in 1935, and the following season the hen began to lay in mid-October, but broke several of the early eggs before settling down to incubate; in all, six young were hatched in mid-December, but the cock died about this time and none of them survived long thereafter. Meanwhile two of the early eggs had been hatched by Bourkes and the chicks were successfully reared by them in January. In 1937 the same hen was mated to the young cock fostered by the Bourkes the previous season, and she started laying late in August and continued to do so until October, breaking most of her eggs soon after producing them. A new hen was obtained at the end of

October, and she laid a clutch of four in mid-November; three of these were fertile and were hatched, and two young survived to leave the nest in the middle of January. This hen died egg-bound in July 1938, and a new hen proceeded to lay eggs throughout September without going broody.

Prior to the next season I obtained a new hen, alleged to be a trapped bird, and mated her with the cock bred in 1937, and this proved to be a very successful mating. In 1939 the first clutch of six eggs was laid in mid-September, and all chicks were hatched, and although three did not survive long, the other three left the nest early in November. A second clutch of four was laid in mid-November, all hatched and three young were reared, leaving the nest early in January. For the next four seasons the same pair had very good results, having two nests each season, and rearing eight young in 1940 and in 1941, seven in 1942, and nine in 1943. In 1944 only one egg was fertile in the first clutch, but the young bird was successfully reared, and although all six eggs comprising the second batch were fertile, three chicks died early and one later on, and only two were reared. The following season all of the first clutch of four were duly reared, but of the second lot of the same number, three chicks died early and the survivor was given to Turquoisines to rear in the hope of a third clutch, which, however, did not materialize.

The year 1946 saw the end of the breeding career of the old hen, who by that time had become extremely fat and sluggish. She hatched five out of her first clutch of six, laid in August, but three young were allowed to die early, and the other two were reared. The second clutch of five, laid late in October, were all hatched and the chicks promptly allowed to die, and the three chicks hatched out of the third clutch of five, laid early in December, were similarly treated.

Since then I have not been particularly successful with Splendids. Two new pairs were tried in 1947, both hens laying in mid-September. One pair threw all their eggs out of the nest and the other hen hatched all of her four eggs just after the cock died; when three of these chicks had died, one after another, the survivor was transferred to a pair of Turquoisines and was reared by them. For the 1948 season the first of the above-mentioned pairs was given another chance, but after they had broken the first lot of eggs the hen was changed. The replacement succeeded in hatching two chicks out of a clutch of five, only to lose one early and the other when it was quite large. A second, entirely new, pair produced a lot of eggs without incubating. For the 1949 season the first pair failed to rear any of three chicks hatched in the first nest, got two good young on the wing out of three hatched in the second, and reared two young in the third. A second pair of birds, bred in 1948, reared one of the two young hatched in the first nest, but failed to rear any of three hatched in both second and third nests.

Later results with this usually easy species were appalling. In 1950 a very fine cock had two eggs laid by his first mate, and they promptly vanished; he was then given another hen who hatched three and four chicks in successive clutches, but reared none of them. Another cock had an early clutch of seven from this hen, and when mated with the other did no more. In 1951 both hens broke their eggs, and one ultimately died egg-bound, and in 1952 one pair did not lay while the hen of a second pair also died egg-bound, and a new hen then hatched two young and they promptly died.

LATHAMUS Lesson
Swift Parrot

The only representative of this genus, the Swift Parrot, has caused much debate as to its correct systematic position. A study of its osteology by Forbes[73] seems to indicate its platycercine affinity, as indeed does the presence of a wing-stripe. Tavistock,[3] who had a remarkable appreciation of behaviour patterns, thought it might be related to the genus *Polytelis*, while Peters[1] placed it, without comment, next to the fig-parrots or lorilets. It has always seemed to me that this may well be its true relationship and that it may be an aberrant southernmost representative of the Opopsittidae. There is a striking resemblance in the red tipping of the inner webs of the innermost secondaries which occurs also in all the Australian fig-parrots. Behavioural studies of these little-known species may well substantiate this relationship.

This species behaves very much as do lorikeets inasmuch as it is predominantly a nectar-feeding bird and it clambers about amongst foliage in very much the same way. However, it has not the typical, jerky movements of the lorikeets, mated pairs do not preen each other nor do they rest close together as do lorikeets, and it is said that the tongue is not as extensively brushed as are those of the typical lorikeets.

Tavistock[3] has described the display and courtship as follows: "When courting the cock Swift gives a curtsey a little reminiscent of one of the actions of a Barraband and then, drawing himself up, feeds the hen, after which he repeats the performance. Later, when she is sitting, the curtsey is omitted before feeding takes place. The hen alone incubates for twenty-one days and both she and her mate are devoted and long-suffering parents, the chicks taking nearly seven weeks before fledging. The youngsters are lazy, selfish and rather ungrateful little beggars, expecting their tired and moulting parents to feed them long after they are well able to look after themselves if they tried. Later, when they do start to feed themselves, they drive their elders away in the most irritable fashion should they desire some delicacy for their own consumption."

The wing-stripe appears to be present in all immatures and rather inconstant in adults, being retained in some males and lost in some females. Its presence may well be considered confirmatory evidence of the platycercine affinity of *Lathamus*.

Swift Parrots bathe very freely in water receptacles in captivity; not being ground feeders, it seems problematical whether they would bathe in the same way in the wild state or whether they would take advantage of wet foliage.

They do use their feet on occasions for holding articles of food, and head-scratching is performed behind the wing.

As the vernacular name implies, the flight is extraordinarily fast and direct and is accompanied by an audible whirring.

57 Swift Parrot

Lathamus discolor (Shaw)

PLATE XIII

Synonyms

Swift Lorikeet, Swift-flying Parrakeet, Red-shouldered Parrakeet, Clink.

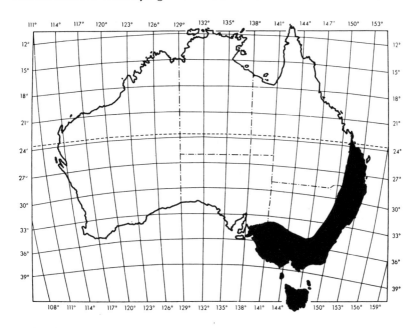

Distribution

The excellent paper on this species by Hindwood and Sharland[74] reaches the conclusion that the bird breeds in Tasmania and possibly in the islands of the Furneaux group, and migrates to spend the winter in southern and eastern Australia.

An amplification of the 1926 R.A.O.U. Checklist distribution would read: Tasmania and islands of the Furneaux group, mainly during spring and summer months; King Island records from M. McGarvie are always in March or September. Migrates to the mainland where it is found principally in autumn and winter.

In South Australia it is rare, occasionally occurring as far north as the

Mount Mary Plains but mainly in the Mount Lofty Ranges and south-east.

In Victoria the species is widespread but probably rarely occurs in the north-west and in the adjacent south-west of New South Wales. In the latter State it is widespread along the coast and Dividing Range with occasional westerly records. Extensions to northern New South Wales and Queensland (as far north as Duaringa) are probably few and far between; L. Nielsen states that there are some records for Chinchilla.

Description

SIZE. About 10 inches (254 mm).

ADULT MALE. General colour above green; lores yellow; forehead and forepart of cheeks crimson; occiput, hind-neck, sides of neck and sides of face green washed with turquoise-blue; shoulder of wing red; remainder of upper wing-coverts and scapulars green; primaries blackish-brown washed with deep blue on basal portion of outer webs, outermost series externally edged with yellow, innermost series with green, narrowly margined with yellow; secondaries blackish-brown, green on their outer webs, and crimson on inner webs of innermost series, all inner webs of quills margined with light yellow; bastard wing and primary coverts dark blue; outer series of greater wing-coverts blue; central tail-feathers dull red, blue at tips; remainder of tail-feathers blue with yellowish-green tips, washed with dull red which decreases in extent towards the outermost feather on each side; throat crimson bordered with yellow; chest, breast, and all the under-surface yellowish-green, slightly darker on sides of breast; flanks a deeper yellow and occasionally splashed with crimson; under tail-coverts dull crimson, the feathers margined with yellow and some of the larger ones centred with green at tips; axillaries and under wing-coverts bright crimson; outer series of lesser under wing-coverts yellowish-green; edge of wing blue; bill fleshy-brown; legs and feet light mealy-grey; eyes yellow-orange.

ADULT FEMALE. Often differs little from the adult male but is generally somewhat duller, lacking the red flecking often present on the breast of the male and with the subcaudals strongly suffused with green; eyes brownish-yellow.

IMMATURE. Generally duller with very little red on the subcaudals, eyes dark. It has been stated that a partial moult, with assumption of brighter plumage, occurs at the age of a few months.

Geographical Variations

None recognized.

Field Notes

Cayley wrote: "The Swift Parrakeet (also called Red-shouldered Parrot, Swift-flying Parrakeet, and Swift-flying Lorikeet) is fairly common in New South Wales. Usually met with in flocks frequenting the flowering eucalypts and other nectar-bearing trees, it is often seen feeding in company with several species of the *Trichoglossi*, being very similar to them in habits and economy. In the north-eastern portion of New South Wales its movements coincide with the flowering of the various species of eucalypts. It appears to be more nomadic than migratory. Aptly named Swift Parrakeet. Generally, one hears its clinking notes, then glimpses a flash of green as it passes overhead. For a nesting-place it selects a hole in the branch of a tree, or a hollow spout—usually of a eucalypt.

"Clutch: usually two eggs; white, and rounded-oval in form; shell close-grained, smooth and lustreless. Breeding-season: November to January."

In years past Swift Parrots used regularly to visit the vicinity of Adelaide in the autumn months and it was on such an occasion that I first made the acquaintance of the species in the wild state. An area of scrubland in the vicinity of Teatree Gully was a favoured spot and it was there in May 1938 that the quite distinct and unmistakable call-notes first drew my attention to the birds, which were feeding on flowering eucalypts in company with Musk and Purple-crowned Lorikeets. In the last twenty or so years there have been remarkably few records of this species in South Australia, contrasting with what previously appeared to have been annual visitations.

In October 1969, in the course of a brief visit to Tasmania, I was delighted to be able to renew my acquaintance with these birds; they were in fact practically the only native birds to be seen in the streets and parks of the city of Launceston where they were to be seen in the exotic trees; whether they were feeding therein was not ascertained. Their rollicking calls could be heard at most times of the day and particularly in the early morning, and individual birds were seen investigating hollows in trees and also in buildings. They were also seen a few miles south of Hobart.

Swift Parrots are relatively easy to identify in the field, the distinctive features being the unusual and unmistakable calls, the extremely rapid, whirring flight, the characteristic silhouette with long, pointed tail and the very obvious red under-wing markings.

Aviary Notes

Cayley wrote: "A pretty and attractive species in an aviary, but quite unsuited to cage life. Very gentle in mixed company, but should be kept housed separately in pairs for the best breeding results.

"Hollow logs provide the most suitable nesting-places; these should be hung in the open flight, and at least two or three should be placed in different positions for the birds to make a selection.

"Simon Harvey, the Honorary Secretary of the Avicultural Society of South Australia, kindly sent me the following notes received by his society from R. Lewitzke, of Enfield, South Australia: '*Comments on breeding Swift Lorikeets*. These birds I had in my possession in a large flight aviary for four years. The first two years they showed no sign of building. The third year they were noted looking for a nesting-site but evidently could not find one suitable, although there were plenty to choose from.

" 'This year they chose one underneath a creeper growing over the aviary, and laid three white eggs, the first one being laid on 21st November and the last on 25th November. The male bird fed the hen the whole time she was sitting, but was not seen to go down the hollow.

" 'The hen was very shy during the incubation period and was only seen out of the hollow early in the mornings and late in the evenings while being fed by the cock. The first young one was hatched on 20th December, the second egg being infertile. The last was hatched on 26th December. All one could see down the hollow was a ball of fluff, until about twelve days later the elder young started to show green feathers on the wings. This young one was doing well until 31st December when it fell out of the nest because of the heat, the temperature in the nest being over the hundred. It died the same night after being put back into the nest.

" 'The diet of the parents, which consisted of hulled oats, hemp and canary-seed, was not changed while they were feeding the young. The remaining young one continued to do well despite the changeable weather, and left the nest on 27th January.

" 'Members will note that this species had taken nearly a fortnight longer to leave the nest than seed-eating parrakeets take. I think this is on account of it being a heavier-built parrakeet; its flights are not strong enough to carry it in its young stage.' "

As far as I am aware, the foregoing success is the only one recorded for Australia. Prestwich[57] states: "Dr Hopkinson tells me that when he was in Tasmania in 1932, he was informed they had occasionally been bred in aviaries there but he did not get any particulars."

My personal experiences with this species have been disappointing. The first four specimens that I possessed did not survive very long, some of them dying suddenly, although apparently in good condition, a characteristic which appears to be not uncommon in recently trapped individuals that have not become accustomed to a captivity diet. Early in 1939 I obtained a fine male from a friend in Melbourne, and a little later I secured a female locally. These birds were noticed feeding in November of the same year, but were not segregated at the time, being housed in a mixed collection without nesting facilities. The following year a different hen was mated to the cock, but it was not until December 1944 that they began to take an interest in a nest log. One egg was laid on 20th December, and a second some days later; of these only one proved fertile and on 9th January a dead young bird, with an empty crop, was found in the nest. For a short time thereafter I thought they would nest again, but no further eggs appeared.

The following season two eggs were laid in October, but they disappeared, probably owing to the activities of an unmated hen Naretha, who was sharing the aviary and subsequently appropriated the nest and laid therein. On her removal the Swifts laid another egg early in January, but it was deserted after about ten days' incubation, and was found to be clear. The next season they appeared to be in breeding condition earlier than usual, but did not lay till just before Christmas; on this occasion both eggs were clear, and soon after this both birds managed to escape.

It was not until 1969 that I was again able to attempt to breed this difficult species. In April of that year I was given a nice pair of aviary-conditioned birds, only to lose the hen within a few weeks. I was fortunate enough to be able to secure a replacement, but no breeding was attempted that summer. The following year the cock died during the winter, but was replaced, and the new pair became interested in a nest-box in the late spring. Eventually three eggs were laid during December; the first was broken but the remaining two were incubated and one proved to be fertile and hatched early in January. The young bird flourished for about a fortnight but was found dead, with a full crop, after an unusually hot day.

It is strange that more successes with this species have apparently not occurred in Australia, especially as there have been several successes in Europe; it is interesting to note that both colony breeding and polygamy have been practised on occasions in overseas collections.

There is no doubt that the feeding requirements of the species in captivity are still imperfectly understood. Birds will survive for long periods on a diet of canary seed and a small amount of sunflower, supplemented with apple and pear and sweetened bread and milk; but are still liable to die suddenly, in good condition although perhaps overfat.

MELOPSITTACUS Gould
Budgerigar

The single species in this genus, the Budgerigar, does not appear to have any close relatives. It certainly has no close affinities with the broad-tailed parrots, and its association with the Ground and Night Parrots appears to be one of convenience, rather than being based on any good evidence.

Budgerigars indulge in mutual preening and, in consequence, are not infrequently known as Lovebirds, a name which should be reserved for the African genus *Agapornis*. The display is well known and is often perpetrated by the tame pet Budgerigar in front of a mirror or other object. It consists of a chirruping on the part of the male whilst rapidly shaking its head in front of the female and intermittently giving her a gentle nudge on the bill; periodically the male will take off on a short flight and then return to continue the performance. Courtship feeding occurs and incubation, lasting about nineteen days, is performed entirely by the female and often commences after the laying of the first egg, so that the brood is frequently of varying ages and sizes; the young remain in the nest for between four and five weeks after hatching, during which time they are fed by both parents.

The down of the chicks is white and the bill of the fledgling tends to have a slightly more creamy colour than that of the adult.

There is a broad wing-stripe present both in adults and immatures; this is in no way comparable to that which occurs in the broadtails.

Budgerigars do not bathe in the strict sense, but enjoy getting wet in damp grass and sometimes in rain or under a spray.

Food is not held in the foot, and head-scratching is over the wing.

An interesting habit that has often been observed is that when large flocks come in to drink, many birds will land on the surface of the water with outstretched wings, drink hurriedly and take off again.

The flight is swift and somewhat erratic; despite this, the flight of a large flock is remarkably well co-ordinated. Small groups tend to fly less rapidly and with more apparent purpose.

58 Budgerigar

Melopsittacus undulatus (Shaw)

PLATE XIII

Synonyms

Shell Parrot, Warbling Grass Parrakeet, Budgerygah, Betcherrygah, Zebra Parrot, Canary Parrot, Flight Bird, Lovebird, Scallop Parrot.

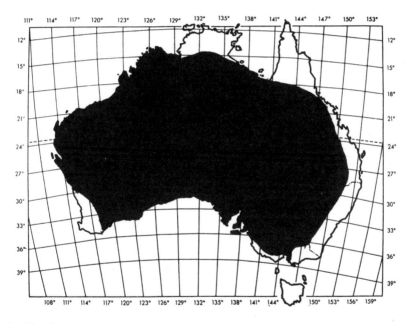

Distribution

This highly nomadic species occurs in the interior of Australia with occasional coastal irruptions. In Western Australia, according to Serventy and Whittell[10] it occurs "all over the State except in the south-west jarrah forest area": there are, however, occasional records of penetrations into this region. Storr[75] states that in the Northern Territory it ordinarily occurs "north to the lower Victoria and upper Roper but at height of dry season sometimes may wander as far north as Pine Creek and in extreme droughts even to Darwin".

In South Australia it occurs throughout the northern parts of the State and at irregular intervals in the more southern parts; it is an irregular visitor to the south-east.

In Victoria the species is recorded from all parts of the State with the exception of approximately the eastern one-third, and in New South Wales it occurs over the whole of the interior of the State but rarely transgresses the Dividing Range.

In Queensland similarly it occurs over most of the interior of the State but rarely reaches the east coast; it does not appear to occur on Cape York Peninsula, north of latitude 18 degrees.

Description

SIZE. About $7\frac{1}{2}$ inches (190 mm).

ADULT MALE. General colour above greenish-yellow, with (except on upper wing-coverts) black transverse bars becoming broader on scapulars; bars on upper wing-coverts dark brown and more crescent-shaped in form; outer webs of quills greenish-blue, dark brown on inner with a whitish band through middle of inner webs of primaries; outer webs of secondaries crossed near their base by a pale green band, inner webs with a broader yellow band; lower back, rump, and upper tail-coverts grass-green, the latter tinged with blue; central pair of tail-feathers dark blue with a greenish-blue tinge on outer margins, remainder greenish-blue crossed with an oblique yellow band; forehead and crown of head straw-yellow; sides of face and ear-coverts yellow, with narrow transverse black bars; lores, forepart of cheeks, chin, and throat rich yellow; on lower cheeks an oblique patch of ultramarine-blue confluent spots (these spots appear violet in some lights); encircling the throat six rounded black spots, three on each side, the uppermost being partly obscured by the violet cheek-patches; remainder of under-surface, and the under wing-coverts and under tail-coverts, rich grass-green; bill greyish-yellow with a bluish shade at base, cere of bill blue, becoming duller in colour during the non-breeding season; legs and feet fleshy-grey; eyes pale yellow; ring round eye blue.

ADULT FEMALE. Similar in plumage to the male, but the violet cheek-patches and black throat-spots are generally smaller, and the cere of the bill is brown or greyish-brown according to the season of the year.

IMMATURE. General colour above and below much duller than the plumage of the adult, with faint transverse undulations on the forehead, crown of head and sides of breast; violet cheek-patches and black throat-spots small and much less clearly defined; cere in both sexes at first a pinkish-violet shade. Adult plumage is obtained by a moult which is usually completed when the bird is about four months old: the sex has usually become obvious earlier by the changes which have occurred in the colour of the cere.

Geographical Variations

None recognized.

Field Notes

Cayley wrote: "My first acquaintance in the field with this dainty parrakeet was in the far north of New South Wales. The season happened to be an exceptionally good one and the birds were in great numbers. It was October, and breeding operations were in full swing, all available nesting-sites being occupied. In many hollow limbs several pairs of birds were nesting: when one knocked on a tree-trunk it was surprising the number of birds that vacated the hollows. Another wonderful sight was to see the limbs and branches of a ring-barked tree literally covered with birds, and as many more flying about looking for a place to settle. The tree had the appearance of being clothed with a glorious green foliage.

"The birds were exceptionally tame, being far too busy carrying out their domestic duties to worry about intrusion. They were constantly on the move, flying to the ground seeking food among the grasses and then back to their brooding mates. During the midday heat small flocks would rise and, after flying around the paddocks, join up in one large flock and fly swiftly away to a fringe of trees bordering a creek. There they would settle among the foliage for hours; then the flocks would take wing, disperse, and return to their several feeding-grounds. Towards evening they flew to the same clump of trees, where they settled for a while; then, in relays, visited the water to quench their thirst.

"Most of the time the birds, presumably the males, kept up a constant chatter. This chirruping note, while not unpleasing, soon becomes monotonous when uttered by many hundreds of birds. Our host whose property we were visiting was an excellent mimic of bird-calls. Occasionally he would give a rendering of the loud cry of the Whistling Eagle. Instantly every bird stopped its chatter; the resultant hush was astounding.

"Nests examined contained both eggs and young in all stages of development, the average clutch and brood being six. In some broods the youngsters were in all stages, from practically naked to nearly fully-fledged birds; in others they were almost uniform in size.

"Visiting the same locality a few years later, the scene had changed. This time the season was a dry one, the heat terrific, and the paddocks nearly burnt up. Only small isolated flocks of Budgerigars were noted, and very few appeared to be breeding. During the heat of the day the birds kept among the foliage of the trees, feeding and drinking in the early morning and towards evening. The nesting-sites examined were mostly unoccupied—only a few had small clutches with an average brood of four. The owner of the property told me that the previous season not a parrot had appeared—the only occasion, to his knowledge, they had missed paying their yearly visit during his twenty years' residence in the district. Since my first introduction to the species, I have met with it in many inland districts, but never in such large numbers or under such favourable conditions. It is a migratory species, usually appearing in the southern portions of the continent in late winter or early spring, departing northwards during February or March. To a certain extent it is nomadic: may make its appearance in a district for one or more seasons, then be absent for many years. These annual movements appear to be regulated by seasonal conditions. There is no record of the species remaining in the southern part of Australia throughout the year.

"Open country, interspersed with belts of timber or patches of scrub, is favoured by the Budgerigar.

"Clutch: five to eight eggs; white, and oval or rounded-oval in form, some specimens being rather pointed at the smaller end; shell close-grained and lustreless. Breeding-season: in New South Wales, normally, from October till the end of December. In times of drought the birds nest after the first heavy rainfall, usually in the autumn."

My own personal experience of the Budgerigar in the field dates back to the years soon after World War I, when it was common on the outskirts of Adelaide, and nested on the Seaton golf links. Since that time I have seen them on numerous occasions in various parts of Australia and in very great numbers in Central Australia at times. Their southern irruptions frequently, but not invariably, coincide with those of Cockatiels and in some seasons both species appear in vast numbers and breed freely along the upper Murray in South Australia.

On a bird-watchers' tour of eastern Queensland in May and June 1970 we observed this species north of Bowen, in the vicinity of Ayr, near Townsville and farther inland, to the south of Clermont.

Aviary Notes

Cayley wrote: "The Budgerigar, quite apart from its beauty and attractive mannerisms, possesses every attribute necessary to make it an ideal subject for breeding experiments. As an aviary bird it has no rival: its adaptability, hardiness, and free-mating propensities, place it in a class quite apart from any other species. Is it any wonder that its popularity as an aviary bird is unparalleled in the history of aviculture?

"A few years after Gould introduced the species into England, this parrakeet was being bred in captivity as readily as the canary. The birds Gould took back with him in 1840 were hand-reared by his brother-in-law Charles Coxen. Presumably they were young birds taken from the nest and not bred and reared in captivity. Begun in the most modest fashion by amateurs, the hobby became so popular that many breeding establishments soon assumed the proportion of industrial undertakings. The Belgians and Dutch were the first to breed the birds on a large scale, to be followed quickly by the French and Germans. Since then, large Budgerigar farms have been established throughout the British Isles, America, Japan and, in a lesser degree, in Australia, the home of the species.

"During recent years societies and clubs devoted to the study of the fascinating Budgerigar have made their advent. The growth of these societies throughout the world has been phenomenal. In Australia, before the beginning of the present century, few, if any, attempts were made to breed Budgerigars in captivity. At that time it was generally known that these charming birds were very popular with oversea breeders, and rumours were rife that several colour varieties had been successfully produced.

"Their popularity with Australians as cage-birds really began with the appearance of the yellow variety, a few pairs being introduced from abroad about 1900. These birds caused considerable speculation and were eagerly sought after, high prices being paid for them and their progeny.

"Today every known coloured variety has been produced in Australia and several new mutations have been established. Many standard books devoted to the 'Cult of the Budgerigar' are available, covering every phase from breeding and management to the higher science of genetics. The two outstanding works on the Budgerigar, which readers are advised to procure, are *The Cult of the Budgerigar* by W. Watmough, and *Genetics of the Budgerigar* by Professor F. A. E. Crew."

I first bred this species when I was a schoolboy during World War I, and still vividly remember my pleasure in successfully rearing five young birds from the first nest. Soon afterwards I was given two yellow cocks, the only mutation known in South Australia at that time, but I never succeeded in breeding from them, although other fanciers were breeding them quite freely then. Since my resumption, in 1935, of avicultural activities, I have frequently kept pairs of Budgerigars, mainly wild greens, for the sake of completeness of the collection, and have bred a number of young, but I have never interested myself in the breeding of colour varieties.

W

PEZOPORUS Illiger
Swamp Parrot

Only one species, the Swamp Parrot, is admitted in this terrestrial genus, but Serventy and Whittell[10] have included the Night Parrot, *Geopsittacus*, in the same genus, a decision that appeals to me.

Little is known or recorded of the behaviour of these birds. Mutual preening was not observed in birds kept in captivity, nor has any form of display been noted. Courtship feeding can be presumed to occur; it is not known whether both sexes incubate, although this seems unlikely. The duration of incubation has not been recorded, nor is it established whether both parents feed the chicks. Forshaw[5] records that young remained in the nest for the first two weeks but thereafter moved out into the surrounding vegetation to meet the parent. When about three weeks old they would leave the nest at the slightest disturbance and a few days later they had vacated it and were found sheltering in nearby tussocks; at this stage they were well feathered but still could not fly. From personal observation I am able to state that the down is greyish-black and the colour of the bill of the newly fledged young is yellow.

A pale yellow wing-stripe is present in both adults and immatures. Bathing was not observed in captive birds and it is presumed that they use wet grass for the purpose.

Food is not held in the foot, and the method of head-scratching has not been recorded.

The birds flush with an audible clatter somewhat reminiscent of the noise produced by a domestic pigeon. The flight is swift and erratic, with rapid wing-beats interspersed with glides; it is usually low over the vegetation and terminates abruptly with the impression of a sudden dive. No call is given in flight.

59 Swamp Parrot

Pezoporus wallicus (Kerr)

PLATE XIII

Synonyms

Ground Parrot, Button Grass Parrot.

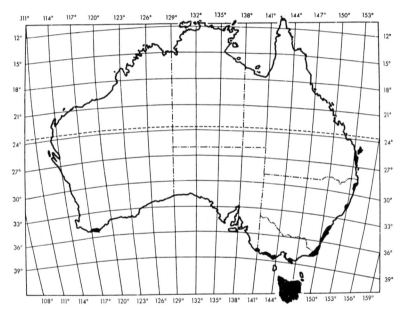

Distribution

In Tasmania this species is widely distributed, but on the mainland the distribution is extremely patchy. There have been no further recordings from Fraser Island since that of Chisholm—see his article "Seeking Rare Birds"[62]—and the only other Queensland record is that of Mrs Carole Bevege[76] who has amplified this to me, stating that the species occurs in localized areas in coastal heathlands from approximately fifty miles north of Brisbane to north-east of Gympie.

In New South Wales there have been records from such widely separated places as Yamba on the north coast, Cape Hawke Peninsula, south of Sydney in the vicinity of Nowra and at Ulladulla, and the Nadgee Fauna Reserve in the far south-east.

In Victoria the species occurs patchily along much of the coast with recordings from Mallacoota, Marlo, Wilson's Promontory, Westernport, Carlisle River, Port Campbell, Port Fairy, Nelson and just across the border to the vicinity of Port Macdonnell, which constitutes the only South Australian record for very many years.

In Western Australia, although this bird originally appears to have extended as far north as Geraldton, the only recordings during the present century are from the south coast at such places as Cheyne Beach, Albany, Wilson's Inlet near Denmark, and Irwin Inlet.

Description

SIZE. About 12½ inches (317 mm).

ADULT MALE. General colour above dark grass-green; forehead deep reddish-orange; feathers of head and hind-neck with a broad stripe of black down the centre; inter-scapular region, scapulars, upper wing-coverts and back crossed by alternate bars of yellow and black on the centre of each feather; rump and upper tail-coverts similarly but more uniformly barred; quills green on their outer webs, blackish-brown on their inner webs and tips, with a large yellow marking on the inner web of all the feathers, and a smaller one on the outer web, with the exception of the first, second and third primaries; two central tail-feathers green tinged with blue on their outer webs and crossed with bars of yellow; the next on either side green on the outer webs, blackish-brown on the inner and barred with yellow; remainder yellow, irregularly barred with dark green on basal portion of outer webs and black on inner webs and tips; centre of throat yellowish-green; sides of face and neck, and chest, grass-green with narrow black shaft lines; breast and sides of abdomen yellow-green, with irregular cross-bars of black, less distinct on centre of abdomen; under tail-coverts greenish-yellow, barred with black; bill slaty-horn colour; legs and feet slaty-brown; eyes buffy-white.

ADULT FEMALE. The shade of green on the head has been stated to be darker but this is not apparent in sexed skins.

IMMATURE. Slightly duller and more yellowish than the adult, and the frontal band is absent; there is no information available as to the time of its acquisition.

Geographical Variations

Western Australian birds, *flaviventris,* are said to differ in having the abdomen bright yellow with indistinct interrupted black barring; whether these differences are constant or not seems to be uncertain.

Field Notes

Cayley wrote: "The Ground Parrakeet or Swamp Parrakeet is chiefly an inhabitant of swamp-lands or low scrub-covered wastes of the coastal districts and islands lying off the mainland. Its range at one time extended from Fraser Island, southern Queensland, right across the continent to the south-western portion of Western Australia; it also occurred on some of the islands of Bass Strait and in Tasmania.

"At one time it was fairly common in neighbourhoods quite close to Sydney. When a youth I observed it at Botany Bay, Long Bay, Maroubra, National Park, Maddcn's Plains, Appin, Narrabeen, the Quarantine Grounds at North Head, and at several localities on the north and south coasts of New South Wales. An isolated pair or two may still remain in some of these localities near Sydney; but it is doubtful, for this bird is an easy prey to domestic cats. Some still exist in certain localities on the north and south coasts of New South Wales, on Fraser Island and at Marlo, Victoria; but of late years few records occur of its existence elsewhere.

"Strangely enough, it used to be considered a good 'sporting' bird, on account of its swift flight, and because, like game-birds, it has a strong smell, and dogs readily stand to it. Its flight, as Gould stated, is very similar to that of quail; its flesh, too, is excellent for table purposes— which no doubt accounts for the scarcity of the species. Once disturbed it is often a difficult matter to flush them again—that is, without the aid of a dog. For, after alighting it runs along the ground some distance before resting, very often doubling back from, or to the right or left of, the spot where it landed. It is remarkable how that parrakeet pitches to the ground. Instead of the usual slanting forward descent of most species, it appears to dive straight down, and very often backwards, from the direction of its flight. This habit is very misleading and makes it difficult to locate where it actually landed, even with the assistance of field-glasses. The nest is a depression in the ground at the base of a tussock of grass or thick clump of rushes or low bush lined with dry, coarse grass or rush.

"Clutch: usually three or four eggs; white, and oval or elliptical in form; shell smooth, close-grained, and more or less lustrous. Breeding-season: September to December."

Having made several fruitless searches in areas where these birds had been frequently seen in the vicinity of Nelson in south-western Victoria, it was not until October 1959 that I first met with the species. In company with Dr Graham Brown and Dr Norman Wettenhall I had spent a considerable time tramping over heathy hillsides in the Carlisle River district of Victoria, where the birds had often been seen, and we were about to abandon the quest when a bird flushed from almost under my feet. Instead of immediately following the bird, fortunately I looked down and discovered a nest containing two very recently hatched chicks and a chipped egg. We flushed the bird on a couple more occasions by following it up but we did not see it again near the nest although we revisited the area again several times during the remainder of the day. However, the nest was kept under observation and the young, which had been banded, were successfully fledged.

In December 1968 several of us tramped the coastal heathlands near Mallacoota, Victoria, and succeeded in flushing several of these birds. Two observations of interest were made: firstly that the birds on flushing made a clapping noise with their wings, somewhat reminiscent of a domestic pigeon only not so loud and, secondly, that after being flushed more than once or twice they invariably sought refuge in the scrub growing on the coastal sandhills.

Aviary Notes

Cayley wrote: "There is no authentic record of this species ever having been bred in captivity. One makes the suggestion that if an attempt be made to do so, it should prove successful.

"North records a note by Percy Peir, of Campsie, near Sydney, which reads: 'About 1885 I had a pair of Ground-Parrakeets (*Pezoporus formosus*) which were caught near a swamp, the present site of the Kensington racecourse, close to Sydney. They lived for some years, but were rather uninteresting, never perching, but always spent their time on the ground. I have seen these birds on and off since that time, and often found tail-feathers scattered about near the edges of swamps at the back of Long Bay and Botany, the birds evidently having fallen victims to Native Cats or other enemies. . . .'

"The only living example I know of in captivity, in Australia or elsewhere, is a bird recently added to the collection of parrots at Royal Park Zoological Gardens, Melbourne."

I have never possessed an example of this species, and my knowledge of its habits are the result of oft-repeated observation of the three birds kept for a long period in the Adelaide Zoo and a couple of brief visits to the collection of A. Leer, at Manly Vale, near Sydney. The birds in the latter's possession always seemed extremely timid, but those in the Adelaide Zoo soon became quite fearless. It was always thought that the first and third of these to be acquired were probably males, and the second possibly a female, but on this bird's death in 1949 it was found to be a male, whilst the other two, which fell victims to rats some year or so earlier, were so mutilated that their sexes were not ascertained. Even if there was a pair amongst these three birds, they never showed any signs of wanting to nest, although I never considered that the enclosure in which they were housed was either sufficiently roomy or well planted enough to encourage them to do so.

There seems little doubt, from the observations of both Manfield[77] and Webber,[78] that this bird has a feeble call-note, resembling that of the Grass Parrakeets; I was never fortunate enough to hear it. This observation has been substantiated by Forshaw.[5]

The Zoo birds never perched in the strict sense of the word, although, as a photograph in *Australian Parrots in Captivity*[45] shows, they occasionally sat on branches placed on the ground. Furthermore, they were never observed to climb the wire-netting of their enclosure, though they would hang awkwardly to it if frightened sufficiently to make them fly, a procedure which was discouraged in the early stages of their captivity by wing-clipping.

The late W. Turner, writing in April 1953 in reply to a query about two Ground Parrots then in the Hallstrom collection, stated: "They were not bred by Sir Edward Hallstrom but by Leer who had a pair in an open top aviary with a lot of shrubbery and grass in it. Arrangements for feeding and watering were made without disturbing the birds and I do not think Leer ever saw the nest. One day he found he had six birds instead of two and it was a pair of these young birds that he gave to Sir Edward who is now trying to repeat the unique performance. Unfortunately the Ground Parrots were later murdered by a pair of Conures which shared their aviary!"

GEOPSITTACUS Gould
Night Parrot

As already mentioned, I lean to the amalgamation of this genus with *Pezoporus*; it has always seemed likely that *Geopsittacus* could be the adaptation of *Pezoporus* to an arid environment.

Virtually nothing is known in regard to the behaviour of this bird.

A pale yellow wing-stripe is in evidence in the few existing skins.

Nothing is recorded in regard to bathing habits, food-holding or method of head-scratching.

The flight has been described as erratic, without undulation.

60 Night Parrot

Geopsittacus occidentalis Gould

PLATE XIII

Synonyms
Western Ground Parrot, Spinifex Parrot.

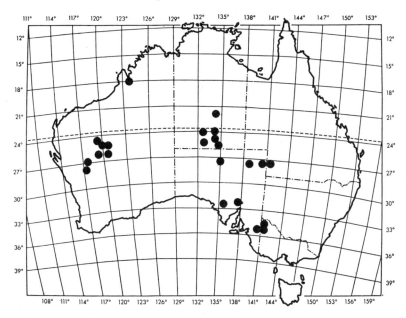

Distribution
The dots on the above map indicate areas where there are reasonably reliable records of the occurrence of this species at some past time. There have been no certain records of this parrot for many years. Wilson[79] related its history very fully. The occurrence of the species in north-western Victoria has never been completely substantiated.

Description
SIZE. About 9½ inches (241 mm).

ADULT MALE. General colour above yellowish-green, with dark brown bases to the feathers and pale markings, the latter in the form of arrow-heads or cross-bars; bastard wing and primary coverts dark brown with olive-green margins to the feathers; primary and secondary quills like the back with a whitish V-shaped mark on the inner webs which commences on the fourth primary and increases in extent on the secondaries; the margins of all the feathers are paler; central tail-feathers dark brown with whitish indentations and greenish margins, the lateral tail-feathers barred with yellowish-white increasing in extent towards the outermost feather on each side; crown of head and nape green with blackish shaft-streaks to the feathers; sides of face green, shading to yellowish-green on throat; foreneck, breast, and sides of body pale green, the feathers barred with black and yellowish-white; centre of breast, abdomen and under tail-coverts lemon-yellow; under wing-coverts pale green becoming pale brown on the greater series; bill slaty-horn colour; legs and feet mealy-brown; eyes brown.

ADULT FEMALE. Stated to be similar to the adult male.

IMMATURE. Undescribed, but stated to be dull and very plain with some yellow on the throat and neck.

Geographical Variations

None recognized.

Field Notes

Cayley wrote: "Practically nothing is known of the life-history of this unique parrakeet, and in recent times there have been no authentic records of its occurrence anywhere. For many years careful search has been undertaken in the haunts where they were once found, without any trace of them; so, apparently, the species has been almost, if not quite, exterminated."

So little is known about this bird that the usual practice in this book has been departed from and there follows in full Andrews's account, given in 1883,[80] of his observations of the species: "During the day this bird lies concealed in the inside of a tussock or bunch of porcupine grass (*Triodia*), the inside being pulled out and a snug retreat formed for its protection. Here, also, its rough nest is formed, and four white eggs laid. When the dark shades of evening have fairly set in it comes out to feed, but generally flies direct to the nearest water, which is often a considerable distance from the nest; in some instances I have known them fly a distance of four or five miles. After drinking and shaking themselves up a little they fly off to feed on the seeds of the porcupine grass, returning to water two or three times during the night. The name given by the aborigines is 'Myrrlumbing', from the supposed resemblance of their whistling note to the sound of that word. They have also a peculiar croaking note of alarm whilst at the water, which much resembles the loud croak of a frog. On one occasion one of these parrots was caught in a hut, where it had apparently been attracted by the light of a bush lamp; it was put into a box, with a handful of dry grass. On examination the next morning, the bird could not be seen; it had placed the dry grass in a heap and drawn out the side straw by straw until it had formed a hole, in which it had concealed itself.

"These birds are pretty generally distributed through the north and north-west of this colony [South Australia]: they come and go according to the nature of the season. When the early season is wet, the porcupine grass flourishes and bears quantities of seed, on which the birds feed; but if, on the contrary, the season is a dry one, the grass does not seed, and no birds are to be seen. I shot some specimens at Cooper's Creek in 1875, when out as collecting naturalist for the late Mr J. W. Lewis, in his exploration of the country about Lake Eyre. They were in that district observed to conceal themselves during the day in thick patches of shrubby samphire on the salt flats bordering the creeks on Lake Eyre."

Wilson summarized all that was known of the history of this bird in his paper in 1937[79] and in the same year Croll[81] published *Wide Horizons*, in which he wrote: "Parrots are not usually regarded as birds of the darkness, but we were in a countryside where one, at least, of the family is credited with nocturnal habits. He is known indeed as the Night Parrot (*Geopsittacus occidentalis*) and, naturally enough, he is one of the rarest of Australian birds. His home is said to be in the porcupine grass; there was abundance of the prickly tussocks about the crest of the rises. On two occasions, late at night, we heard bird-calls which we could not associate with any nightbird known to us, and which very definitely suggested the cry of a parrot. Since a certain expedition a few years ago, the Night Parrot has interested the bushmen, and they are watching for it. Aborigines are also taking a hand in the pursuit of this elusive bird. An observant station owner, who has a fine aviary at his homestead, pointed out the large eyes of the Bourke Parrots and said that these parrots assuredly fly by night. He had camped at waterholes and noted that the Bourkes always came to drink after darkness had set in. They would arrive in a flock, and with them, quite often, would be a single bird, or perhaps a couple, with a different beat of wing. They could not be seen, of course—it was only his keen ears, trained to recognize every bush sound, that could distinguish something strange. This happened repeatedly. The Night Parrot is so commonly alone, on the rare occasions when he is seen, that the bushmen have named him the Solitaire, so it is quite possible that the individual bird which joins the Bourkes in their evening drink is *Geopsittacus*."

Since 1937 there have been several reports of sightings but none have been positively confirmed. Perhaps the most interesting one is that of Powell,[82] a station manager who, in the spring of 1969, while mustering sheep west of the Flinders Ranges in South Australia, flushed two birds on one occasion and a single bird on another. He is certain the three were Night Parrots.

Aviary Notes

Cayley wrote: "Sclater (*Proc. Zool. Soc. Lond.*, p. 891, 1867) records the receipt of a living specimen of this parrakeet from Dr Ferdinand Müller, who wrote: 'This peculiar parrot was presented to me by Mr Ryan, on whose sheep station, on the Gawler Ranges west of Spencer Gulf, it was obtained. The most extraordinary circumstance connected with this bird is, that it is *nocturnal!* It lives in the rocky caves of the ranges, and comes out at night to feed.'

"Apparently this bird did not live long, for in the next volume (p. 158) Murie records its death, stating: 'I need only add two facts mentioned by Mr Bartlett: one, that it shows a preference for green food; the other, that its voice was a double note, harsh and loud.' "

H. Manfield, formerly head bird-keeper at the Adelaide Zoo, always maintained that, as a lad, he saw examples of this species in Foglia's bird-shop in Rundle Street, Adelaide; this would be round about the turn of the century.

APPENDIX
Keeping Australian Parrots in Captivity

The corresponding section in the first edition of this book was written by the late R. R. Minchin, then Director of the Adelaide Zoological Gardens. Many of the advances made in this field have been the direct result of his enthusiasm and early experiences and I am particularly indebted to him for his assistance and encouragement.

HOUSING

The modern methods of housing Australian parrots have almost certainly developed from the prototype aviaries erected for that specific purpose at the Adelaide Zoo in 1932; many modifications and improvements have evolved since then, but the basic design remains virtually unchanged. For the aviculturist, who usually keeps more than one species, blocks of aviaries with communicating doors have proved efficient as well as being economical as regards ground space and building material. Over the years I have experimented with various modifications and have reached the conclusion that the present design of my aviaries is the best that I have developed. The plan and elevation are shown in this Appendix, with particular emphasis on the important features. The aviaries should be designed not only to give the greatest protection from cold winds but to receive the maximum amount of morning sun, particularly in winter; this usually means that they should face between north and east. This pattern of housing implies the use of one aviary for each pair of birds; very occasionally it may be feasible to house two docile, unrelated pairs, such as Superb and Turquoise Parrots, in the one aviary, provided it is roomy enough. It is highly undesirable to house closely related species in adjoining aviaries: unless double divisions are used, there will be loss of toes and even upper mandibles as a result of fighting, and there will be many distractions during the nesting season.

Flights

In designing the flight of an aviary, length is of paramount importance in order to afford the maximum exercise for the inmates: width is of relatively little concern and height should only be sufficient to allow of easy, comfortable maintenance and uninterrupted viewing. I consider that the minimum dimensions of the flight should be 6 feet in length, 3 feet in width and 6 feet in height for the smallest species, for example the Neophemas, but it is stressed that 9 feet in length for the smaller species and 15 feet for the larger is decidedly advantageous and that $6\frac{1}{2}$ to 7 feet in height is an improvement. For the largest species, such as Kings, 4 feet width and for Cockatoos 5 feet width and 20 feet or more length is much to be desired. The framework of the flight is most satisfactorily constructed of galvanized water piping of either $\frac{1}{2}$-inch or $\frac{3}{4}$-inch gauge; a wide range of fittings enabling it to be held together are available and they make construction very easy and permanent. The netting used is generally $\frac{1}{2}$-inch mesh and it is desirable to use the heaviest gauge obtainable; even so, some of the stronger-billed parrots, such as Twenty-eights, are prone to bite holes in it. Netting with $\frac{3}{8}$-inch mesh has the advantage of being practically mouse-proof but it is expensive and not readily obtainable in heavy gauge. For cockatoos and for some of the larger parrots, galvanized chain wire of 1-inch mesh is essential. This is sparrow- and rat-proof but not, as I have found since living in the Mount Lofty Ranges, finch-proof, and my larger aviaries are now daily invaded by clouds of Red-browed Finches (*Aegintha temporalis*) which obtain an easy living thereby! The flights are made rat- and mouse-proof by bordering the external boundaries with flat galvanized sheet iron, which is sunk into the ground for 18 inches and extends a further 18 inches above ground level.

The floor of the flights is comprised of natural earth, which needs periodic raking and turning and may, with advantage, have slaked lime dug in at intervals.

Shelters

The shelters are placed, as shown in the diagram, at the rear of the flights. They are, perhaps, best built of brick of single thickness, but are more cheaply constructed on a framework of piping and may consist either of small-fluted galvanized iron or of asbestos sheeting: the latter has the advantage of being both warmer and cooler but tends to become brittle as it weathers.

Half the front of each shelter should be closed in order to afford greater privacy and protection from wind.

The roof is 18 inches higher at the front, sloping away to the rear; the front of the recess thus produced is constructed either of glass impregnated with wire netting or of some translucent material, such as Windowlite; if the latter is used, it needs to be protected from the birds' attentions by a lining of wire netting on the inside. The advantage of such a recess is that the birds almost invariably seek the highest point at which to roost and are attracted by the light and consequently obtain the maximum shelter. The floor of the shelter is best constructed of concrete, which allows of easy cleaning.

Doors

The entrance and intercommunicating doors are most conveniently placed, as shown, at the extreme rear of the shelters. By so doing, undue interference with the inmates is avoided, as they leave for the front of the flight as the shelter is entered. In addition, the food and water receptacles can be serviced from this position with a minimum of inconvenience and can be placed clear of the perches, as shown in the diagram. The intercommunicating doors should be so fashioned as to open in either direction; the external doors should preferably open outwards only.

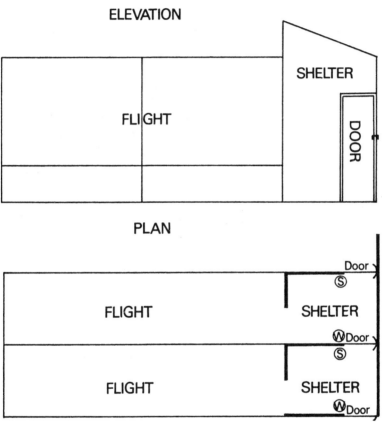

Aviary designed by A. H. Lendon: plan. Scale ¼ in. = 1 ft.
W = Water. S = Seed.

AVIARY FITTINGS

Perches should be relatively few and far between in order to encourage the maximum of exercise. In the type of aviary shown in the diagram, one perch is placed about 12 inches from the back of the shelter and another farther forward and higher up, about 6 inches behind the translucent recess. In the flight, one perch is placed about 6 inches from the front of the aviary. Ordinary dowelling is generally used, the size varying with the size of the inmates, but this will need frequent replacement for the stronger-billed species.

Natural branches with the bark left on are probably advantageous in that they provide amusement and exercise for the inhabitants. For cockatoos, perches of jarrah or other hard woods are more durable; the Yellow-tailed and White-tailed Black Cockatoos are particularly destructive to most types of wood and it has been found that olive wood is the most resistant to their powerful bills.

With few exceptions nests are best constructed from natural hollow logs, the internal diameter and length varying according to the size of the bird. Both ends should be closed, either with wood or galvanized iron, the lower end permanently and the upper hinged so as to allow of inspection and cleaning. A hole should be bored near the upper end and this should be of a size which will just admit the prospective user comfortably; most species do not like an unduly large entrance and some, such as Blue Bonnets, appear to prefer a very small one, through which they can only just squeeze. The nests should usually be suspended obliquely as high as possible in the shelter, and it is wise to give each pair the choice of two nests. The logs are filled to a depth of several inches with a mixture of decayed wood and earth obtained from the bottom of a woodheap. Care must be taken to ensure that the birds do not eject all of this material before laying.

I remove the nesting logs at the end of the breeding season and replace them at the beginning of the following one: this manoeuvre always seems to stimulate considerable interest on the part of the birds at the appropriate time. However, in the case of Lorikeets, it is probably desirable to leave them all the year round, as they are often used for roosting purposes. Some species, especially Kings and Red-wingeds, appear to prefer a very long log with its base resting on the ground and standing practically vertically; in such cases it is desirable to include an internal "ladder" of wire-netting. Artificial nest-boxes are favoured by

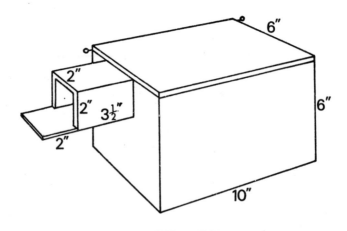

THE NEST – BOX
Nest-box designed by Sir Edward Hallstrom.

some aviculturists: I have never used them except for Golden-shouldereds, which seem to prefer them, and the design favoured by the late Sir Edward Hallstrom has been followed (see diagram). Other species with unusual breeding sites, such as Hoodeds and Rocks, have been found to take readily to the usual hollow logs.

FEEDING

With the exception of the lorikeets and fig-parrots, the basic diet in captivity consists of a seed mixture, which varies according to the size of the birds. Thus, for the rosellas and birds of similar size, a suitable mixture consists of approximately two parts each of sunflower and canary seed with one part each of hulled oats and of one of the millets, usually panicum.

In the days before World War II hemp seed was readily available and was greatly relished; nowadays it has to be sterilized, is very expensive and is seldom used.

Although sorghum (milo) is frequently added to commercial parrot mixtures, it is usually ignored; this is strange because crops are extensively raided, especially by cockatiels: presumably it is only palatable when green. For the smaller species, such as the grass parrots, a mixture of equal parts of canary seed and panicum with a small amount of hulled oats is usually given; very occasionally they will take a little very small sunflower seed.

For the larger species, the proportion of sunflower should be increased and wheat may be added, while for the white cockatoos the basic diet should consist of sunflower, oats and wheat with a little canary seed. Black cockatoos will subsist satisfactorily on an exclusive seed diet of sunflower and will rarely eat other seeds. The requirements of Gang-gangs have never been satisfactorily resolved; some will undoubtedly survive for long periods on a seed diet but many become feather biters and it is to be presumed that this is the result of some dietary deficiency; possibly wattle seed, which they eat extensively in the wild state, would be the answer if available.

I supply the seed mixture in shallow trays on a stem about 12 inches high, mounted on a heavy base, in order to protect it from the attentions of the occasional intruding mouse.

Green food, in some form or other, is readily accepted by most seed-eating species. Lettuce or silver beet is frequently fed, and most seeding grasses, especially *Poa* and *Erharta*, are greatly appreciated. Sow thistles, particularly the flowering heads, are also valuable.

Fruit is appreciated by most of the large parrots and less so by the cockatoos. Apple is by far the best, pear being a good second. Grapes are usually readily accepted and some species will eat banana. Many berries, such as *Pyracantha*, are relished when ripe.

Nuts are a useful and much sought after supplement to the seed mixture, especially for cockatoos and the larger parrots. Peanuts are readily accepted but are expensive to feed regularly; almond rejects can be obtained very cheaply and are very suitable for most species. The nuts of the stone pine (*Pinus pinea*) are relished by the black cockatoos and macadamia nuts (*Macadamia ternifolia*) are favoured by the palm cockatoos, whose powerful mandibles are ideally adapted for cracking the extremely hard shells.

Dried seed sprays, especially of the various millets, are used frequently overseas but are seldom available commercially in Australia. Sprouted seeds, especially wheat, are often appreciated and boiled maize is a useful additive for cockatoos.

The correct feeding of lorikeets in captivity has never been solved to everyone's satisfaction. Although it is undisputed that some of the larger species will survive, and even breed, on a diet of seed alone, it is certain that they will thrive better if provided with an abundance of fruit and some form of nectar substitute, of which sweetened stale bread or toast, soaked in scalded milk, appears to be the most widely used. Some seed, especially canary, should always be provided and sweetened maize meal is often fed. The smaller lorikeets will certainly not survive on seed alone and various types of artificial nectar must be tried, either sweetened bread and milk, some adaptation of infant foods or some mixture which uses diluted honey as a base.

Swift parrots, which in their natural state are principally nectar feeders, do well in captivity on a diet of plain canary seed, apple and sweetened bread and milk.

Fig-parrots have rarely been kept in captivity, and I am indebted to J. Forshaw for the information he has supplied regarding the bird which he has kept successfully for a long period. He states: "The basic food for my fig-parrot is millet or canary seed and he gets this every day. Also every day he gets about ten sultanas, soaked overnight in water, and a few slices of apple. Each second day he is also given half a dried fig (Sanitarium brand) which is soaked overnight with the sultanas in water to which has been added a few drops of Vetemul concentrate. Note that the vitamin concentrate is added to the water only when fig is given, that is, every second night. Canned cherries are given regularly as a variation, and fresh fruits, particularly grapes, cherries and loquats, are given when available. The bird will not eat fresh figs and has shown no interest whatever in live food."

Grit, in some form, is an essential. Shell grit is commonly supplied but I prefer cuttlefish bone, which is readily available on most beaches and is eagerly nibbled, especially in the breeding season. It may have an additional virtue as a source of salt.

WATER

Drinking water is best supplied in relatively shallow, glazed, earthenware dishes in which the birds can also bathe if so disposed. It should be changed at least every second day and it is remarkable how frequently birds will bathe immediately after it has been changed. As indicated elsewhere, not all species will bathe, and those that do not, as well as those that do, will frequently appreciate a spray from a garden sprinkler or similar arrangement. It is noteworthy that, whilst some seem to prefer a fine spray, others like a coarser one; whether the latter are rainforest-living species, which are used to heavier rain, has not been determined.

GAZETTEER

All co-ordinates are expressed to the nearest degree of south latitude and east longitude.

Abbreviations

A.C.T. Australian Capital Territory
N.S.W. New South Wales
N.T. Northern Territory
Q. Queensland
S.A. South Australia
T. Tasmania
V. Victoria
W.A. Western Australia

	S.lat. E.long.		S.lat. E.long.
Abminga, N.T.	26 x 135	Bega, N.S.W.	37 x 150
Adavale, Q.	26 x 145	Bellenden-Ker Ra., Q.	17 x 146
Adelaide, S.A.	35 x 138	Bellinger River, N.S.W.	30 x 153
Adelaide River, N.T.	13 x 131	Belyando River, Q.	23 x 147
Ajana, W.A.	28 x 115	Benalla, V.	37 x 146
Albany, W.A.	35 x 118	Bendigo, V.	37 x 144
Alberga, S.A.	27 x 135	Biloela, Q.	24 x 150
Albury, N.S.W.	36 x 147	Bindoon, W.A.	31 x 116
Alice Springs, N.T.	24 x 134	Bingara, N.S.W.	30 x 151
Ammaroo, N.T.	22 x 135	Binnaburra, Q.	28 x 153
Angas Downs, N.T.	25 x 132	Blackall, Q.	24 x 146
Archer River, Q.	13 x 142	Blackall Ra., Q.	27 x 153
Arkaroola, S.A.	30 x 139	Black Rock, V.	38 x 145
Arnhem Land, N.T.	13 x 134	Bogan River, N.S.W.	31 x 147
Arrino, W.A.	29 x 116	Bonython Ra., N.T.	24 x 129
Ashbourne, S.A.	35 x 139	Booligal, N.S.W.	34 x 145
Atherton, Q.	17 x 145	Bordertown, S.A.	36 x 141
Augathella, Q.	26 x 147	Borroloola, N.T.	16 x 136
Ayers Rock, N.T.	25 x 131	Boulia, Q.	23 x 140
Ayr, Q.	20 x 147	Bowen, Q.	20 x 148
		Boyne River, Q.	26 x 151
Backstairs Passage, S.A.	36 x 138	Breakfast Creek, N.S.W.	33 x 150
Banka Banka, N.T.	19 x 134	Brisbane, Q.	27 x 153
Barcaldine, Q.	24 x 145	Bridgetown, W.A.	34 x 116
Barellan, N.S.W.	34 x 147	Broken Hill, N.S.W.	32 x 141
Barham, N.S.W.	36 x 144	Broome, W.A.	18 x 122
Barmera, S.A.	34 x 141	Bulloo, Q.	28 x 142
Barrington, N.S.W.	32 x 152	Bundaberg, Q.	25 x 152
Barrow Creek, N.T.	22 x 134	Bungaree, S.A.	34 x 139
Bateman's Bay, N.S.W.	36 x 150	Bunya Mountains, Q.	27 x 152
Baudin Rocks, S.A.	37 x 140	Burketown, Q.	18 x 139

	S.lat. E.long.		S.lat. E.long.
Buronga, N.S.W.	34 x 142	Darling Downs, Q.	27 x 151
Burra, S.A.	34 x 139	Darling Ra., W.A.	31 x 116
Byrock, N.S.W.	31 x 146	Darling River, N.S.W.	32 x 143
		Darwin, N.T.	12 x 131
Cairns, Q.	17 x 146	Dawson River, Q.	26 x 150
Calliope River, Q.	24 x 151	Delungra, N.S.W.	30 x 151
Caltowie, S.A.	33 x 138	Deniliquin, N.S.W.	35 x 145
Camooweal, Q.	20 x 138	Denmark, W.A.	35 x 117
Canning Dam, W.A.	32 x 116	Devil's Marbles, N.T.	20 x 134
Cape Barren Is., T.	40 x 148	Dharug, N.S.W.	33 x 151
Cape Hawke, N.S.W.	32 x 153	Dimbulah, Q.	17 x 145
Cape Jervis, S.A.	36 x 138	Dirranbandi, Q.	29 x 148
Cape River, Q.	21 x 146	Dongara, W.A.	29 x 115
Cape York Pen., Q.	14 x 143	Dorrigo, N.S.W.	30 x 153
Cardwell, Q.	18 x 146	Duaringa, Q.	24 x 150
Carlisle River, V.	39 x 143	Dubbo, N.S.W.	32 x 149
Carnamah, W.A.	30 x 116	Dundas, W.A.	32 x 122
Carriewerloo, S.A.	32 x 137	Dunedoo, N.S.W.	32 x 149
Casino, N.S.W.	29 x 153	Dunmarra, N.T.	17 x 133
Castlereagh River, N.S.W.	31 x 148	Dwarda, W.A.	33 x 117
Central Mt Stuart, N.T.	22 x 133		
Charleville, Q.	26 x 146	Eidsvold, Q.	25 x 151
Charters Towers, Q.	20 x 146	Elkedra, N.T.	21 x 135
Chauncey's Line, S.A.	36 x 139	Ellery Creek, N.T.	24 x 133
Cheyne Beach, W.A.	35 x 118	Elliott, N.T.	18 x 134
Chichester, N.S.W.	32 x 152	Elsey, N.T.	15 x 134
Chinchilla, Q.	27 x 151	Emerald, Q.	24 x 148
Clare, S.A.	34 x 139	Ernabella, S.A.	26 x 132
Clarence River, N.S.W.	29 x 152	Esperance, W.A.	34 x 122
Claudie River, Q.	13 x 143	Eucla, W.A.	32 x 129
Clermont, Q.	23 x 148	Eulo, Q.	28 x 145
Cloncurry, Q.	21 x 141	Eungella Ra., Q.	21 x 148
Cobar, N.S.W.	32 x 146	Euston, N.S.W.	35 x 143
Cobbora, N.S.W.	32 x 149	Everard Ra., S.A.	27 x 132
Cobram, V.	36 x 146	Eyre Pen., S.A.	33 x 135
Cocklebiddy, W.A.	32 x 126		
Coen, Q.	14 x 143	Finke, N.T.	26 x 135
Collarenebri, N.S.W.	30 x 149	Finley, N.S.W.	36 x 146
Condamine River, Q.	27 x 150	Fitzroy River, W.A.	18 x 124
Cooktown, Q.	15 x 145	Fleurieu Pen., S.A.	36 x 138
Coolgardie, W.A.	31 x 121	Flinders Chase, K. Is., S.A.	36 x 137
Coonabarabran, N.S.W.	31 x 149	Flinders Is., T.	40 x 148
Coonamble, N.S.W.	31 x 148	Flinders Ra., S.A.	32 x 138
Coorong, S.A.	36 x 140	Florina, N.T.	14 x 132
Coorow, W.A.	30 x 116	Forbes, N.S.W.	33 x 148
Cootamundra, N.S.W.	35 x 148	Fortescue River, W.A.	22 x 117
Corrigin, W.A.	32 x 118	Fowler's Bay, S.A.	32 x 132
Cowra, N.S.W.	34 x 148	Fraser Is., Q.	25 x 153
Culburra, S.A.	36 x 140	Furneaux Group, T.	40 x 148
Cunderdin, W.A.	32 x 117		
Cunnamulla, Q.	28 x 146	Garah, N.S.W.	29 x 150
Cunningham's Gap, Q.	28 x 152	Gascoyne River, W.A.	25 x 114
		Gawler Ra., S.A.	32 x 136
Daly Waters, N.T.	16 x 133	Gayndah, Q.	26 x 152
Dandaragan, W.A.	31 x 116	Genoa River, V.	37 x 150
Dandenong Ra., V.	38 x 145	Georgetown, Q.	18 x 144

	S.lat.E.long.		S.lat.E.long.
Geraldton, W.A.	29 x 115	Jardine River, Q.	11 x 142
Gibson Desert, W.A.	24 x 125	Jerilderie, N.S.W.	35 x 146
Gilbert River, Q.	17 x 142	Jurien Bay, W.A.	30 x 115
Gilgandra, N.S.W.	32 x 149		
Gingin, W.A.	31 x 116	Kaban, Q.	18 x 145
Gin Gin, Q.	25 x 152	Kalannie, W.A.	30 x 117
Gippsland, V.	38 x 147	Kalgoorlie, W.A.	31 x 121
Gladstone, S.A.	33 x 138	Kangaroo Is., S.A.	36 x 137
Glen Innes, N.S.W.	30 x 152	Kaniva, V.	36 x 141
Goodparla, N.T.	13 x 136	Katherine, N.T.	15 x 132
Goomalling, W.A.	31 x 117	Katoomba, N.S.W.	34 x 150
Grafton, N.S.W.	30 x 153	Kellerberrin, W.A.	32 x 118
Grass Valley, W.A.	32 x 117	Keilor, V.	38 x 145
Great Australian Bight	37 x 132	Keith, S.A.	36 x 140
Great Victoria Desert	29 x 128	Kerang, V.	36 x 144
Gregory River, Q.	19 x 139	Kiata, V.	36 x 142
Grenfell, N.S.W.	34 x 148	Kimba, S.A.	33 x 136
Griffith, N.S.W.	34 x 146	Kimberleys, W.A.	16 x 126
Groote Eylandt, N.T.	14 x 137	King Is., T.	40 x 144
Gulf St Vincent, S.A.	35 x 138	Kingoonya, S.A.	31 x 135
Gumlu, Q.	20 x 148	Kingston, S.A.	37 x 140
Gunnedah, N.S.W.	31 x 150	Knuckey's Lagoon, N.T.	12 x 131
Gympie, Q.	26 x 153	Kogan, Q.	27 x 151
		Koondrook, N.S.W.	36 x 144
Hale River, N.T.	24 x 136	Kununurra, W.A.	16 x 129
Hamilton Downs, N.T.	23 x 133	Kuranda, Q.	17 x 146
Hattah, V.	34 x 142	Kweda, W.A.	32 x 117
Hawkesbury River, N.S.W.	34 x 151	Kynuna, Q.	22 x 142
Hay, N.S.W.	34 x 145		
Hayes River, Q.	13 x 144	Lachlan River, N.S.W.	34 x 145
Healesville, V.	38 x 146	Lake Albacutya, V.	36 x 142
Helenvale, Q.	16 x 145	Lake Alexandrina, S.A.	36 x 139
Herberton, Q.	17 x 145	Lake Barrine, Q.	17 x 146
Hermannsburg, N.T.	24 x 133	Lake Callabonna, S.A.	30 x 140
Hermidale, N.S.W.	32 x 147	Lake Eacham, Q.	17 x 146
Hervey Bay, Q.	25 x 153	Lake Eyre, S.A.	29 x 137
Hindmarsh Tiers, S.A.	36 x 138	Lake Grace, W.A.	33 x 118
Hobart, T.	43 x 147	Lake Muir, W.A.	35 x 117
Howell's Ponds, N.T.	17 x 133	Lake Victoria, N.S.W.	34 x 141
Hugh River, N.T.	24 x 134	Lambinna, S.A.	27 x 134
Humpty Doo, N.T.	13 x 131	Langhorne Creek, S.A.	35 x 139
Hunter River, N.S.W.	33 x 151	Larrimah, N.T.	15 x 133
Huon River, T.	43 x 147	Launceston, T.	41 x 147
		Laverton, W.A.	29 x 122
Illawarra, N.S.W.	35 x 151	Leeton, N.S.W.	35 x 146
Inglewood, Q.	28 x 151	Leonora, W.A.	29 x 121
Innamincka, S.A.	28 x 141	Lismore, N.S.W.	29 x 153
Innisfail, Q.	17 x 146	Lithgow, N.S.W.	33 x 150
Inverell, N.S.W.	30 x 151	Little River, V.	38 x 145
Iron Knob, S.A.	33 x 137	Lockhart River, Q.	13 x 143
Iron Ra., Q.	13 x 143	Longreach, Q.	23 x 144
Irwin Inlet, W.A.	35 x 117	Loongana, W.A.	31 x 127
Israelite Bay, W.A.	34 x 124	Lower Everton, V.	36 x 147
Ivanhoe, N.S.W.	33 x 144		
		McArthur River, N.T.	16 x 136
Jandowae, Q.	27 x 151	Macdonald Downs, N.T.	22 x 135

	S.lat.	E.long.		S.lat.	E.long.
MacIntyre River, N.S.W.	29 x 151		Muswellbrook, N.S.W.	32 x 151	
Mackay, Q.	21 x 149		Mutooroo, S.A.	32 x 141	
Macleay River, N.S.W.	31 x 153				
McPherson Ra., Q.	28 x 153		Nadgee, N.S.W.	37 x 150	
Macquarie River, N.S.W.	31 x 147		Nagambie, V.	37 x 145	
Mallacoota, V.	38 x 150		Namban, W.A.	31 x 116	
Mambray Creek, S.A.	32 x 138		Nambour, Q.	27 x 153	
Manning River, N.S.W.	32 x 152		Nappamerrie, Q.	28 x 141	
Mannum, S.A.	35 x 139		Naracoorte, S.A.	37 x 141	
Manya, V.	35 x 141		Naretha, W.A.	31 x 125	
Mareeba, Q.	17 x 145		Narrabri, N.S.W.	30 x 150	
Marlo, V.	38 x 149		Narrandera, N.S.W.	35 x 147	
Marne River, S.A.	35 x 140		Narran Lake, N.S.W.	30 x 147	
Marree, S.A.	30 x 138		Narrogin, W.A.	33 x 117	
Mary Kathleen, Q.	20 x 139		Narromine, N.S.W.	32 x 148	
Maryborough, Q.	26 x 153		Narrung, S.A.	36 x 139	
Marysville, V.	38 x 146		Nelson, V.	38 x 141	
Massey Creek, Q.	14 x 144		Nesbit River, Q.	14 x 144	
Mataranka, N.T.	15 x 133		Newcastle Waters, N.T.	17 x 133	
Mathoura, N.S.W.	35 x 145		New Norcia, W.A.	31 x 116	
Meandarra, Q.	27 x 150		Nicholson River, N.T.	18 x 138	
Melbourne, V.	38 x 145		Nogoa River, Q.	24 x 148	
Melrose, S.A.	33 x 138		Normanton, Q.	18 x 141	
Melville Is., N.T.	12 x 131		Norseman, W.A.	32 x 122	
Menindee, N.S.W.	32 x 142		Nourlangie, N.T.	13 x 132	
Meningie, S.A.	36 x 139		Nowra, N.S.W.	35 x 151	
Menzies, W.A.	30 x 121		Numery, N.T.	24 x 136	
Merredin, W.A.	32 x 118		Nyabing, W.A.	34 x 118	
Merriwa, N.S.W.	32 x 150		Nyngan, N.S.W.	32 x 147	
Monto, Q.	25 x 151				
Mooliabeenee, W.A.	31 x 116		Oakwood, Q.	26 x 146	
Moora, W.A.	31 x 116		Oodnadatta, S.A.	28 x 136	
Moore River, W.A.	31 x 116		Ord River, W.A.	15 x 129	
Mooroopna, V.	36 x 145		Orroroo, S.A.	33 x 139	
Morawa, W.A.	29 x 116		Otway Ra., V.	39 x 144	
Moree, N.S.W.	29 x 150		Ovens River, V.	37 x 147	
Morgan, S.A.	34 x 139		Outer Harbour, S.A.	35 x 138	
Moulamein, N.S.W.	35 x 144				
Moura, Q.	25 x 150		Palm Valley, N.T.	24 x 133	
Mt Barrow, T.	41 x 147		Parkes, N.S.W.	33 x 148	
Mt Isa, Q.	21 x 139		Partacoona, S.A.	32 x 138	
Mt Lofty, S.A.	35 x 139		Pascoe River, Q.	13 x 143	
Mt Mary, S.A.	34 x 139		Patersonia, T.	41 x 147	
Mt Tamborine, Q.	28 x 153		Peach River, Q.	14 x 143	
Mt Wellington, T.	43 x 147		Peak Hill, N.S.W.	33 x 148	
Mt Wilson, N.S.W.	33 x 150		Pennefather River, Q.	12 x 142	
Mudgee, N.S.W.	33 x 150		Penola, S.A.	37 x 141	
Mullewa, W.A.	29 x 115		Perth, W.A.	32 x 116	
Mundrabilla, W.A.	32 x 128		Petermann Ra., N.T.	25 x 129	
Murchison River, W.A.	28 x 115		Pilbara, W.A.	21 x 118	
Murphy's Creek, Q.	27 x 152		Pilliga, N.S.W.	30 x 149	
Murray Bridge, S.A.	35 x 139		Pine Creek, N.T.	14 x 132	
Murray Mallee, S.A.	35 x 140		Pine Plains, V.	35 x 142	
Murrumbidgee River, N.S.W.	34 x 145		Pingelly, W.A.	33 x 117	
Musgrave Ra., S.A.	26 x 132		Pinnaroo, S.A.	35 x 141	

	S.lat. E.long.		S.lat. E.long.
Pooncarie, N.S.W.	33 x 143	Tansey, Q.	26 x 152
Port Augusta, S.A.	32 x 138	Tarlton Downs, N.T.	23 x 137
Port Campbell, V.	39 x 143	Tea Tree Gully, S.A.	35 x 138
Port Fairy, V.	38 x 142	Temora, N.S.W.	34 x 148
Portland, V.	38 x 142	Tenterfield, N.S.W.	29 x 152
Port Lincoln, S.A.	35 x 136	Three Springs, W.A.	30 x 116
Port Macdonnell, S.A.	38 x 141	Tibooburra, N.S.W.	29 x 142
Port Phillip Bay, V.	38 x 145	Timber Creek, N.T.	16 x 131
Princess Charlotte Bay, Q.	14 x 144	Tocumwal, N.S.W.	36 x 146
Puckapunyal, V.	37 x 145	Todd River, N.T.	24 x 134
		Tomkinson Ra., S.A.	26 x 129
Quairading, W.A.	32 x 117	Toodyay, W.A.	32 x 116
Quilpie, Q.	27 x 144	Toowoomba, Q.	28 x 152
		Torres Strait, Q.	10 x 142
Rand, N.S.W.	36 x 147	Tottenham, N.S.W.	32 x 147
Rankin's Springs, N.S.W.	34 x 146	Townsville, Q.	19 x 147
Ravenshoe, Q.	18 x 145	Tweed River, N.S.W.	28 x 154
Rawlinna, W.A.	31 x 125	Two Wells, S.A.	35 x 138
Redbank, Q.	27 x 153	Tumut, N.S.W.	35 x 148
Renmark, S.A.	34 x 141		
Renner's Springs, N.T.	19 x 134	Ulladulla, N.S.W.	35 x 150
Richmond, Q.	21 x 143	Undoolya, N.T.	24 x 134
Ringwood, N.T.	24 x 135	Upper Hunter, N.S.W.	33 x 152
Riverina, N.S.W.	35 x 145	Urangan, Q.	25 x 153
Robe, S.A.	37 x 140		
Rochester, V.	36 x 145	Victor Harbour, S.A.	36 x 139
Rockhampton, Q.	23 x 151	Victoria River Downs, N.T.	16 x 131
Rocky River, Q.	14 x 144		
Roper River, N.T.	15 x 134	Waddington, W.A.	31 x 116
		Wagga, N.S.W.	35 x 147
Salt Creek, S.A.	36 x 140	Wangaratta, V.	36 x 146
Sandstone, W.A.	28 x 119	Warby Ra., V.	37 x 146
Santa Teresa, N.T.	24 x 134	Warialda, N.S.W.	30 x 151
Scone, N.S.W.	32 x 151	Warlock Ponds, N.T.	15 x 133
Scrubby Creek, Q.	17 x 145	Warra, Q.	27 x 151
Selwyn Ra., Q.	21 x 140	Warren, N.S.W.	32 x 148
Seymour, V.	37 x 145	Warren Gorge, S.A.	32 x 138
Shark Bay, W.A.	25 x 113	Warrumbungles, N.S.W.	31 x 149
Shepparton, V.	36 x 145	Warwick, Q.	28 x 152
Sherbrooke. V.	38 x 145	Watson River, Q.	13 x 142
Shoal Bay, N.T.	12 x 131	Wauchope, N.T.	21 x 134
Spencer, N.S.W.	33 x 151	Wellington, N.S.W.	33 x 149
Spencer's Gulf, S.A.	34 x 137	Wellington East, S.A.	35 x 139
Spring Creek, W.A.	17 x 129	Wentworth, N.S.W.	34 x 142
South Alligator River, N.T.	13 x 132	Westernport, V.	38 x 145
Southern Cross, W.A.	31 x 119	West Wyalong, N.S.W.	34 x 147
Southport, Q.	28 x 154	Wickepin, W.A.	33 x 118
Stanthorpe, Q.	29 x 152	Williams, W.A.	33 x 117
St George, Q.	28 x 149	Williams River, N.S.W.	32 x 152
Strathbogie, V.	37 x 146	Wilmington, S.A.	33 x 138
Sutherlands, S.A.	34 x 139	Wilson's Inlet, W.A.	35 x 117
Swan Reach, S.A.	35 x 139	Wilson's Promontory, V.	39 x 147
Sydney, N.S.W.	34 x 151	Wiluna, W.A.	27 x 120
		Wimmera. V.	36 x 142
Tailem Bend, S.A.	35 x 139	Windorah, Q.	25 x 143
Tanami, N.T.	20 x 130	Winton, Q.	22 x 143

	S. lat. E. long.		S. lat. E. long.
Wiseman's Ferry, N.S.W.	33 x 151	Yarra River, V.	38 x 145
Wongan Hills, W.A.	31 x 117	Yarrawonga, V.	37 x 146
Wongulla, S.A.	35 x 140	Yass, N.S.W.	35 x 149
		Yeppoon, Q.	23 x 151
Yamba, N.S.W.	29 x 153	Yorke Peninsula, S.A.	34 x 138
Yaninee, S.A.	33 x 135	You Yangs, V.	38 x 144

REFERENCES
to published works

1. J. L. Peters, *Checklist of Birds of the World*, vol. 3. 1937.
2. A. J. Cain, "A Revision of *Trichoglossus haematodus* and of the Australian Platycercine Parrots", *Ibis*, vol. 97, 1955, pp. 432-79.
3. Marquess of Tavistock, *Parrots and Parrot-like Birds*. 1929.
4. M. Sharland, *Tasmanian Birds*, 3rd ed. 1958.
5. J. M. Forshaw, *Australian Parrots*. 1969.
6. St G. Mivart, *A Monograph of the Lories or Brush-tongued Parrots, comprising the family Loriidae*. 1896.
7. T. Salvadori, *Catalogue of Birds in the British Museum: Psittaci* (vol. 20). 1891.
8. A. Brooksbank, *Avicultural Magazine*, 5th ser., vol. I, no. 7, July, 1936, pp. 192-93.
9. J. L. Mitchell, "My Observations Whilst Breeding the Varied Lorikeet", *Bird-keeping in Australia*, vol. 9, no. 2, Feb. 1966, pp. 24-25.
10. D. L. Serventy and H. M. Whittell, *Birds of Western Australia*, 4th ed. 1967.
11. "The Breeding of the Purple-crowned Lorikeet", *Birdkeeping in Australia*, vol. 7, no. 4, April 1964, pp. 41-42.
12. A. J. Keast, "Bird Speciation on the Australian Continent", *Bull. Mus. Comp. Zool., Harvard*, vol. 123, 1961, pp. 307-495.
13. Marquess of Tavistock, "The Western Golden-headed Dwarf Parrot", *Avicultural Magazine*, 5th ser., vol. 3, no. 6, June 1938, pp. 149-50.
14. P. A. Bourke and A. F. Austin, "Notes on the Red-browed Lorilet", *Emu*, vol. 46, 1947, pp. 286-94.
15. A. J. Campbell, *Nests and Eggs of Australian Birds*, p. 599. 1900.
16. T. Iredale, "A New Australian Parrot", *Emu*, vol. 46, part I, July 1946, pp. 1-2.
17. E. J. Boosey, "Double-eyed Dwarf Parrot", in *Foreign Bird-keeping*, pp. 159-61, 1957.
18. J. M. Forshaw, "Some Field Observations on the Great Palm Cockatoo", *Emu*, vol. 63, 1964, pp. 327-31.
19. D. F. Thomson, *Birds of Cape York Peninsula*. 1935.
20. H. G. Barnard, "Field Notes from Cape York", *Emu*, vol. 11, 1911, pp. 17-32.
21. W. Macgillivray, "Notes on Some North Queensland Birds", *Emu*, vol. 13, 1914, pp. 132-86.
22. E. A. D'Ombrain, "Notes on the Great Black Palm Cockatoo", *Emu*, vol. 33, 1933, pp. 114-21.
23. G. M. Mathews, *The Birds of Australia* (12 vols 1910-27), vol. 6, 1917.
24. E. N. T. Vane, "Some Observations on the Cacatuinae—the Cockatoos", *Avicultural Magazine*, vol. 65, 1959, pp. 9-16.
25. G. F. Taylor, "The Aviary Breeding of Black Cockatoos", *Australian Aviculture*, vol. 25, 1971, no. 11, pp. 176-77.
26. I. C. Carnaby, "Variation in the White-tailed Black Cockatoo", *Western Australian Naturalist*, vol. 1, 1948, pp. 136-38.

27. D. H. Perry, "Black Cockatoos and Pine Plantations", *Western Australian Naturalist*, vol. 1, no. 7, Dec. 1948, pp. 133-35.

28. John Gould, *The Birds of Australia*, 7 vols, 1840-8 and Supplement 1869.

29. R. T. Lynn, "Breeding of the Yellow-tailed Black Cockatoo in Captivity", *Journal of the Parrot Society*, vol. 1, no. 8, August 1967, pp. 9-12.

30. E. F. C., "Breeding the Banksian Cockatoo", *Avicultural Magazine*, 5th ser., vol. 5, no. 5, May 1940, p. 136.

31. E. J. L. Hallstrom, "Breeding of Glossy Black Cockatoos", *Avicultural Magazine*, vol. 60, no. 5, Sept.-Oct. 1954, pp. 163-64. Also "Some Breeding Results in the Hallstrom Collection", *Avicultural Magazine*, vol. 65, no. 3, May-June 1959, p. 80.

32. S. A. Parker, "Critical Notes on the Status of Some Northern Territory Birds", *South Australian Ornithologist*, 1970, vol. 25, p. 117.

33. F. E. Blaauw, "On the Breeding of the Bare-eyed Cockatoo of Australia", *Ibis*, 12th ser., vol. 3, no. 3, July 1927, pp. 425-26.

34. A. H. Lendon, "First Breeding of the Long-billed Corella", *Birdkeeping in Australia*, vol. 12, April 1969, no. 4, p. 50.

35. H. J. Frith and J. H. Calaby, "The Superb Parrot in Southern New South Wales", *Emu*, vol. 53, 1953, pp. 324-30.

36. L. C. E. Gee, "The Rarest Parrots in the World—The Princess Alexandra Parrakeets—found only in Central Australia", in *Bush Tracks and Gold Fields: Reminiscences of Australia's Back of Beyond*, pp. 55-57. 1926.

37. E. J. Boosey, "The Princess of Wales's Parrakeet", *Avicultural Magazine*, May 1935, 4th ser., vol. 13, no. 5, pp. 119-20.

38. C. N. Austin, "Range Extensions of Three Bird Species", *Emu*, vol. 56, 1956, pp. 80-81.

39. D. L. Serventy, "The King Parrot of Western Australia", *Emu*, vol. 37, 1938, pp. 169-72.

40. A. H. Lendon, "The 'Wing-stripe' in Broadtailed Parrots", *South Australian Ornithologist*, vol. 15, 1940, pp. 87-94.

41. H. T. Condon, "The Australian Broad-tailed Parrots (subfamily Platycercinae)", *Records of the South Australian Museum*, vol. 7, 1941, pp. 117-44.

42. R. H. Lovell, "Far from the Madding Crowd", *Birdkeeping in Australia*, vol. 13, no. 10, October 1970, p. 132.

43. A. H. Lendon, "The Breeding in Captivity of the Cloncurry Parrakeet", *Avicultural Magazine*, 5th ser., vol. 5, no. 4, April 1940, pp. 91-93.

44. E. Ashby, "Description of a New Subspecies of *Platycercus elegans*", *Emu*, vol. 17, 1917, pp. 43-45, 117.

45. A. H. Lendon, *Australian Parrots in Captivity*. 1951.

46. H. L. White, "Notes on the Yellow-mantled Parrot", *Emu*, 1916, vol. 15, pp. 169-71.

47. M. Symonds Clark, "Our Native Parrots", *Proc. Field Naturalists Sec., Royal Society of South Australia*, 1889, pp. 28-46.

48. J. Ford and E. H. Sedgwick, "Bird Distribution in the Nullarbor Plain and Great Victoria Desert Region, Western Australia", *Emu*, vol. 67, 1967, pp. 99-124.

49. H. L. White, "Notes on the Naretha Parrot", *Emu*, vol. 21, 1921, pp. 81-83.

50. J. H. Calaby, "Recent Observations on the Naretha Parrot", *Western Australian Naturalist*, vol. 6, 1958, p. 153.

51. H. Manfield, "The Breeding in Captivity of the Naretha or Little Blue Bonnet Parrakeet", *Avicultural Magazine*, 5th ser., vol. 10, 1945, pp. 7-8.

52. A. H. Chisholm, "Birds of the Gilbert Diary", *Emu*, vol. 44, 1945, pp. 184-86.

53. W. T. Greene, *Parrots in Captivity*, vol. 2. 1884-88.

54. C. Lumholtz, *Among Cannibals*. 1887.

55. A. F. Wiener, *Foreign Cage Birds.* 1879.

56. C. W. Gedney, *Foreign Cage Birds.* ca. 1876.

57. A. A. Prestwich, *Records of Parrots Bred in Captivity.* 1950-2. Also additional published records, 1954.

58. D. Seth-Smith, *Parrakeets.* 1903.

59. D. Seth-Smith, "Notes on my Visit to Australia", *Avicultural Magazine*, 1910, 3rd ser., vol. 1, p. 206.

60. Marquess of Tavistock, "Threatened Extermination of Grass Parrakeets", *Avicultural Magazine*, 4th ser., vol. 2, no. 3, March 1924, pp. 64-65.

61. A. J. Campbell, "Missing Birds", *Emu*, vol. 14, part 3, Jan. 1915, pp. 167-68. Also reply from C. Barnard, ibid., p. 167.

62. A. H. Chisholm, "The 'Lost' Paradise Parrot", *Emu*, vol. 22, 1922, pp. 4-17. Also his "Seeking Rare Parrots", *Emu*, vol. 24, 1924, pp. 25-32.

63. A. H. Chisholm, *Mateship with Birds*, pp. 171-88. 1922.

64. A. H. Chisholm, *Birds and Green Places*, pp. 103-7, 1929.

65. A. H. Lendon, "An Appreciation of the late A. Wachsmann", *Avicultural Magazine*, 5th ser., vol. 5, 1940, pp. 105-6.

66. K. Immelmann, *Australian Parrakeets*, 1968.

67. A. R. McGill, "Parrots of the genus *Neophema* in New South Wales", *Emu*, vol. 60, 1960, pp. 39-46.

68. J. Ford, "The Increase in Abundance of the Bourke Parrot in Western Australia, 1938-1960", *Emu*, vol. 61, 1961, pp. 211-17.

69. H. E. A. Jarman, "The Orange-breasted Parrot", *Australian Bird Watcher*, vol. 2, no. 6, December 1965, pp. 155-67.

70. H. E. A. Jarman, "The Turquoise Parrot", *Australian Bird Watcher*, vol. 4, no. 8, March 1973, pp. 239-50.

71. H. E. A. Jarman, "The Scarlet-chested Parrot", *Australian Bird Watcher*, vol. 3, no. 4, December 1968, pp. 111-22.

72. S. Harvey, "Breeding the Splendid or Scarlet-chested Parrakeet", *Avicultural Magazine*, 1933, 4th ser., vol. 11, pp. 8-12.

73. W. A. Forbes, "On the Systematic Position of the genus Lathamus", *Proc. Zool. Soc., London*, 1879, pp. 166-74.

74. K. A. Hindwood and M. Sharland, "The Swift Parrot", *Emu*, vol. 63, 1964, pp. 310-26.

75. G. M. Storr, *List of Northern Territory Birds.* Special publication of W.A. Museum, no. 4, 1967.

76. C. Bevege, "Calling of the Ground Parrot", *Emu*, vol. 67, 1968, pp. 209-10.

77. H. Manfield, "The Australian Ground Parrot in Captivity", *Avicultural Magazine*, 5th ser., vol. 6, 1941, pp. 172-74.

78. L. C. Webber, "The Ground Parrot in Habitat and Captivity", *Avicultural Magazine*, vol. 54, 1948, pp. 41-45.

79. H. Wilson, "Notes on the Night Parrot, with reference to Recent Occurrences", *Emu*, vol. 37, 1937, pp. 79-87.

80. F. W. Andrews, "Notes on the Night Parrot", *Proc. Roy. Soc. S.A.*, vol. 6, 1883, pp. 29-30.

81. R. H. Croll, *Wide Horizons*, p. 51, 1937.

82. B. Powell, "The Night Parrot", *South Australian Ornithologist*, vol. 25, 1970, pp. 208-9.

New References

The publications that have appeared since 1973 give new information on the taxonomy, distribution and other aspects of the natural history of Australian parrots. These works add to or, in some cases, modify the information given in Lendon's book.

References to significant recently published papers and books are given below.

Readers interested in keeping and breeding Australian parrots also will find much of interest in the avicultural magazines. For Australian aviculturists the most important of these are:

Australian Aviculture, monthly magazine of The Avicultural Society of Australia.

The Avicultural Magazine, published bimonthly by The Avicultural Society (London).

J. Le G. Brereton, A survey of parrots, September 1965. *Emu*, vol. 77, 1977, pp. 143-5.

N. A. Campbell and D. A. Saunders, Morphological variation in the White-tailed Black Cockatoo, *Calyptorhynchus baudinii*, in Western Australia: a multivariate approach. *Australian Journal of Zoology*, vol. 24, 1976, pp. 589-95.

H. T. Condon, Checklist of the birds of Australia. Part 1. Non-passerines, 1975 (R.A.O.U., Melbourne).

J. Courtney, Comments on the taxonomic position of the Cockatiel. *Emu*, vol. 74, 1974, pp. 97-102.

J. Eckert, Range of the Bourke Parrot. *South Australian Ornithologist*, vol. 27, 1975, pp. 18-9.

C. D. Fisher, E. Lindgren and W. R. Dawson, Drinking patterns and behaviour of Australian desert birds in relation to their ecology and abundance. *Condor*, vol. 74, 1972, pp. 111-36.

J. Ford, Naretha Parrot in South Australia. *Emu*, vol. 73, 1973, p. 27.

J. M. Forshaw, *Parrots of the world*, 1973 (Landsdowne Press, Melbourne).

J. M. Forshaw, P. J. Fullaghar and J. I. Harris, Specimens of the Night Parrot in museums throughout the world. *Emu*, vol. 76, 1976, pp. 120-6.

R. Henderson, First record of Naretha Parrot in South Australia. *Emu*, vol. 72, 1972, p. 114.

R. C. Henderson, Breeding records of the Scarlet-chested Parrot in the Great Victoria Desert, and further records in the lower North-east. *South Australian Ornithologist*, vol. 27, 1977, pp. 222-3.

D. T. Holyoak, The relation of *Nymphicus* to the Cacatuinae. *Emu*, vol. 72, 1972, pp. 77-8.

D. T. Holyoak, Comments on taxonomy and relationships in the parrot subfamilies Nestorinae, Loriinae and Platycercinae. *Emu*, vol. 73, 1973, pp. 157-76; vol. 74, 1974, p. 106.

K. Immelmann, *Die australischen Plattschweifsittiche*, 1972 (Wittenberg Lutherstadt).

L. Joseph, Recent records of the Scarlet-chested Parrot. *South Australian Ornithologist*, vol. 27, 1976, pp. 144-5.

L. C. Llewellyn, New records of red-tailed black cockatoos in south-eastern Australia with a discussion of their plumages. *Emu*, vol. 74, 1974, pp. 249-53.

J. D. Macdonald, Name of southern subspecies of Little Corella. *Emu*, vol. 74, 1974, p. 195.

R. S. McInnes and P. B. Carne, Predation of cossid moth larvae by Yellow-tailed Black Cockatoos causing losses in plantations of *Eucalyptus grandis* in north coastal New South Wales. *Australian Wildlife Research*, vol. 5, 1978, pp. 101-21.

D. Milledge, The Orange-bellied Parrot in Tasmania. *South Australian Ornithologist*, vol. 26, 1972, pp. 56-8.

D. A. Saunders, The function of displays in the breeding of the White-tailed Black Cockatoo. *Emu*, vol. 74, 1974, pp. 43-6.

D. A. Saunders, The occurrence of the White-tailed Black Cockatoo, *Calyptorhynchus baudinii*, in *Pinus* plantations in Western Australia. *Australian Wildlife Research*, vol. 1, 1974, pp. 45-54.

D. A. Saunders, Subspeciation in the White-tailed Black Cockatoo, *Calyptorhynchus baudinii*, in Western Australia. *Australian Wildlife Research*, vol. 1, 1974, pp. 55-69.

D. A. Saunders, Breeding of the White-tailed Black Cockatoo in captivity. *Western Australian Naturalist*, vol. 13, 1976, pp. 171-2.

D. A. Saunders, Red-tailed Black Cockatoo breeding twice a year in the south-west of Western Australia. *Emu*, vol. 77, 1977, pp. 107-10.

D. A. Saunders, Breeding of the Long-billed Corella at Coomallo Creek, W.A. *Emu*, vol. 77, 1977, pp. 223-7.

D. A. Saunders, The effect of agricultural clearing on the breeding success of the White-tailed Black Cockatoo. *Emu*, vol. 77, 1977, pp. 180-4.

D. A. Saunders, Measurements of the Little Corella from Kununurra, W.A. *Emu*, vol. 78, 1978, pp. 37-9.

D. J. Schultz, Diseases of parrots. Pp. 223-44 *in* Proceedings No. 36 of Course for Veterinarians, 1978. (University of Sydney Post-graduate Committee in Veterinary Science).

D. L. Serventy and H. M. Whittell, *Birds of Western Australia*. 5th Ed., 1976 (University of Western Australia Press, Perth).

G. A. Smith, Systematics of parrots. *Ibis*, vol. 117, 1975, pp. 18-66.

G. M. Storr, *List of Queensland birds*. Western Australian Museum Special Publication No. 5, 1973.

G. M. Storr, The Rainbow Lorikeet (*Trichoglossus moluccanus*) in Perth, Western Australia. *Western Australian Naturalist*, vol. 12, 1973, p. 116.

G. M. Storr, *Birds of the Northern Territory*. Western Australian Museum Special Publication No. 7, 1977.

INDEX